CW01021682



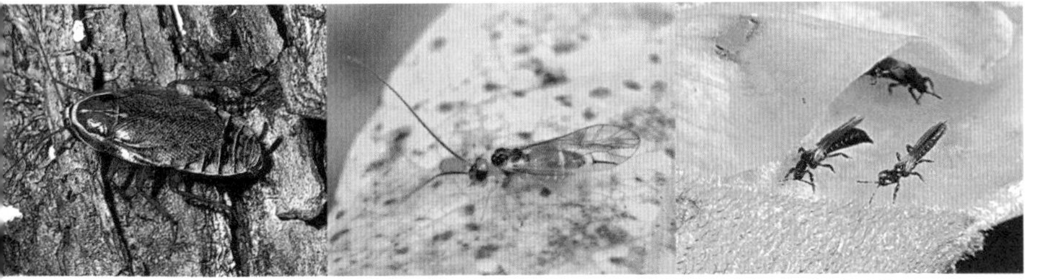

# A photographic guide to INSECTS OF SOUTHERN EUROPE & THE MEDITERRANEAN

by Paul D. Brock

Copyright © Paul D. Brock (2017)
Copyright © of the photographs remains with the photographers

All rights reserved. No part of this publication may be reproduced, stored in a retrieval system or transmitted, in any form or by any means electronic, mechanical, photocopying, recording or otherwise, without the prior permission of the publishers.

First published 2017.

British-Library-in-Publication Data
A catalogue record for this book is available from the British Library.

ISBN 978-1-874357-79-7

Designed and published by Pisces Publications

Pisces Publications is the imprint of NatureBureau, 36 Kingfisher Court, Hambridge Road, Newbury, Berkshire RG14 5SJ
www.naturebureau.co.uk

Printed and bound in Turkey by Imago

**Visit our bookshop**
**www.naturebureau.co.uk/bookshop/**

# CONTENTS

# ACKNOWLEDGEMENTS

I have been bug-hunting since the 1960s, starting in my back garden whilst a toddler. Whilst for much of that time, I have specialised in the mainly tropical and subtropical stick and leaf insects, I have always been fascinated by all insects. It is not, however, possible to be expert in every insect order and I have consulted many publications (books and papers), visited the Natural History Museum, London entomological collection and library, as well as discussed these insects with professional and amateur entomologists. Countless hours have been spent in the field observing insects as well and all my images are taken after 2010, mainly using Nikon cameras.

The majority of the photographs are mine. Particular thanks are due to the following photographers, whose initials otherwise appear by each photo, along with the main order(s) for those where several images are used: Jim Asher [JA], Janet Ashwell [JAs], Ken Bailey [KB] Lepidoptera (butterflies from his many trips), Tristan Bantock (www.flickr.com/people/tristanba/) [TB] Hemiptera, Keith Bensusan [KBe] ants, John Bingham [JB], Helen Brock [HB], Nuno Camejo [NC], Richard Coomber [RC], David Barros Cardona [DBC], David Cook [DC], Lucinda Creed [LC], Peter Creed [PC], Jeremy Early [JE], Peter Eeles [PE], George Else [GE], Teresa Farino (iberianwildlife.com) [TF], Paolo Fontana [PF], Conrad Gillett [CG], António A. Gonçalves [AG], Paul Goriup [PG], Wolfram Graf [WG], Janet Graham [JG], Rhian Guillem [RG], Penny Hale [PH], Thomas Haynes [TH], Jeff Higgott [JH], Gus Jones [GJ], Maria Justamond [MJ], Roger Key [RK], Christodoulos Makris [CM], Gilles San Martin (www.flickr.com/photos/sanmartin/) [GSM], Jim McCusker [JM], Kate McCusker (www.trikimages.co.uk) [KM], Tim Norriss [TN], Simon Oliver (www.flickr.com/photos/126688171@N06/) [SO] various orders, Nick Owens [NO], Trevor and Dilys Pendleton (www.eakringbirds.com) [TP], Ross Piper (www.rosspiper.net) [RP], Tony Pittaway [ARP] Lepidoptera (moths), Rosemary Powell [RPo], Maurice Pugh [MP], Stéphane Puissant [SP] Cicadidae, Nikola Rahmé [NR] (www.flickr.com/photos/eurythyrea/albums) Coleoptera, Pierre Rasmont [PR], Stuart Read [SR] various orders, David Rentz [DR], Mick Richardson [MR] (www.lojawildlife.com/) Odonata, Paul Ritchie [PRi], Francisco Rodriguez (Faluke) (www.biodiversidadvirtual.org/Insectarium/Francisco-Rodriguez-(Faluke)-usr3588.html and http://faluke.blogspot.com.es/) [FR], Daniel Rojas [DRo] & Miguel Ángel Rojas [MRo] various orders, Michael Skelton [MS] Lepidoptera (butterflies), Orthoptera, Peter Sutton [PS], Clive Turner [CT], Brian Valentine [BV], Pablo Valero [PV], John Smit [JS], Wolfgang Wagner (http://pyrgus.de/) [WW] , David Walker [DW] and Rosemary Winnall [RW]. Of these, I decided to leave perusing Simon Oliver's and Francisco Rodriguez's Spanish insect photos until a late stage, as I knew both had numerous high quality photos to fill gaps. Such keen naturalists as these do a great service to others hoping to find or help identify insects, as they tend to photograph all orders and readily make these available. Whilst a number of images by the above-mentioned photographers might do well in photographic competitions, I single out Nikola Rahmé's stunning Coleoptera images, among the best insect photos I have ever seen.

Whilst working on his massive life-time's work on British bees, George Else found time to give constructive guidance on the introduction and Hymenoptera section. Other specialists kindly commented on drafts of other sections of the book: Richard Askew (Odonata), Max Barclay and Conrad Gillett (Coleoptera) [Conrad provided much needed help with certain maps], Wolfram Graf (Plecoptera), Penny Hale (part of Lepidoptera: moths, who also showed us the many moths attracted to moth traps in her garden in Casares, Spain), Agostino Letardi (Neuroptera), Jude Lock (Lepidoptera: butterflies (http://borderlinehols.com/) and Judith Marshall (Orthoptera and relatives). The photographers and others named above occasionally assisted in other ways such as Mick Richardson proving expert guiding in Sierra Nevada and elsewhere, along with the following, who helped with discussions on the insect fauna, finding insects, confirming identification from specimens or photographs, or in other ways: David Baldock, Bob Buckler (www.wingspanbirdtours.com), Oskar Conle, Ian Cross, Emmanuel Delfosse, Joan Barat Domenech, Michael Geiser, John Hale, Sigfrid Ingrish, Darren Mann, Dan Powell, Chris Raper, Martin Rejzek, David Simpson (http://dordognebutterflybirdwatching.co.uk/), Tihomir Stefanov and Dr José Luis Yela. My apologies to others I may have omitted. My sister, Helen Brock has accompanied me on many bug-hunts often finding rarities. Peter Creed (NatureBureau www.naturebureau.co.uk) has been enthusiastic about the project from the very outset, providing various photographs from his own trips and has done an excellent job on the user-friendly design and layout of the pages, and seeing the book through to publication. Aurea Paquete worked hard producing the maps. Any errors in identification and omissions remain firmly mine.

***Paul D. Brock 2017***

# INTRODUCTION

## About this book

Why a book on insects of southern Europe and the Mediterranean? There has not been a book with good photographic coverage in English on the subject, featuring the type of spectacular insects keen naturalists might encounter on holiday in this biodiversity hotspot. Indeed, most books cover mainly British insects even if they add Europe to the title – but naturalists from Britain will quickly discover many species from southern Europe are not found in the north, rendering most books frustrating to use. Yet the Mediterranean is the most popular area for British naturalists; realistically only butterflies, moths, dragonflies and damselflies are well covered. It is reported that 80% of holidays from Britain are to Europe, with millions of holidaymakers going to Spain and France every year; other popular areas include Italy, Greece and Portugal. Gerald Durrell inspired thousands of naturalists to visit Corfu following publication of *My Family and Other Animals* and a popular television series on the same subject. Various trips for naturalists and butterfly watchers are now more popular than ever and are organised in most parts of Europe, often promising a density of butterfly life rarely seen in Britain. Many species are restricted to certain countries, others are aliens, sometimes evading the authorities and arriving on imported materials from various parts of the world.

My book *A comprehensive guide to insects of Britain & Ireland* (Pisces, 2014) features 2,100 species out of 24,000 species in 524 pages. The Mediterranean and southern European fauna is massive in comparison with Britain (66,000 species is a conservative estimate), but with fewer pages, I can only cover representative species from most insect orders, concentrating on what the naturalist, photographer or holidaymaker is likely to notice and wonder what it is. Anyone wanting to know about tiny flies or others will need to check the specialist scientific literature, or leave this to an expert. A lot remains to be learned about the smaller fauna of the region, with plenty of species still new to science.

The world of insects is fascinating, anyone browsing through this book will notice photos of some beautiful species, many never featured in other books. These are easily within reach of the British naturalist after just a few hours journey by plane, although some prefer car or ferry. Some insects have a bad reputation among the general public, are disliked or dismissed as having no use. A typical question from a member of the public might be 'what use are they?' However, for many naturalists several hours can be lost watching the antics of some of these insects, or trying to obtain photographs of quick-moving insects in flight. Insects are the most abundant and successful animals on Earth; they are everywhere and cannot be avoided! The European fauna is a tiny percentage of the well over a million insects described in the world, with many still undescribed. It is hoped that readers will gain some understanding about the fauna which regularly features in the news, albeit sadly often bad news: a decline in bees, butterflies and moths or possible arrivals from afar, with resulting concerns about pollination, pest control, loss of suitable habitat and climate change. Whilst some species are rare in Britain, they may be plentiful in southern Europe, although in recent years there have been noticeable declines in populations of some monitored species, which organisations involved with

**Near Lalinde, Dordogne, France**: holidaying in accommodation surrounded by nature.

conservation are addressing. Understandably, agriculture and income are important to countries, but this is increasingly having an adverse effect on wildlife. There are growing concerns about not just redevelopment of land with loss of habitat, but also agricultural changes, such as land abandonment. Air pollution in Europe, not only affects human health, but threatens biodiversity and the use of pesticides (including neonicotinoids), particularly by aerial spraying, is also causing major concerns. EU bans on some products may not be permanent. Climate change is influencing changes in populations of some insect species. Insects are vital to the well-being of many other animals and birds, as well as humans.

The layout of this book avoids the need for highly technical keys or having to use a microscope. However, these may be vital tools for some families, with tiny lookalike species; the introductory text to orders gives some guidance on this. Many naturalists are now using good quality binoculars with close focus from 50 cm suitable for insects and enjoy just watching insects from a distance. Many photographs show fascinating, sometimes seldom observed behaviour of insects; marching around a site to tick off a list of species seen will rarely reveal this type of activity, but methodical searches and observation will reward those with time and patience.

**Southern Europe & Mediterranean**

The Mediterranean conjures up thoughts of warm countries and although variably used, usually means lands bordered by the Mediterranean Sea. In this book there is concentrated coverage on the European countries, but excluding Central to Eastern Europe (Switzerland, Austria. Hungary, Romania, Moldova and Ukraine) with its colder climate and, to some extent, different vegetation – although this does not necessarily prevent some Mediterranean insect species from breeding or migrating north. Spain, Portugal and southern France feature strongly, and east to the Balkans and Turkey. The ever popular Greek islands are included in the coverage, also the Balearic Islands, Corsica, Sardinia, Sicily and Cyprus. Many of the European insects also occur in North Africa, beyond the scope of this book, hence only occasionally specifically mentioned; likewise the Middle East. The map below (with mountain ranges above 1,000 m in brown) shows the area covered by this book (the countries with darker shading are not covered by this book).

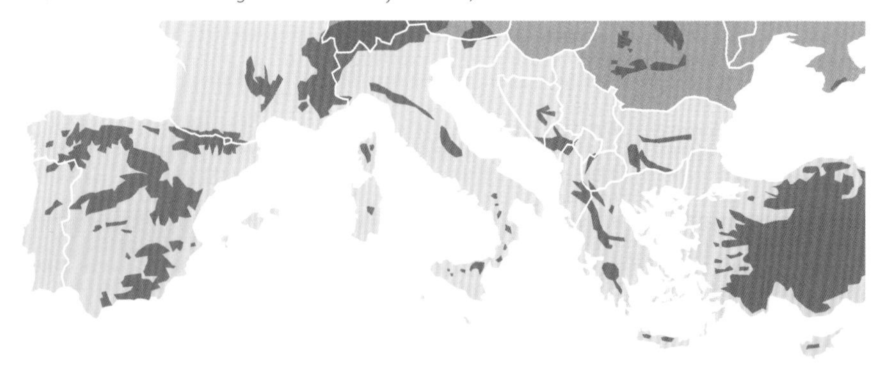

**Maps** – indicative distribution is only widely known for certain major groups of popular insects; invariably, data is incomplete for lesser studied groups – sometimes they may not be widely found in the countries shown or may occur elsewhere. Fauna Europaea maps exclude some countries, including Turkey, so for some orders information may be incomplete. Wherever possible, searches have been undertaken to ensure the maps are accurate, at least to country level.

**Habitat** – details of typical habitat types have been provided for many species.

**Hotspots** – given only as an indication of sites or countries where the insects discussed may be plentiful, in order to assist photographers or enthusiasts. There are always many other sites across Europe. To find sites near the area being visited, consult guide books and relevant websites such as Butterfly Conservation, European Interest Group.

**References** – key identification guides are listed here, including websites.

**Season** – an indication of the months during which adults can be found; these may differ across the range due to varying climate and different altitude.

**Sex symbols** – ♂ used for male, ♀ used for female throughout the book.

**Classification** – follows the division of insects into major groups called orders, such as Coleoptera (beetles) = sheath wings. Each order is divided into families, whose name ends in –idae i.e. Cerambycidae (longorn beetles). Families are divided into a genus or genera (plural) containing one or more closely related species, with names obtained from the latest accepted checklist or publication(s). The most used English name (where given), follows by the scientific name. As they are in usage worldwide, scientific names are often preferred by entomologists, as the English name would not mean much to a biologist in another country. There are examples where a dragonfly has both English and European names. Changes may be made by entomologists, i.e. some recent publications list the Six-spotted Longhorn Beetle *Anoplodera sexguttata* as *Leptura sexguttata*. In this example, the genus *Leptura* has changed to *Anoplodera* following revision, whilst the species name [*sexguttata*] remains the same. The English name is derived from the Latin *sexguttata*, i.e. six-spotted. Names are often made up of features, habitat, or the collector. Few insects have a stable classification, followed by all researchers studying the group and modern genetics work is leading to some changes in nomenclature, even to previously familiar names, for example among butterflies.

**Status categories** – most of the insects featured in this book are widespread. Using butterflies as examples, the Large White *Pieris brassicae* is clearly a widespread species, found practically everywhere. Two-tailed Pasha *Charaxes jasius* is local i.e. infrequently encountered, in relatively few areas or well scattered locations, although they may be common in those areas. Sadly more and more species are now regarded as rare and are often Red List category [= Red Data Book] species. Some species are considered endangered i.e. close to becoming extinct and may have a conservation programme in place. The rarest species are usually very restricted and often rarely seen. The False Ringlet *Coenonympha oedippus* is endangered in Europe, although across its global range is regarded as 'near threatened' or in decline. The Red List status is usually periodically updated. Rarer species featured are listed in Appendix 2. Some species are immigrants, wandering in from outside Europe, although they are not normally permanently established, perhaps due to the variation in climate, or restrictive foodplants. The best known is a butterfly, the Monarch *Danaus plexippus*, a true migrant as it also make a return journey, unlike some immigrants. Formerly restricted to the Canary Islands, it now breeds in Madeira, Portugal and southern Spain. Numbers fluctuate, but 2016 was a particularly good year for them in the Mediterranean. A number of rarer insects have at least partial protection and, in several cases, full protection by law. The regulations periodically change and the latest information should be checked. If surveying for insects which cannot be identified in the field, collecting permits are required in some countries for National Parks; others have a complete ban on collecting anywhere without permits, including Spain. Regulations need to be checked when planning a trip, as they can and do periodically change. Nowadays butterfly nets are often frowned upon and one is much more likely to see naturalists use a camera.

Enjoy the insect fauna, if not already an entomologist (someone of any age, who takes an interest in insects, and studies them), you may become one. No expensive equipment is needed, you can go outdoors and explore in your holiday accommodation or back garden. Or better still, take a trip to the great outdoors and take time to watch and learn – it's a fascinating world!

## Learning more

There are many nature tours throughout Europe by reputable organisations and individuals, usually for small groups, most offering a full package with an emphasis on Lepidoptera or Odonata. If being part of a group of photographers is not for you (and some tour leaders can irritate photographers by insisting on frequently netting butterflies or other insects so they can be closely examined), many people hire a car and go searching for insects themselves or take public transport. Planning and preparation is vital. Or there are plenty of guides with local knowledge providing individual tours, particularly with expertise in the better known insect groups.

# HABITATS

There is a wide selection of habitats in the Mediterranean where one can see mountains, rivers, deserts, forests and many islands. No wonder then that it is regarded as one of the Global Biodiversity Hotspots. However, a drive along some areas shows how developed many of these are, particularly on the coast. There is an ever-increasing demand for housing, tourist related activities and vast agricultural usage. Alien ornamental vegetation is spreading and impacts on native plant species and, consequently, the insects which rely on such vegetation. Nevertheless, compared with Britain, some areas are still full of insect life, well adapted to the Mediterranean climate and habitats, with its rich native, plant life. Even so, one must always be wary of the risks associated with habitat loss and degradation, as well as invasive plants and animals. Despite conservation efforts for some orders, many species are increasingly under threat and action or even inaction by landowners can have a devastating effect on wildlife.

### Coastal habitats

Some sites on the coast may be garrigue, but sand dunes and saltmarshes support an interesting array of specialist plants and insects. Many beautiful palm trees enjoyed by visitors to coastal resorts and parks for hundreds of years, have been devastated by the Red Palm Weevil, an Asian species which reached the Middle East in the 1980s via infected palm trees and rapidly spread to Europe, leaving thousands of dead and dying palm trees.

### Garrigue and maquis

These terms are familiar to those visiting the Mediterranean and typically means low evergreen shrub-dominated habitat on deep, acid soils. Maquis is the French term in the Mediterranean basin, otherwise known as mattoral (Spanish) or macchia (Italian); typical plants include holm oak *Quercus ilex* and rosemary *Rosmarinus officinalis*. Garrigue is the low-lying version, often on coastal limestone where vegetation is even more stunted. A wide range of often aromatic, fragrant plants is associated with this habitat, capable of withstanding a summer drought and supporting numerous populations of insects.

### Montane habitats

In the Mediterranean, higher mountains tend to occur in the south and low to medium in the north. These mountains receive more precipitation than other Mediterranean zones. Natural vegetation is deciduous or coniferous forests (often beech forests in the north, oak in the south), but other shrub formations and grasslands are also common. At higher altitude, vegetation can be sparse leaving mainly rocky areas.

### Woodlands

These are typically pine and oak woodlands, some of which may be of economic importance for their wood. They provide welcome shelter to visitors. Some oaks are often at higher altitude due to increased rainfall. The understory is home to many shrubs and flowers which attract a wide range of insects, including butterflies that enjoy shady conditions.

### Agricultural land

These were formerly evergreen oak forests. Many crops are grown on agricultural lands across the region, not just wheat, rice, vegetables, citrus fruits and grapes, but vast areas of almond *Prunus dulcis*, carob *Ceratonia siliqua*, fig *Ficus carica* and olive *Olea europaea*, the latter being a source of olive oil. Such lands invariably include at least pockets of wild flowers and habitats for a wide range of insects. Some lands are left natural, being mainly meadows full of flowers and consequently rich in insect life.

### Other habitats

Entomologists like to examine disturbed habitats wherever flowers grow, whether large botanical gardens or smaller private gardens, roadsides and disused land. These often include a wide range of alien plants. Those interested in dragonflies and damselflies will seek out freshwater habitats, looking for rivers which have not run dry by summer, ponds or temporary pools. Because freshwater habitats are relatively isolated, the larger wetlands sites are well known for rarer, endemic species. The Taberas Desert in Almería, Spain, is a semi-desert (with the only true desert climate in Europe), with a limited, but specialist flora and fauna.

**Sand dunes in the Tróia peninsula, Portugal** attract a wide range of insects, including various day-flying moths such as *Cerocala scapulosa* (pictured above [TF]) (Erebidae) in March. [TF]

**Dalyan Delta, Dalyan, south-west Turkey**, surrounded by various habitats, including productive agricultural areas. *Graphosoma semipunctatum* (pictured above [PC]) is one of the most attractive bugs seen on flowers. [SR]

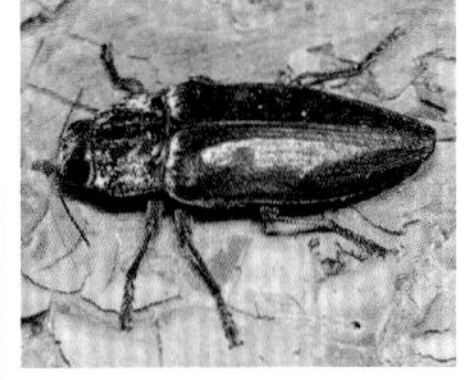

**West Peloponnese, Greece**: intact dune systems are a good habitat for many beetles including the impressive ground beetle *Scarites buparius* (Carabidae), and the jewel beetle *Chalcophora detrita* (Buprestidae) (pictured above [TB]) on dead pine stumps. [CG]

**Parco Nazionale di Abruzzo, Lazio e Molise, Italy**: diverse mountainous landscape containing a wealth of excellent insect habitats harbouring a rich fauna, including many Appenine mountain endemics. *Polyommatus damon* (pictured above [KB]) is one of the various high altitude butterfly species in the Appenines. [CG]

**Smolyan landslide lakes, southern Bulgaria** include pine forests, lakes and meadows of the biodiversity-rich East Rhodopes. Insects to be seen in this area include Odonata such as *Coenagrion hastulatum* and insects associated with pines. The woodwasp *Xeris spectrum* (12–28 mm) (above) oviposits in dead pine tree trunks.

An incredibly rich area of garrigue at low elevation (400 m.) on the **Mount Olympos massif, Greece**. Species present include *Saga* sp., *Nemoptera sinuata* (pictured above [TB]), *Megascolia maculata flavifrons*, *Charaxes jasius*, *Protaetia speciosissima*, and many longhorn beetles [CG]

Cork Oak forest, **Pinheiro, Portugal**. *Euproctis chrysrrhoa* moth larvae (pictured above) are known to defoliate Cork Oak trees in Iberia. [TF]

Olive groves in **Sierra de los Filabres, Almeria, Spain**. The larvae of the attractive micro-moth *Palpita vitrealis* (adult pictured above [PC]) feed on Olive *Olea* leaves. [TF]

**Barèges, France**: typical fast-flowing habitat for *Perla* spp., including *Perla grandis* (pictured above [WG]) and other stoneflies (Plecoptera).

# PHOTOGRAPHY

Some insects are easy to photograph, such as stick insects, or moths at rest. Tiny insects and others including fast-moving bees, flies and dragonflies in-flight are often photogenic, but they present more of a challenge to photographers than many other insects. Ideally, the photographer wants to take good images of insects in clear focus, in their natural habitat, showing aspects such as their habitat and behaviour. True macro (close-up) photography involves taking photos of the subject matter greater than life size and to achieve this, suitable camera equipment is necessary. Many keen entomologists use a digital single lens reflex camera, often choosing one manufactured by the market leaders Canon and Nikon, which offer a wide range of interchangeable lenses and accessories. Even fairly inexpensive cameras produce sharp, clear pictures, which can be transferred to computer and are suitable for publication.

## Equipment

Camera. Ideally this should be a lightweight, digital single lens reflex model around twenty megapixels upwards, allowing one to crop images as appropriate, without significant loss of quality. Which model to choose? Why not visit a large camera shop and try some out for weight or features. Modern cameras have ultra-fast auto-focusing, with motor drives firing the shutter several times a second; some cheaper compact cameras also produce fairly good quality results. Although a camera can be used with a good quality kit lens, the serious photographer combines it with a genuine macro lens and macro flash system, which adds to the initial cost. However, alternative, cheaper options are available, as discussed below.

Macro lens. Check dedicated manufacturer's macro lenses. For example, the highly regarded Nikon Micro-Nikkor 105 mm f.2.8G ED IF AF-S VR lens focuses from infinity to the all-important life size (1:1) for macro work although it is heavier than basic Nikon cameras such as the D5500. Importantly, a built-in image stabiliser helps with camera shake on hand held images. It is possible to save money on the macro lens itself by purchasing another manufacturer's model with a Nikon-fit, but these are invariably not the same quality. If considered necessary, the macro lens can be combined with a screw-on close-up lens, for example, the Marumi DHG Achromat Macro 200 (+5). This gives a magnification factor of +5, ideal when photographing tiny insects. However, the downside is that instead of standing back and taking the insect photo from a distance of a foot (0.314 m.), one needs to just centimetres away from the subject. Screw-in close-up attachments are an inexpensive way of taking macro photographs with ordinary lenses, but they vary in quality, often producing images that are soft around the edges. Achromatic attachments are preferable, but more expensive. Other options for close-up work include extension tubes and bellows.

Macro flash. The Nikon R1C1 package includes two wireless remote speedlights perched on a lens attachment ring, controlled by a wireless commander on the hot shoe connection. Further speedlights can be added and the comprehensive kit includes various diffusers. This is a fully automated system, using lithium batteries, producing high quality images in nature even at night. The speedlights can be angled, as required. Less expensive ring flashes may, however, eliminate shadows more fully when photographing dead specimens in collections. Spare batteries are needed in the field.

Dudley Cheesman enjoying finding and photographing a Southern White Admiral *Limentis reducta*.

Memory cards. A high quality memory card is required, perhaps 32GB, along with a spare. Details of compatible cards will be found in the camera instruction booklet.

Camera bag. Always carry the equipment in a suitable sized camera bag, along with a spare charged-up camera battery. Some use rucksacks, but these may not offer adequate protection.

**Techniques for photographing insects**

Subject, composition and lighting are crucial. Automated settings mean that everything is calculated for a perfect, sharp picture, the flash synchronising with the camera. It is recommended that aperture priority is used with an aperture of f.16-f.22 which provides additional depth of field (range of sharp focus). Refer to camera manuals for specific guidance on macro work and a book covering your camera or macro photographic techniques; different settings may be are preferred by photographers, for example some only use manual autofocus. Framing the subject is also important and those wanting competition photographs might want to use f.8-f.11 which creates a more blurred background. Combined with a sturdy tripod and, perhaps, electronic cable release, flash equipment may not be needed or desired by the user, if the light is good. However, in bright light, macro flash provides a fill-in flash, helping to eliminate undesirable, harsh shadows. Occasionally, some insects anticipate the camera flash and for these, it may need to be switched off.

In sunny weather, insects are much more active and observing their behaviour can help to decide on the best strategy for photographs; in any case approach cautiously without sudden movement and avoid casting a shadow over the insect. Focus on the head and thorax and try to hold the camera parallel with the whole body, trying to fill much of the frame with the insect, unless habitat is also required. Hand-held images are often perfectly acceptable and many featured in this book, involve speedily taken images in nature where the insect may only remain a split second or two before flying away. The camera must obviously be held steady and using a tripod or monopod is not always a viable option. If photographing insects in flight, a tripod may be useful. The most straightforward images involve insects at rest. If there is the luxury of several seconds or minutes to take images, composing the photo is important, in order to avoid unsatisfactory, cluttered backgrounds. Where insects are actively flying, in flight images showing sensation of movement are preferable. These could be frozen at high speed but some cameras have a maximum 1/200th of a second shutter speed with flash and the shutter needs to be precisely released. Although not adequate for some fast-moving insects, the low shutter speed is a compromise, still allowing reasonable depth of field. Without flash, some use the camera on Manual setting, using a high shutter speed.

In extreme cases, the insects are so fast the only solution to obtain a photo is to catch one [where one is allowed to do so] and bring it back home, placing it is the fridge for c.30 minutes or so, before taking a photograph in as natural conditions as possible; it may die if kept in the fridge overnight. If it does not fly, it can be released where caught. In warm weather some insects tend to fly within seconds of release though, so it is necessary to set the camera up ready prior to placing the insect in position for photographs; some specimens may have to be retained by entomologists in order to confirm identification. In order to avoid confusion, images should be processed and labelled speedily, particularly as some insects are very similar in appearance. This can cause a dilemma for the photographer, as it is vital to know which species the insect belongs to, but also important to obtain images. It is good practise to make notes in the field.

Editing software such as Photoshop is useful and can be used to make various adjustments, such as better framing of the subject and slight changes to sharpness and colour. RAW files are the choice of advanced, demanding photographers, as they allow greater creative control and RAW does not apply destructive compression associated with JPEG. However, files are large and therefore take up much more space on your memory card and computer; processing can also take up considerable time. Most photographers take JPEG Fine (high quality) images without any noticeable loss of quality. It is important to take quality images in situ, rather than spending hours on Photoshop. If fortunate, there may be time to check the images in the viewfinder. One can invariably tell when images have been taken in artificial surroundings, whether due to unnatural position of the insect (still alive?!) or poor background choice, sometimes resulting in a black surround due to insufficient light in the background. But perhaps the most important message is if one spots a rarity, or unusual behaviour, be ready! The opportunity may never present itself again.

As always in photography though, there is a potential conflict between the entomologist regarding accuracy in representation and others who have a subjective view, perhaps photographing an insect on a flower it would not visit, or inappropriate habitat.

# PRIMITIVE INSECT ORDERS

Whilst the classification is subject to different opinions, there are usually considered to be two orders of primitive wingless insects, with immature stages resembling small adults. These are the rather similar Silverfish (Zygentoma [=Thysanura]) and the Bristletails (Archaeognatha [=Microcoryphia]).

## Order ZYGENTOMA – SILVERFISH

**Southern Europe & Mediterranean: many of Europe's c.60 species**

The best known of these quick-moving species are sometimes pests in houses and bakeries; three slender tails are a similar length. These insects are appropriately named due to their fast movement resembling the wiggling of a fish and silver scales.

### Family Lepismatidae

***Lepisma saccharina*** **Silverfish**

Body length: 11 mm. Covered in silvery scales. Antennae approximately two-thirds of body length. **HABITAT** Likely to be encountered in cool, damp parts of houses, particularly where there is food available, such as cereals. **SEASON** All year.

***Thermobia domestica*** **Firebrat**

Body length: 11–13 mm. Brown, large hairs on thorax and abdominal segments. Antennae as long or longer than body. **HABITAT** Eats materials such as paper and plant debris, living near ovens and hot pipes. Outdoors they can sometimes be found under rocks or leaf litter. ♀s can lay c.6,000 eggs in a 3 to 5 year lifespan. **SEASON** All year.

## Order ARCHAEOGNATHA – BRISTLETAILS

**Southern Europe & Mediterranean: many of Europe's c.200 species**

Distinguished by a humped thorax and three tails at the end of the abdomen, the central one longer than the others.

### Family Machilidae

***Dilta hibernica***

Body length: c.11 mm. Brown. **HABITAT** Places with dense vegetation cover. **SEASON** June to September.

***Dilta littoralis*** **Heath Silverfish**

Body length: 10–11 mm. Brown. Males can be separated from other *Dilta* species, by differences in pattern of spines on the 2nd segment of the labial palp. **HABITAT** Grasslands and heathlands under debris, often coastal. **SEASON** June to September.

## A FEW NOTES ON NON-INSECTS

Formerly regarded as insects, but now generally listed as non-insect Hexapods, are the Proturans [Protura], Springtails [Collembola] and Diplurans [Diplura]. Common springtail species are shown: ***Pogonognathellus longicornis*** (c.6 mm), which is often seen in woodlands and recognised by its fairly large size and abdominal hairs, the globular ***Dicyrtomina saundersi*** (2–3 mm) and the hairy ***Orchesella villosa*** (c.4 mm). Other arthropods (animals without a backbone), but with more than six legs present in insects are the Myriapods, which include Millepedes [Diplopoda] and Centipedes [Chilopoda]. The Arachnids include Ticks and Mites [Acari] and Spiders [Araneae], the Crustacea include Woodlice [Isopoda].

*Lepisma saccharina*

*Thermobia domestica*

*Dilta hibernica*

*Dilta littoralis*

*Pogonognathellus longicornis*

*Dicyrtomina saundersi*

*Orchesella villosa*

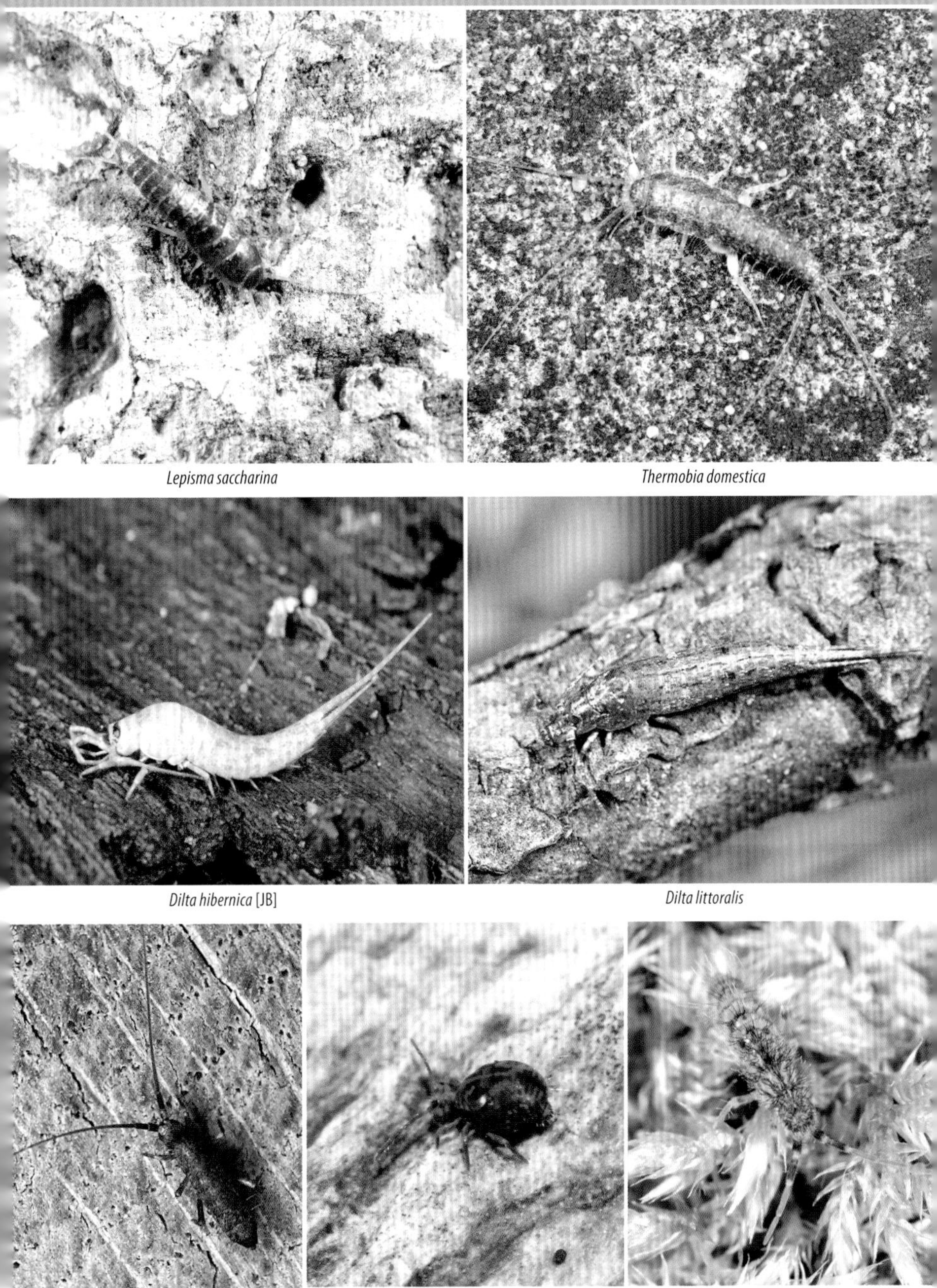

*Lepisma saccharina*

*Thermobia domestica*

*Dilta hibernica* [JB]

*Dilta littoralis*

*Pogonognathellus longicornis*

*Dicyrtomina saundersi* [PC]

*Orchesella villosa* [JB]

# Order EPHEMEROPTERA – MAYFLIES

**Southern Europe & Mediterranean: most of Europe & North Africa's 369 species**

Well known to trout fishermen (who tie artificial mayflies), many people will have seen the weak fluttering of mayflies over waterbodies. They have one or two pairs of densely veined, almost transparent wings (forewings much larger), characteristic short antennae and two or three slender, long, trailing 'tails'. The name Ephemeroptera means 'living for a day' and in some species this is true. However, the larvae are aquatic, spending a year or more under water, feeding on vegetation and small fragments of organic matter. Mayflies are the only insects to moult when fully-winged. When freshly emerged, the non-feeding adults are known as duns and are rather dull, but they moult within a few hours. The mature adults, known as spinners, rest with the wings held vertically above the back and some days swarms of thousands of these insects are seen flying around in mating 'dances', above the water or nearby. The life cycle is one of incomplete metamorphosis (development), so ♀s lay eggs which hatch into nymphs (*Ephemera danica* pictured left), from which eventually an adult emerges. A nymph (with three thread-like tails) can take about two years to complete its life cycle and may be found by examining the underside of stones in fast-flowing streams; others burrow in the silt or are active swimmers. Whilst damselfly nymphs also have three tails, these tend to be plate-like; gills are never external as in mayfly nymphs, which have up to seven pairs of gills. Other water creatures have fewer than three tails, so are unlikely to be confused. Some mayfly species have exacting habitat requirements and are particularly noticed at beauty spots in Europe in spring and summer; representative species are illustrated.

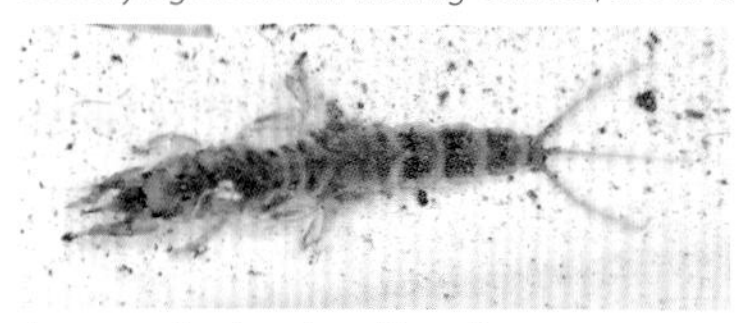

**HABITAT** Mayflies can be found in rivers, lakes, streams and ponds.

**HOTSPOTS** Many sites good for dragonflies, or used by anglers are suitable. Research varies across Europe. 106 species are recorded from Italy, but only 50 from Croatia, presumably reflecting under-recording.

## Family Baetidae

Two tails, hindwings small or absent.

### *Centroptilum luteolum* Small Spurwing

Body length: 6–7 mm. Small species with large, turret-like eyes. **HABITAT** Pools or margins of rivers or streams. **SEASON** April to November.

*Centroptilum luteolum*

### *Cloeon dipterum* Pond Olive

Body length: 6–10 mm. Medium sized species which lacks hindwings. **HABITAT** Pools or margins of rivers or streams. ♀s are known to lay c.1,200 eggs on the water surface 10–14 days after mating, with eggs hatching immediately. **SEASON** May to October.

*Cloeon dipterum*

## Family Ephemeridae

Three tails, large hindwings (dark marks on forewings), distinctive markings on abdomen.

### *Ephemera danica* Green Drake Mayfly

Body length: c.25 mm. Large species; forewing with several dark patches. **HABITAT** Lakes, rivers and streams with sandy or gravel bed. ♀s are known to lay up to 8,300 eggs. **SEASON** April to November.

*Ephemera danica*

### *Ephemera vulgata* Drake Mackerel Mayfly

Body length: c.25 mm. Large species with distinctive abdominal pattern of dark triangles and lines; forewing with several dark patches. **HABITAT** Slow rivers and ponds. **SEASON** May to August.

*Ephemera vulgata*

*Centroptilum luteolum*

*Cloeon dipterum*

*Ephemera danica*

*Ephemera vulgata* [PC]

# Order ODONATA – DRAGONFLIES & DAMSELFLIES

**Southern Europe & Mediterranean: c.125 species [23 endemic to the Mediterranean]**

Adults of these popular insects are large, fast, day-flying predators with amazing aerial skills, flying at up to 36 km/h (dragonflies) or more gracefully (damselflies). They have large eyes, tiny antennae and two pairs of wings, with a complex network of veins. The abdomen is long, slender and often brightly coloured, enabling them to be identified in flight. In fact, some rarely settle, making photography difficult. Immature forms and colour forms may add to confusion, but there are excellent guide books available. The life cycle is incomplete metamorphosis, involving egg, larva and adult. The predatory larvae are aquatic, feeding on insect larvae (including of the same species) and larger larvae eat tadpoles and small fish. The exuviae (larval skin) is often observed clinging onto reeds or waterside vegetation. Many photographers use large lenses on a tripod, taking photos from some distance away. However, it is possible to get close to the subject by careful stalking, avoiding sudden movement, although the insect may fly off to chase insects, possibly returning to the same perch. Adults catch various insects as prey, including other Odonata. Popular European vernacular names are provided, where significantly different to UK names, the latter are included in square brackets.

**HABITAT** Waterbodies with aquatic vegetation such as canals, ditches, lakes, ponds, rivers and streams, particularly if there is suitable habitat nearby with a plentiful supply of insect prey to hunt.

**HOTSPOTS** Numerous sheltered sunny sites can be productive on warm, still days. A visit in mid morning to early afternoon is usually best, but many photographers like an early start to potentially see emerging insects. Examples of productive sites include the Camargue in France and Doñana National Park in Spain. Dragonfly watchers can go on organised excursions looking for Odonata in various areas, including Sardinia, with 43 species recorded (Italy is good, with 88 species). France has 89 species, with other species found in Corsica, Spain has 79 species, including migrants from Africa, whilst European Turkey boasts 56 species.

**Laguna Grande, Malaga province, Spain.** Part of the Lagunas de Archidona Nature Reserve, with two saltwater lakes: Laguna Grande ['Big Lake'] and Laguna Chica ['Small Lake']. The smaller lake can dry up in extreme weather. This is a productive habitat for many Odonata, from large hawkers to skimmers, darters, dropwings and damselflies. The surrounding vegetation is also attractive to a wide range of other insects.

**Kerkini Lake, northern Greece** is regarded as one of Europe's most important wetlands. c.40 species of Odonata have been recorded here, including the exotic-looking *Lindenia teraphylla* Bladetail [pictured below], which flies along lakeside paths, occasionally settling. The various habitats are also excellent for a wide range of orther insects.

*Ischnura graellsii* damselflies mating, ♂ above

*Ischnura pumilio* damselfly egglaying

*Orthetrum trinacria* ♂ with prey (left), teneral eating a *Sympetrum fonscolombii* (right)

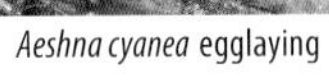

*Aeshna cyanea* egglaying

A dragonfly keeping watch for prey

# Suborder Zygoptera – DAMSELFLIES

The slender-bodied damselflies have a weak flight and usually rest with the wings held vertically above the body, although some rest with wings at least partly open. Damselflies tend to be much commoner at ponds and streams than the larger dragonflies; as such areas can only support a modest population. There may be hundreds of damselflies alongside some streams, where they spread out on vegetation, and ♂s form territories; different species may occupy other zones. ♀s are eagerly awaited and will often be seen paired, or egg-laying, often the ♀ oviposits in tandem with the ♂, which prevents rival ♂s mating. Sperm is stored by the ♀ in specialised organs. Fresh adults are known as teneral (not fully mature in colours), which can confuse observers until the normal adult colour is reached after a few days. The flight and colour of individuals helps to identify species. Larvae are carnivorous, taking approximately one year to complete their development under water.

## Family Lestidae – SPREADWINGS & WINTER DAMSELS [EMERALD DAMSELFLIES]

***Lestes barbarus* Migrant Spreadwing** [Southern Emerald Damselfly]
Body length: 40–45 mm. Similar to *L. sponsa* i.e. metallic green body but less blue pruinescence in the ♂; only on final abdominal segment if at all. Easy to confirm identification by the black and white wing spots (only black or brown in related species). ♀ ovipositor pale. **HABITAT** Seasonal waters and pools, in meadows and others. **SEASON** March to October.

***Lestes dryas* Robust Spreadwing** [Scarce Emerald Damselfly]
Body length: 35–40 mm. Like *L. sponsa*, but slightly broader abdomen. In the ♂, end of the anal appendage is curved, rather than straight (best viewed laterally); also there is usually less blue pruinescence, particularly on the first abdominal segments, where it covers the first one and a half segments. The eyes are normally deeper blue. **HABITAT** Well vegetated still waters. **SEASON** April to October.

***Lestes macrostigma* Dark Spreadwing**
Body length: 39–48 mm. Never as bright in ♂ as other species and often dark; blue pruinescence in both sexes distinctive, covering head, thorax, first two and final three abdominal segments. Wing spots large and dark. **HABITAT** Scattered populations, usually coastal shallow waters with dense rushes and sedges such as *Bolboschoenus maritimus*; also some inland wetlands. **SEASON** Late February to August.

***Lestes sponsa* Common Spreadwing** [Emerald Damselfly]
Body length: 35–39 mm. Body metallic green; ♂ with blue pruinescence on both sides of the thorax and the first and last two abdominal segments. **HABITAT** Well vegetated standing waters. The flight is very fluttering and at rest the wings are often held away from the body. Eggs overwinter. **SEASON** May to October.

***Lestes virens* Small Spreadwing**
Body length: 30–39 mm. Small, delicate species, some populations resembling *L. barbarus*. Back of the head yellow. ♂ blue pruinescence restricted to final two abdominal segments. **HABITAT** Seasonal waters and pools, in meadows and others; rather damper boggy areas further north. **SEASON** April to November.

***Chalcolestes viridis* Western Willow Spreadwing**
[Willow Emerald Damselfly]
Body length: 39–48 mm. Like *Lestes sponsa*, but conspicuously longer and ♂ without blue eyes or blue pruinescence. **HABITAT** Any well vegetated areas of still or slow-flowing water, with overhanging trees; eggs are laid into twigs overhanging water. Holds wings well spread and has a habit of vanishing in vegetation. **SEASON** May to November.

***Sympecma fusca* Common Winter Damsel**
Body length: 34–39 mm. Pale brown, with dark markings. **HABITAT** Well vegetated standing waters. **SEASON** All year but mainly April to September.

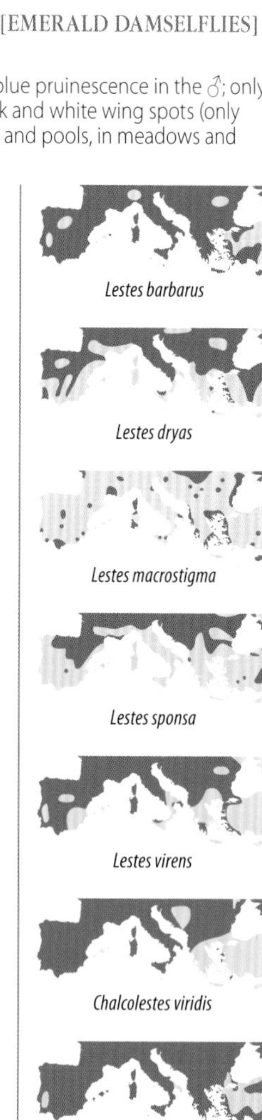

*Lestes barbarus*

*Lestes dryas*

*Lestes macrostigma*

*Lestes sponsa*

*Lestes virens*

*Chalcolestes viridis*

*Sympecma fusca*

*Lestes barbarus* ♂

*Lestes virens* ♂

*Lestes macrostigma* ♀

*Lestes sponsa* ♂

*Lestes dryas* ♂

*Chalcolestes viridis* ♀ (left), ♂ (right)

*Sympecma fusca* ♀ (left), ♂ (right)

## Family Calopterygidae – DEMOISELLES

### *Calopteryx haemorrhoidalis* Copper Demoiselle

Body length: 45–48 mm. Often metallic copper-red ♂ (can be other dark colours; if in doubt underside of abdomen is pink) with mainly dark wings (clear at base), ♀ metallic bronze to green body, hindwing with dark tip. **HABITAT** Streams and rivers with running water, in shade or sun. **SEASON** May to September.

*Calopteryx haemorrhoidalis*

### *Calopteryx splendens* Banded Demoiselle

Body length: 45–48 mm. ♂ body metallic blue; band of blue on otherwise translucent wing, usually not reaching tip. The ♀ has a metallic green body, with greenish-yellow wing with bold white tip. Some variation; rather darker form in Turkey, where outer half of wing is coloured (brown in female). **HABITAT** Open flowing streams and rivers. **SEASON** Late April to October.

*Calopteryx splendens*

### *Calopteryx virgo* Beautiful Demoiselle

Body length: 45–49 mm. Metallic bluish-green ♂ with almost completely blue wings, ♀ metallic bronze-green body, brownish wing with white tip. **HABITAT** Streams and rivers with running water, often shaded. ♀s lay eggs alone, with ♂s standing guard nearby. **SEASON** May to September.

*Calopteryx virgo*

*Calopteryx virgo* ♂. Subspecies *meridionalis* (illustrated, photographed in Spain) has a clear basal area, otherwise wings are bluish with dark tips. This occurs in the western Mediterranean and French Atlantic areas, with the entirely blue males of subspecies *festiva* found in southern Italy to Turkey. There is an overlap of these subspecies in Italy.

### *Calopteryx xanthostoma* Western Demoiselle

Body length: 45–48 mm. ♂ body metallic blue; band of blue on outer half of wings, extending to tip. The ♀ has a mainly metallic green body, difficult to separate in the field from *C. splendens*, but the last three abdominal segments are brown. **HABITAT** Rivers and canals with running water. More restricted distribution than other European demoiselles, also known to hydridise with *C. splendens*. **SEASON** April to September.

*Calopteryx xanthostoma*

## Family Euphaeidae – ODALISQUES

### *Epallage fatime* Odalisque

Body length: 40–50 mm. Robust species, blue ♂, ♀ pale, black patterned body. Dark wing tips in both sexes, more extensive in some females. **HABITAT** Rocky streams with running waters, also rivers. **SEASON** Late April to mid August.

*Epallage fatime*

*Calopteryx haemorrhoidalis* ♂ (left), ♀ (right) [PC]

*Calopteryx splendens* ♂ (left), ♀ (right)

*Calopteryx virgo* ♂ (left), ♀ (right)

*Calopteryx xanthostoma* ♂

*Epallage fatime* ♂ [KB]

## Family Platycnemididae – FEATHERLEGS

**_Platycnemis acutipennis_ Orange Featherleg**
Body length: 34–37 mm. Orange body, blue eyes in ♂. **HABITAT** Running waters. **SEASON** Late May to mid August.

*Platycnemis acutipennis*

**_Platycnemis latipes_ White Featherleg**
Body length: 33–37 mm. Both sexes with white body (mating pair pictured left); blue eyes in ♂. Black markings on abdominal segments. **HABITAT** Running waters. **SEASON** May to September.

*Platycnemis latipes*

**_Platycnemis pennipes_ Blue Featherleg** [White-legged Damselfly]
Body length: 35–37 mm. Blue (tenerals are white), white-legged ♂ with blue eyes. Black markings on final abdominal segments, typical of some featherlegs. **HABITAT** Various waters. **SEASON** May to October.

*Platycnemis pennipes*

## Family Coenagrionidae –BLUETAILS, BLUETS, BRIGHTEYES, RED DAMSELS & ALLIES

**_Ceriagrion tenellum_ Small Red Damsel**
Body length: 25–35 mm. Fairly small species, with a bronze thorax and reddish spots on the wings. The ♂ has an all red abdomen, but the amount of black and red on the abdomen varies in the ♀. **HABITAT** Small streams and seepages, including bogs. **SEASON** April to October.

*Ceriagrion tenellum*

**_Coenagrion caerulescens_ Mediterranean Bluet**
Body length: 30–33 mm. Similar to *C. scitulum*. With much more black than most related species, but with some variation. **HABITAT** Well vegetated streams, seepages and rivers. **SEASON** May to August.

*Coenagrion caerulescens*

**_Coenagrion hastulatum_ Spearhead Bluet** [Northern Damselfly]
Body length: 31–33 mm. Blue and black ♂, green and black ♀, only likely to be confused with the rather brighter *Enallagma cyathigerum*. ♂ with a spearhead mark on 2nd abdominal segment. **HABITAT** Various well vegetated acidic and other waters, with sedges. **SEASON** May to July.

*Coenagrion hastulatum*

**_Coenagrion mercuriale_ Mercury Bluet** [Southern Damselfly]
Body length: 27–31 mm. A small species, both sexes with slim thoracic stripes Many observers look for the black 'mercury' sign on the 2nd abdominal segment. The ♂ is blue and black, the ♀ black and yellow, green or greenish. **HABITAT** Streams with rich aquatic vegetation. **SEASON** May to August.

*Coenagrion mercuriale*

**_Coenagrion puella_ Azure Bluet**
Body length: 33–35 mm. ♂ bright blue and black with a characteristic 'U' shaped mark on the 2nd abdominal segment. The ♀ is green and black, occasionally a blue form occurs. **HABITAT** Various waters. **SEASON** April to September.

*Coenagrion puella*

**_Coenagrion pulchellum_ Variable Bluet**
Body length: 34–38 mm. Similar to *C. puella*, but appears a darker blue as it has more extensive black coloration. The ♂ has a 'Y' shaped mark on the 2nd abdominal segment, but this is variable. The ♀ has a dark and blue form with distinctive shaped markings on the pronotum. **HABITAT** Well vegetated still and slow-flowing waters. **SEASON** April to mid September.

*Coenagrion pulchellum*

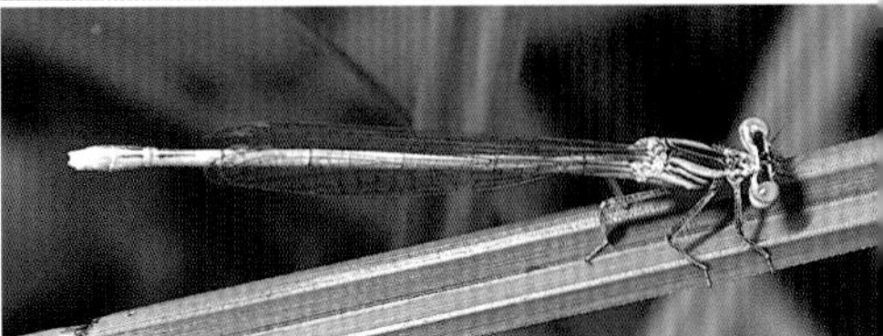

*Platycnemis acutipennis* ♂ (left), ♀ (right)

*Platycnemis latipes* ♂

*Platycnemis pennipes* ♂

*Ceriagrion tenellum* ♂

*Coenagrion caerulescens* ♂

*Coenagrion hastulatum* ♂

*Coenagrion mercuriale* ♂

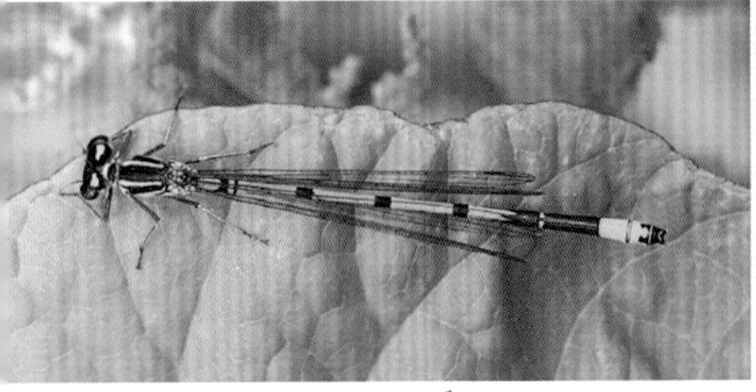

*Coenagrion puella* ♂

*Coenagrion pulchellum* ♂

**_Coenagrion scitulum_ Dainty Bluet**
Body length: 30–33 mm. Delicate blue and black species with yellowish underside; could be confused with *C. caerulescens* where these overlap. **HABITAT** Still and slow-flowing waters with rich aquatic vegetation. **SEASON** April to September.

*Coenagrion scitulum*

**_Enallagma cyathigerum_ Common Bluet**
Body length: 29–36 mm. ♂ bright blue and black with a characteristic club shaped black mark on the 2nd abdominal segment, also all blue segments 8–9. The ♀ is blue and black, often a dull green colour form occurs. The side of the thorax has only a single stripe. **HABITAT** Ponds, lakes and slow-flowing rivers. **SEASON** Late April to October.

*Enallagma cyathigerum*

**_Erythromma lindenii_ Blue-eye**
Body length: 29–36 mm. Black lanceolate abdominal markings characteristic, including blue tip. ♂ has a goblet-shaped mark on the 2nd abdominal segment. **HABITAT** Large waters with rich aquatic vegetation. **SEASON** March to October.

*Erythromma lindenii*

**_Erythromma najas_ Large Redeye**
Body length: 30–36 mm. Black with distinctive red eyes. The ♂ has light blue on the sides of the thorax (in ♀, yellow), the first and last two abdominal segments. **HABITAT** Still waters with rich aquatic vegetation, including floating leaves, which they often rest on. **SEASON** April to August.

*Erythromma najas*

**_Erythromma viridulum_ Small Redeye**
Body length: 26–32 mm. Very similar to *E. najas* and sometimes found together, may be initially noticed by the slightly smaller size. Again, black with distinctive red eyes. The ♂ has light blue on the sides of the thorax, the first and last two abdominal segments, but the sides of 2nd and 8th segments are blue (black in *E. najas*). **HABITAT** Still waters with rich aquatic vegetation, which they often rest on. **SEASON** May to September.

*Erythromma viridulum*

**_Ischnura elegans_ Common Bluetail** [Blue-tailed Damselfly]
Body length: 30–34 mm. Fairly small, the ♂ has a black abdomen with blue on the 8th abdominal segment. The ♀ is variable, with several colour forms. The normal form is similar to the ♂, others are green or brown. Immature forms have a pink or violet thorax. **HABITAT** Running and still waters, where they usually stay nearby. Adults spend up to six hours mating, hence are often seen paired. **SEASON** Late April to September.

*Ischnura elegans*

**_Ischnura graellsii_ Iberian Bluetail**
Body length: 26–31 mm. Small, similar to *I. elegans*, but often lacks side stripes on thorax. Hind part of pronotum lacking upright projection in *elegans*. **HABITAT** Running and still waters, where they usually stay nearby. Overlaps and hybridises with *I. elegans* in parts of Iberia. **SEASON** March to November.

*Ischnura graellsii*

**_Ischnura pumilio_ Small Bluetail** [Scarce Blue-tailed Damselfly]
Body length: 26–31 mm. A small species, similar to *I. elegans*, the ♂ abdomen is black with blue on the tip of the 8th and all of the 9th abdominal segments (the latter may have a pair of tiny black marks). The ♀ is black with a greenish thorax lacking clear side stripes; the orange immature form *aurantiaca* is unmistakeable. **HABITAT** Small ponds, pools and ditches. **SEASON** March to October.

*Ischnura pumilio*

**_Pyrrhosoma nymphula_ Large Red Damsel**
Body length: 33–36 mm. Thorax black in both sexes, with red stripes, abdomen red with dark bronze to black on final segments in ♂; in ♀ yellow band encircling each abdominal segment. There are several ♀ colour forms. **HABITAT** Various waters, often resting on vegetation on occasion well away from water. **SEASON** April to August.

*Pyrrhosoma nymphula*

*Coenagrion scitulum* ♂

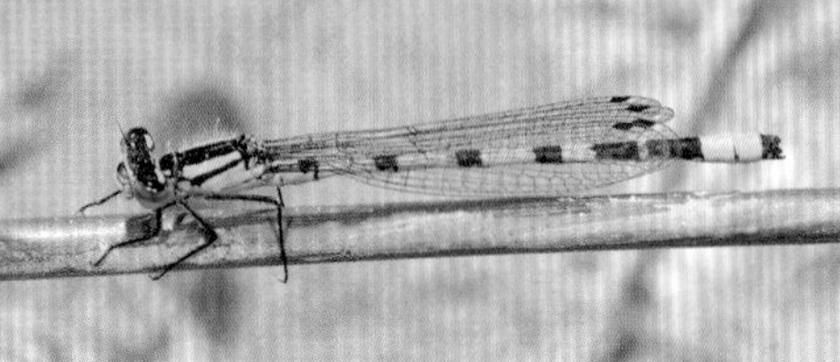

*Enallagma cyathigerum* ♂

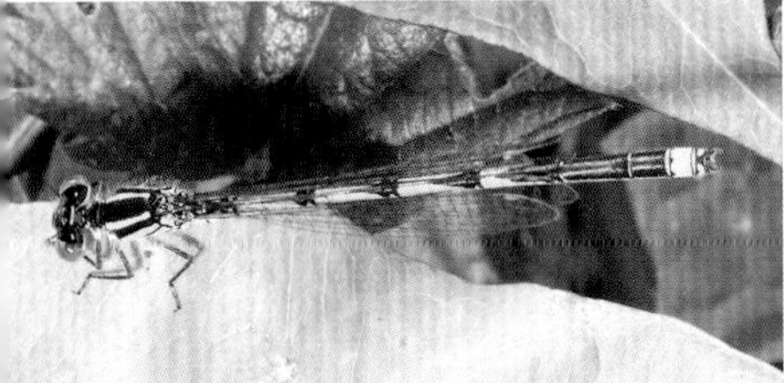

*Erythromma lindenii* ♂

*Erythromma najas* ♂ [PRi]

*Erythromma viridulum* ♂

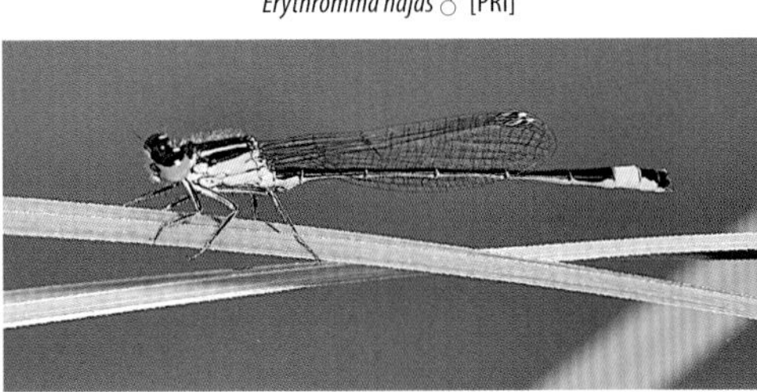

*Ischnura elegans* ♂

*Ischnura graellsii* ♂ (left), ♀ orange teneral form (right)

*Ischnura pumilio* ♂

*Pyrrhosoma nymphula* ♂

## Suborder Anisoptera – DRAGONFLIES

The dragonflies are larger and stouter than damselflies, with the hindwing broader than the forewing. Often powerful flyers, appearing to rarely stop, they rest with the wings fully open. Hawkers stay on the wing longest, patrolling their territories much of the day, sometimes stopping to eat a meal. They often catch bees, flies, wasps, butterflies, moths and even damselflies or smaller dragonflies. They are not seen paired as often as damselflies, except in the case of some darters. Egglaying is, however, often observed, with ♀s either ovipositing on their own, in tandem with the ♂, or with a ♂ on guard. Other dragonflies will attempt to chase them off their territories. Fresh adults are known as teneral (not fully mature in colours). The flight, colour and to some extent behaviour, of individuals helps to identify species. Larvae are carnivorous, as with damselflies taking two or more years to complete their development under water, depending on species.

### Family Aeshnidae – HAWKERS, EMPERORS & SPECTRES

**_Aeshna affinis_ Blue-eyed Hawker** [Southern Migrant Hawker]
Body length: 57–66 mm. Similar to *A. mixta*, but ♂ with side of thorax all green and all blue abdominal spots. **HABITAT** Still, often overgrown waters that dry up in summer. **SEASON** May to August.

**_Aeshna cyanea_ Blue Hawker** [Southern Hawker]
Body length: 67–76 mm. Appears greener in flight than other hawkers. Both sexes have a narrow yellow triangle on the 2nd abdominal segment and large yellow spots on the thorax, as well as green bars (blue in ♂) on last three abdominal segments. **HABITAT** Woodland and other sheltered ponds, including those in gardens. Adults are often found hunting in woodlands. Although the flight is powerful, they often hover and appear to be inquisitive, flying close to observers and readily perching low down. **SEASON** June to November.

**_Aeshna grandis_ Brown Hawker**
Body length: 70–77 mm. A large hawker, easily recognised in flight by the golden brown wings. Both sexes are similar. **HABITAT** Still waters with bankside vegetation. Adults are often found hunting in woodlands. **SEASON** Late May to early October.

**_Aeshna isosceles_ Green-eyed Hawker** [Norfolk Hawker]
Body length: 62–67 mm. A brown hawker, easily recognised by its clear wings. Both sexes are similar, with green eyes and a conspicuous yellow triangle on the 2nd abdominal segment. **HABITAT** Ponds, marshes and lakes with rich vegetation; may occur on running water. Often perches up. **SEASON** May to August.

**_Aeshna juncea_ Moorland Hawker** [Common Hawker]
Body length: 65–80 mm. Registers as brown and blue in flight. Both sexes have narrow yellow stripes on the thorax. The ♂ has blue abdominal spots (always rounded), usually yellow in the ♀. Upper forewing and hindwing vein (costa) noticeably yellow. **HABITAT** Acidic ponds, lakes and pools in lowlands, various waters elsewhere. ♂s are often found flying low over water searching for ♀s, or speeding along hunting for prey, in open areas or woodland rides. They are not easy to photograph, as they often perch out of reach. **SEASON** June to November.

**_Aeshna mixta_ Migrant Hawker**
Body length: 56–64 mm. A small hawker, similar to *A. affinis*, but has a small yellow triangle on the 2nd abdominal segment. Paired abdominal spots in ♂ blue; smaller marks on some segments yellow. ♀ abdomen is brown with yellow or green markings (rarely spots are blue). **HABITAT** Various still or slow-flowing waters. ♂s are often found flying along woodland rides. **SEASON** May to December.

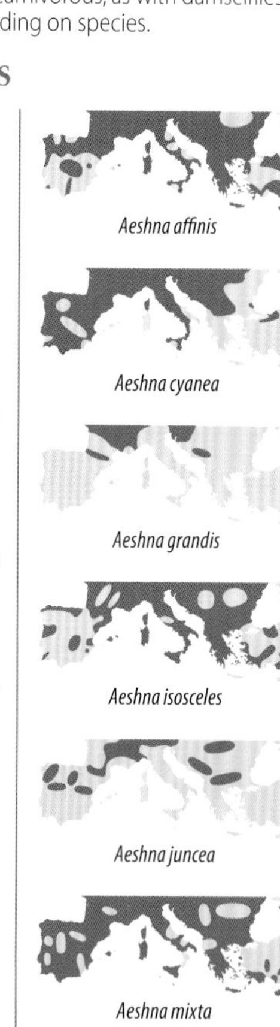

*Aeshna affinis* ♂ (left), ♀ (right) [both RPo]

*Aeshna cyanea* ♂

*Aeshna grandis* ♂

*Aeshna isosceles* ♂

*Aeshna juncea* ♂

*Aeshna mixta* ♂

### *Anax ephippiger* Vagrant Emperor

Body length: 61–70 mm. Similar to *A. parthenope* but blue saddle usually restricted to dorsal side only of 2nd abdominal segment in ♂ (less easy to see in flight) otherwise brown. The ♀ is similar but duller, the blue saddle less conspicuous. **HABITAT** Shallow pools and lakes where this migrant from Africa may regularly breed in the Mediterranean. **SEASON** All year.

*Anax ephippiger*

### *Anax imperator* Blue Emperor

Body length: 66–84 mm. A colourful large hawker, with a green thorax and green abdomen in the ♀ (sometimes blue), brilliant blue in the ♂. In both sexes, the abdomen has a broad central line. **HABITAT** Well vegetated, often large still waters but also small garden ponds. ♂s often patrol waters, rarely perching; small prey are eaten on the wing. They are seldom straightforward to photograph, but they sometimes perch low down on vegetation; by comparison it is straightforward to obtain ♀ egglaying photographs (see below). **SEASON** March to November.

*Anax imperator*

*Anax parthenope*

*Brachytron pratense*

*Boyeria irene*

### *Anax parthenope* Lesser Emperor

Body length: 62–75 mm. Similar to *A. imperator* but with green eyes and brown thorax. The ♂ only has the dorsal and lateral surface of the 2nd and 3rd abdominal segments blue (conspicuous in flight), otherwise brown and similar to *A. ephippiger*. The ♀ is similar but duller, although confusingly, a blue form sometimes occurs. **HABITAT** Still, large waters. **SEASON** March to November.

### *Brachytron pratense* Hairy Hawker

Body length: 54–63 mm. A small, early flying hawker, with a hairy thorax. The ♂ has a blue spotted abdomen, yellow in ♀s. **HABITAT** Still waters with rich aquatic vegetation, including canals and marshes. **SEASON** Late March to early August.

### *Boyeria irene* Western Spectre

Body length: 63–71 mm. A slender hawker, rather pale with mottled markings. **HABITAT** Partly shaded streams and rivers, where they patrol slowly. More likely in the open at dusk, when they are hunting. **SEASON** Late June to September.

*Anax ephippiger* ♀ [DRo]

*Anax imperator* ♂ [PC]

*Anax parthenope* mating pair, ♂ top

*Brachytron pratense* ♂

*Boyeria irene* ♀ [MR]

## Family Gomphidae – CLUB-TAILS, PINCERTAILS & ALLIES

### *Gomphus graslinii* Pronged Clubtail

Body length: 47–50 mm. Bright yellow (sometimes green), ♂ easily recognised by forked abdominal appendages alone. **HABITAT** Slow-flowing sections of large rivers in hilly areas. **SEASON** June to August.

### *Gomphus pulchellus* Western Clubtail

Body length: 47–50 mm. Yellow or tinged greenish, less bright and slenderer than other clubtails, with pale blue eyes (♀ pictured left). **HABITAT** Still and slow-flowing waters, often rivers and side channels. **SEASON** Late March to August.

### *Gomphus vulgatissimus* Common Clubtail

Body length: 45–50 mm. Black (more than in related species) and yellow or yellowish green, with greenish eyes. The ♂ has abdominal segments 8–9 more obviously clubbed than the ♀. **HABITAT** Slow-flowing waters, including large lakes and reservoirs. **SEASON** April to June.

### *Onychogomphus forcipatus* Small Pincertail

Body length: 46–50 mm. Black and yellow with large appendage in ♂, see *O. uncatus* for differences. **HABITAT** Often rocky rivers and streams. **SEASON** May to September.

### *Onychogomphus uncatus* Large Pincertail

Body length: 50–53 mm. Black and yellow, distinguished from *O. forcipatus* by the more extensive yellow abdominal markings, top of the head all black (yellow mark in *O. forcipatus*) and yellow thoracic collar broken by black (not broken in *O. forcipatus*). **HABITAT** Streams with flowing water, sometimes rivers. **SEASON** Late May to September.

*Onychogomphus forcipatus* ♂ (left) showing yellow unbroken collar and top of head with yellow mark; *Onychogomphus uncatus* ♀ (right) showing yellow collar broken by black and top of head all black

### *Paragomphus genei* Green Hooktail

Body length: 46–50 mm. Green face and thorax, with mottled abdomen (♀ pictured below). ♂ with flaps on abdominal segments 8 & 9. Appendages characteristic. **HABITAT** Still or slow-flowing waters, including seasonal pools, where they often perch with raised abdomen. **SEASON** April to October.

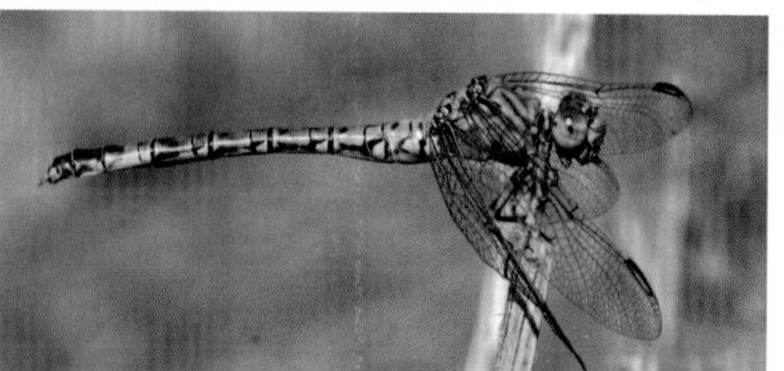

*Paragomphus genei* ♀ [MR]

*Gomphus graslinii*

*Gomphus pulchellus*

*Gomphus vulgatissimus*

*Onychogomphus forcipatus*

*Onychogomphus uncatus*

*Paragomphus genei*

*Gomphus graslinii* ♂ [MR]

*Onychogomphus forcipatus* ♂ [PC]

*Gomphus pulchellus* ♂

*Onychogomphus uncatus* ♂ [PC]

*Gomphus vulgatissimus* ♂ [PRi]

*Paragomphus genei* ♂ [MR]

## Family Cordulegastridae – GOLDENRINGS

### *Cordulegaster boltonii* Common Goldenring

Body length: 74–84 mm. A large hawker, easily recognised by its green eyes, yellow thoracic stripes and black and yellow banded abdomen. The ♀ has a long pointed ovipositor at the end of her abdomen. **HABITAT** Streams and small rivers in open areas and woodlands. ♂s patrol small stretches of water, with regular fights between encroaching rivals. The egglaying differs from other hawkers, the ♀ hovers in an upright position and repeatedly stabs into the streamside margins to deposit her eggs; in good spots she may stay for several minutes before speeding away to another site. The larval stage lasts two to five years. Photography is straightforward, as they often return to the same perch. **SEASON** Late May to August. **SIMILAR SPECIES** There are six other *Cordulegaster* species in the Mediterranean, including ***C. heros* Balkan Goldenring** and ***C. trinacriae* Italian Goldenring** [not illustrated].

*Cordulegaster heros* ♂, note larger abdominal bands

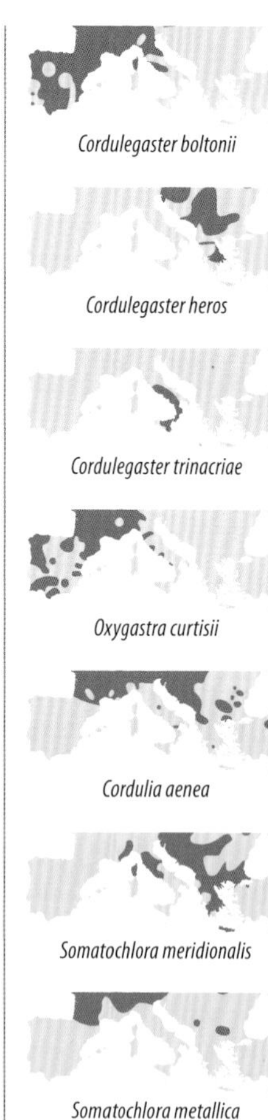


## Family Corduliidae – EMERALDS & CRUISERS

### *Oxygastra curtisii* Orange-spotted Emerald

Body length: 47–54 mm. Slender club-shaped abdomen, dark with yellow or orange streaks. Green eyes. **HABITAT** Slow-flowing rivers and streams. **SEASON** Late May to August.

### *Cordulia aenea* Downy Emerald

Body length: 47–55 mm. Greenish-black to bronze abdomen and yellowish-green eyes. **HABITAT** Well vegetated large ponds, lakes and other waters in woodlands and open areas, where ♂s patrol fast and low over the water, rarely stopping, and making photography more difficult. Feeding may be high in trees. **SEASON** Late April to July.

### *Somatochlora meridionalis* Balkan Emerald

Body length: 50–55 mm. Body metallic green. The wings have yellow bases. There are pairs of small yellow marks on abdominal segments 2–3, as well as one (rarely two) yellow spots on the thorax sides. Anal appendages long

in both sexes. Front of eyes with yellow bar (pictured left). **HABITAT** Shaded streams and rivers with running water. **SEASON** June to August. **SIMILAR SPECIES** ***S. metallica* Brilliant Emerald** [not illustrated] is almost identical in the field, but lacks the yellow spot on the side of the thorax.

### *Macromia splendens* Splendid Cruiser

Body length: 70–75 mm. Similar in general appearance to *Cordulegaster boltonii*, but with a clubbed abdomen and different markings. **HABITAT** Slow-flowing, warm rivers with plentiful vegetation; also known to breed in reservoirs. This species is aptly named a cruiser and rarely settles, presenting a challenge for photographers. **SEASON** Late May to mid August.

*Cordulegaster boltonii* ♂

*Oxygastra curtisii* ♂

*Cordulia aenea* ♂

*Macromia splendens* ♂ [DRo]

*Somatochlora meridionalis* ♂

## Family Libellulidae – GROUNDLINGS, WHITEFACES, CHASERS, SKIMMERS, DARTERS & DROPWINGS

***Brachythemis impartita*** **Northern Banded Groundling**
Body length: 25–34 mm. Easily recognised by the ♂ s dark wing bands, absent in more than half of ♀s (pictured left). The ♂ abdomen becomes black with age. Cream wing spots in both sexes, with dark outer margin. **HABITAT** Still waters such as lakes and pools, often with bare ground. This species often flutters low down in groups, settling periodically. **SEASON** April to October.

***Crocothemis erythraea*** **Broad Scarlet** [Scarlet Darter]
Body length: 36–45 mm. All red, broad bodied ♂. ♀s (pictured left) brown with white dorsal stripe on thorax. **HABITAT** Various open stagnant waters. **SEASON** March to October.

***Diplacodes lefebvrii*** **Black Percher**
Body length: 25–34 mm. Small, black ♂s, whilst ♀s straw coloured with hindwing base yellowish. Appendages in both sexes often pale. **HABITAT** Edges of lakes and marshes, perching on vegetation. **SEASON** April to November.

***Leucorrhinia dubia*** **Small Whiteface** [White-faced Darter]
Body length: 31–36 mm. A small species, the ♂ black with red spots and markings on the thorax and abdomen, which are white in the ♀. The common name derives from a distinctive white 'face'. **HABITAT** Often in acidic bog pools, ponds and lakes in forests. Often perches up, ♂s fly low over water to defend a territory. **SEASON** Mid April to early September.

***Libellula depressa*** **Broad-bodied Chaser**
Body length: 39–48 mm. A rather broad, flattened abdomen. The ♂ has a powdery blue abdomen with yellow spots along the side, whilst in the ♀ (pictured left [PC]) the blue is replaced by golden brown. Both sexes have brown eyes with dark brown wing bases. **HABITAT** Various small stagnant waters. The ♂ guards the ♀ whilst egglaying, by hovering nearby. This species is easy to photograph as this species often return to the same sunlit perch, the ♂ defending its territory by flying to intercept possible intruders. **SEASON** Late April to mid September.

***Libellula fulva*** **Blue Chaser** [Scarce Chaser]
Body length: 42–45 mm. The abdomen is not as broad as in the similar *L. depressa* and ♂'s powdery blue abdomen has distinctive darker areas in the centre (mating scars); the final three segments are black. The ♀ has an orange to brown abdomen (darkens with age) with black mid line markings broadening and rather triangular shaped towards the tip. The ♂ has bluish grey eyes; both sexes have dark brown wing bases. **HABITAT** Well vegetated, slow-flowing waters, ponds and others. **SEASON** Late April to early August.

***Libellula quadrimaculata*** **Four-spotted Chaser**
Body length: 39–48 mm. Brown, with narrow tapering abdomen, bordered by yellow on segments 3–9. Additional spot in middle of wings, in addition to yellow veins on fore and hindwings. In the fairly common form *praenubila* the black spots on the wings are more extensive. Both sexes have dark brown hindwing bases. **HABITAT** Still waters, often perched up. **SEASON** Late April to mid September.

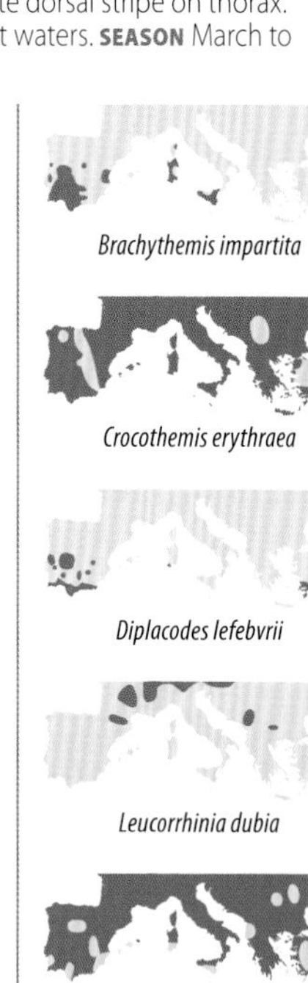

*Libellula quadrimaculata*

*Brachythemis impartita* ♂

*Libellula depressa* ♂

*Crocothemis erythraea* ♂

*Libellula fulva* ♂

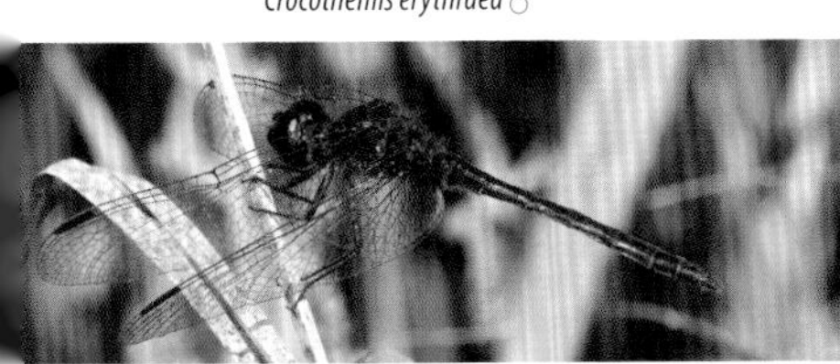
*Diplacodes lefebvrii* ♂

*Leucorrhinia dubia* ♂

*Libellula quadrimaculata* ♂

### *Orthetrum albistylum* White-tailed Skimmer

Body length: 45–50 mm. Slender and similar to *O. cancellatum*, pale blue ♂, with black tipped abdomen, ♀ brown with black longitudinal curved bands on abdomen. Both sexes with pale stripe on thorax and between wings and whitish appendages (rarely black); last abdominal segment also white in ♀. **HABITAT** Open ponds and lakes. **SEASON** Late May to mid September.

*Orthetrum albistylum* ♀

### *Orthetrum brunneum* Southern Skimmer

Body length: 41–49 mm. Fairly broad blue ♂, brown ♀. **HABITAT** Running waters. **SEASON** April to September.

### *Orthetrum cancellatum* Black-tailed Skimmer

Body length: 44–50 mm. Black-tipped pale blue abdomen in ♂, yellow in ♀ (pictured below) with two longitudinal black lines. **HABITAT** Larger still or slow-flowing waters, where they often rest on bare earth. **SEASON** Late April to early September.

*Orthetrum cancellatum* ♀

### *Orthetrum chrysostigma* Epaulet Skimmer

Body length: 39–48 mm. Slender blue ♂, with waisted abdomen, brown ♀. 'Epaulet' refers to an ornamental shoulder, a white band bordered with black. **HABITAT** Larger still waters, often streams in open areas. **SEASON** April to September.

### *Orthetrum coerulescens* Keeled Skimmer

Body length: 36–45 mm. Slender, mid to dark brown thorax, with pale stripes. The abdomen is powdery blue with pale stripes in the ♂ (sometimes all blue thorax and abdomen in parts of the south), golden yellow in the ♀, with a black central line. **HABITAT** Running waters, often streams. **SEASON** April to November.

*Orthetrum albistylum*

*Orthetrum brunneum*

*Orthetrum cancellatum*

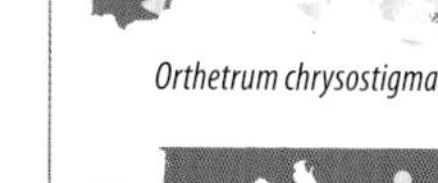

*Orthetrum chrysostigma*

*Orthetrum coerulescens*

*Orthetrum albistylum* ♂ [KM]

*Orthetrum cancellatum* ♂

*Orthetrum brunneum* ♂ (top), ♀ (bottom)

*Orthetrum chrysostigma* ♂

*Orthetrum coerulescens* ♂

**Sotogrande, Andalucía, Spain.** Close to the largest privately owned residential development in Andalucía, the River Guadiaro and Estuary is part of a reserve well known to birdwatchers, watching migratory birds. The pool by the seafront (illustrated, left) and nearby is remarkably productive, with the likes of *Orthetrum* species including *O. trinacria, Diplacodes lefebvrii, Brachythemis impartita, Lestes macrostigma* and a number of commoner species.

### *Orthetrum nitidinerve* Yellow-veined Skimmer

Body length: 46–50 mm. Blue ♂, brown ♀. Distinguished from *O. brunneum* by yellow veins on wings and yellow spots. **HABITAT** Still and running waters in hot, dry areas. **SEASON** April to October.

### *Orthetrum sabina* Slender Skimmer

Body length: 43–50 mm. Easily recognised by the slender black and white abdomen; appendages white. **HABITAT** Still and slow-flowing waters, where they often perch very briefly on the ground or twigs before speeding away. **SEASON** April to October.

### *Orthetrum taeniolatum* Small Skimmer

Body length: 33–38 mm. Small species, blue ♂ brown ♀ with black central line; two whitish stripes on the thorax (in old males the body can appear as all blue). **HABITAT** Still and slow-flowing waters, where they often perch on sandy ground or on rocks. **SEASON** May to September.

### *Orthetrum trinacria* Long Skimmer

Body length: 51–67 mm. A large, slender skimmer, bluish black ♂, brown striped ♀. Appendages noticeably longer than in other related species. **HABITAT** Still, large waters, such as lakes, where they are often seen eating other sizeable dragonflies. **SEASON** May to October.

*Orthetrum trinacria* mating pair, ♂ top

*Orthetrum nitidinerve*

*Orthetrum sabina*

*Orthetrum taeniolatum*

*Orthetrum trinacria*

*Orthetrum nitidinerve* ♂

*Orthetrum sabina* ♀ [SR]

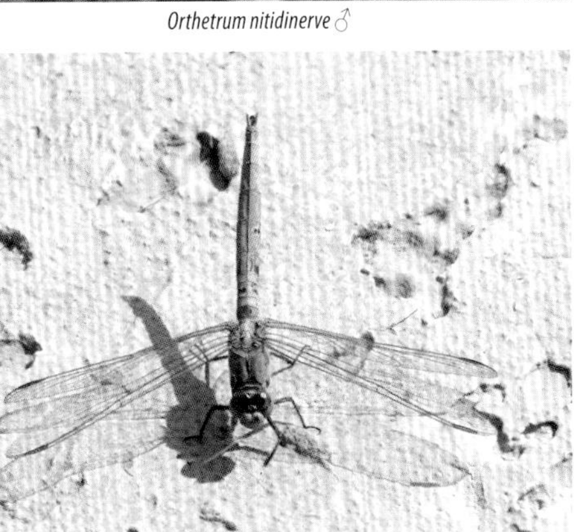

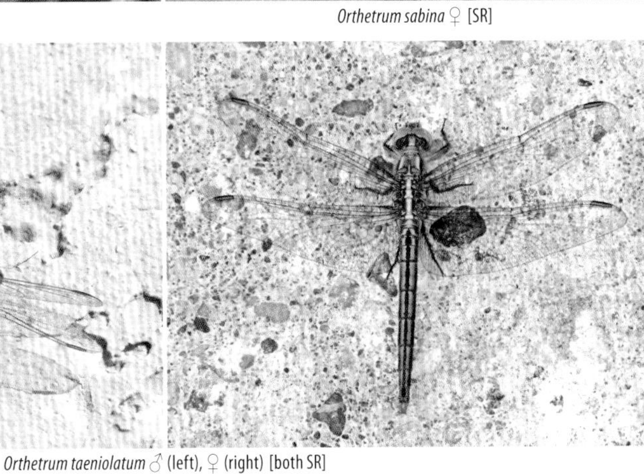

*Orthetrum taeniolatum* ♂ (left), ♀ (right) [both SR]

*Orthetrum trinacria* ♂ (left), ♀ (right)

*Selysiothemis nigra* ♀

### *Selysiothemis nigra* Black Pennant

Body length: 30–38 mm. Small, large-headed species with black ♂, brown ♀ (pictured above). Wings broad with mainly pale veins, pterostigma forming a black '=' sign. **HABITAT** Still, shallow waters. **SEASON** Mid May to September.

### *Sympetrum danae* Black Darter

Body length: 29–34 mm. A small species (mating pair pictured left), with black ♂, with yellow markings along the sides of the thorax and abdomen. The ♀ is yellow abdomen, with a black triangle on the thorax; sides strongly marked in black. **HABITAT** Acidic waters, including bogs. **SEASON** Mid June to early November.

### *Sympetrum flaveolum* Yellow-winged Darter

Body length: 32–37 mm. Easy to identify from the yellow wings. **HABITAT** Shallow, well vegetated waters. **SEASON** Late May to October.

### *Sympetrum fonscolombii* Red-veined Darter

Body length: 33–40 mm. Distinguished from other red darters by the red or yellow veins on the basal half of each wing, yellow base to wings and colour of eyes (pictured right [PC]), which are red above (brown above in ♀) and blue below. The ♀ (pictured left) is yellow with black markings, the thorax has greenish yellow sides. **HABITAT** Warm still waters. **SEASON** All year.

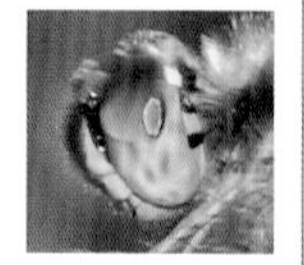

### *Sympetrum meridionale* Southern Darter

Body length: 35–44 mm. Plainer than related species, with few black markings. **HABITAT** Still waters. **SEASON** June to October.

### *Sympetrum pedemontanum* Banded Darter

Body length: 28–35 mm. Easily recognised by brown wing bands. Red spot on wings in ♂. **HABITAT** Hilly areas with slow-flowing waters. **SEASON** July to mid October.

*Selysiothemis nigra*

*Sympetrum danae*

*Sympetrum flaveolum*

*Sympetrum fonscolombii*

*Sympetrum meridionale*

*Symptetrum pedemontanum*

*Selysiothemis nigra* ♂

*Sympetrum danae* ♂ [TH]

*Sympetrum flaveolum* ♀ [PC]

*Sympetrum fonscolombii* ♂

*Sympetrum meridionale* ♂ [MRo]

*Symptetrum pedemontanum* ♂ [RPo]

*Sympetrum sanguineum* pair, ♂ on right

**_Sympetrum sanguineum_ Ruddy Darter**
Body length: 34–39 mm. ♂ with a much brighter red abdomen than relatives, with black marks on the side of abdominal segments, also centre of 8th and 9th segments. The ♀ has a yellow abdomen. **HABITAT** Well vegetated waters. **SEASON** April to October.

**_Sympetrum striolatum_ Common Darter**
Body length: 35–44 mm. A slender insect with brown thorax, with pale stripes dorsally and on the sides, the ♂ has a red abdomen, yellowish brown in the ♀ (pictured left), with black side markings. **HABITAT** Various. Mating pairs are a frequent sight, the ♀ oviposits in tandem with the ♂. **SEASON** All year.

**_Trithemis annulata_ Violet Dropwing**
Body length: 32–38 mm. Broad bodied species, striking violet male ♂, colourful ♀; both sexes with yellow base to wings. **HABITAT** Various waters, often perched on branches. **SEASON** April to October.

**_Trithemis festiva_ Indigo Dropwing**
Body length: 31–37 mm. Dark blue male ♂, sometimes with dark wing tips. And dark basal patch on hindwings. ♀ abdomen black, yellow streaked. **HABITAT** Streams and small rivers. **SEASON** Late April to September.

**_Trithemis kirbyi_ Orange-winged Dropwing**
Body length: 30–34 mm. Conspicuous red ♂ with orange wings, ♀ brown, with less orange on wings. **HABITAT** Small waters in open hot, dry areas, such as rocky streams, where they perch on vegetation, rocks or bare ground. **SEASON** May to October.

**_Zygonyx torridus_ Ringed Cascader**
Body length: 50–60 mm. Large member of the family, black with yellow spotted abdomen. **HABITAT** Fast flowing waters, such as rivers including waterfalls, where they only rarely perch on vegetation. Breeding is, so far, only confirmed for Sicily and Spain: the southern tip of Andalucía and the border of the province of Valencia. **SEASON** April to September.

*Sympetrum sanguineum*

*Sympetrum striolatum*

*Trithemis annulata*

*Trithemis festiva*

*Trithemis kirbyi*

*Zygonyx torridus*

*Sympetrum sanguineum* ♂

*Sympetrum striolatum* ♂

*Trithemis annulata* ♂ (left), ♀ (right)

*Trithemis festiva* ♂ [SR]

*Trithemis kirbyi* ♂

*Zygonyx torridus* ♂

# Order PLECOPTERA – STONEFLIES

**Southern Europe & Mediterranean: some of Europe's 426 species**

A group of mainly brown or yellowish insects found in flowing, aquatic habitats, particularly in temperate areas. The adults have two pairs of wings (shortened in some species), folded flat over the body, or wrapped around the abdomen. The end of the body has two threadlike tails in some species, but absent in most. The long antennae are threadlike, mouthparts are designed for chewing, but some larvae are carnivorous, whilst others feed on aquatic vegetation. Larvae grow to 40 mm in some species and many cling to stones on the stream bed, preferring fast-running water. Most adults do not feed (some graze on lichens and algae) and generally live for a few weeks. They attract the opposite sex by drumming (banging) the abdomen. The flight (where made) is slow and rather clumsy, with some species appearing at any time of year. There is an incomplete metamorphosis: egg, nymph and adult, most species completing the cycle in a year. Identification to species level can be difficult and involves using a microscope to examine genitalia. A few representatives are illustrated.

**HABITAT** Rivers and streams, few species dwell in standing waters. Adults are likely to be found at rest on nearby vegetation, rocks or buildings. Sometimes they are seen fluttering around. Nymphs may be seen crawling at the water's edge, prior to emergence, where skins are often noticed by naturalists.

**HOTSPOTS** A number of endemic species occur in the Alps and in the Mediterranean, particularly in France, Italy, Spain and the Balkans, not least due to mountainous territory.

## Family Nemouridae – SMALL BROWN STONEFLIES

Species without tails; wings with obvious ladders, held flat over the abdomen.

### *Protonemura ichnusae*

Body length: 3–7 mm. Typical of the family; brownish medium-sized stonefly. **HABITAT** Streams and rivers, endemic in Sardinia. **SEASON** March to April.

*Protonemura ichnusae*

## Family Chloroperlidae – SMALL YELLOW SALLIES

Small to medium, pale yellowish green species with two tails; wings without obvious ladders.

### *Siphonoperla torrentium* Common Small Yellow Sally

Body length: c.6 mm. Pale yellow. **HABITAT** Stony waters, flowing and still. **SEASON** April to August.

*Siphonoperla torrentium*

## Family Perlodidae – PERLODID STONEFLIES

Medium to large species with two tails; some species with conspicuous yellow or orange stripe on thorax; short and long-winged forms occur.

### *Isoperla curtata*

Body length: 6–16 mm. Yellowish body and additional dark markings. Characteristic short wings. **HABITAT** Springs and trickles, endemic species of the Iberian Peninsula. **SEASON** May to August.

*Isoperla curtata*

## Family Perlidae – STONEFLIES

The largest stoneflies in Europe, in general brown to black body coloration, with two tails; larvae carnivorous.

### *Perla grandis*

Body length: c.40 mm. Large species, with characteristic orange head. **HABITAT** Mountainous species of cold streams. **SEASON** Mainly mid May to July. **SIMILAR SPECIES** ***P. marginata***, similar size and some overlapping in range. Can only be reliably distinguished from differences in ♂ genitalia and egg chorion structure.

*Perla grandis*

*Perla marginata*

### *Perla pallida*

Body length: up to 25 mm. Yellowish general appearance. **HABITAT** Streams and rivers, widespread in the Balkans. **SEASON** Mainly May to June.

*Perla pallida*

### *Perlodes microcephalus* Orange-striped Stonefly

Body length: c.20 mm. Dark brown with bold orange-striped thorax. **HABITAT** Flowing waters. **SEASON** March to July.

*Perlodes microcephalus*

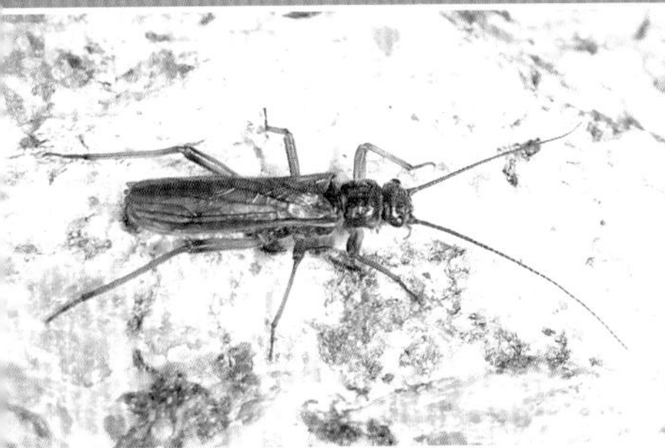

*Protonemura ichnusae* [WG]

*Siphonoperla torrentium*

*Isoperla curtata* [WG]

*Perla marginata* [WG]

*Perla grandis* (left), larval skin (right)

*Perla pallida* [WG]

*Perlodes microcephalus* [PC]

# Order DERMAPTERA – EARWIGS

**Southern Europe & Mediterranean: many of Europe's c.80 species**

Easily recognised by the large forceps (modified cerci, used in predation, defence and during mating) at the end of the abdomen, these insects are often seen by gardeners, as they eat flower buds or young plants. However, they are found almost everywhere, feeding on plant or animal material. Earwigs vary from having fully developed wings beneath flap-like forewings (but rarely fly), to having reduced wings, absent in some species. These mainly nocturnal insects have an unusual behaviour, in that ♀s guard their young until they are able to fend for themselves. Even the eggs are carefully kept clean. A few representative species are illustrated, two of them cosmopolitan.

## Family Anisolabididae

### *Euborellia annulipes* Ring-legged Earwig

Body length: 9–11 mm. Wingless, usually dark brown; legs are yellowish, the femora with a darker central band. **HABITAT** Various, under stones; a cosmopolitan species. **SEASON** All year, but often stays underground in winter.

*Euborellia annulipes*

## Family Forficulidae

### *Forficula auricularia* Common Earwig

Body length: 10–15 mm. A shiny, dark chestnut-brown species with yellowish legs. The tips of the folded hindwings project beneath the forewings. The forceps are large and robust, almost straight in the ♀, strongly curved in the ♂ in form *forcipata*. **HABITAT** Various. **SEASON** All year.

*Forficula auricularia*

### *Forficula lesnei* Lesne's Earwig

Body length: 6–7 mm. A small, pale species, with hindwings absent or greatly reduced. ♂ forceps strongly curved. **HABITAT** Various. **SEASON** May to October.

*Forficula lesnei*

## Family Labiduridae

### *Labidura riparia* Giant Earwig

Body length: 12–30 mm. Yellowish species, with variable dark brown markings. ♂ forceps long and gently curved, almost straight in ♀. **HABITAT** Often coastal, in sandy areas, where ♀s nest under rocks, but also found inland in farmlands and other habitats. **SEASON** All year, with 2-3 generations a year, the final brood hibernating until spring.

*Labidura riparia*

*Labidura riparia* habitat

*Euborellia annulipes* ♂ [FR]

*Forficula lesnei* ♂

*Forficula auricularia* form *forcipata* ♂ (left), ♀ (right)

*Labidura riparia* ♂

# Order ORTHOPTERA – BUSH-CRICKETS, CRICKETS & GRASSHOPPERS

**Southern Europe & Mediterranean: many of Europe's c.1,000 species**

This group of insects usually has two pairs of wings in adults, although a few lack wings. The antennae are long or short; eyes are large. Most characteristic are the large hind legs, which are modified for jumping. In all cases the life cycle shows incomplete metamorphosis (development), so adults lay eggs into plants or soil which hatch into nymphs; these resemble small adults and shed their skins several times before reaching the adult, breeding stage. Adults of several species tend to be very variable in colour so it is important to note certain key features when identifying species. The distinctive songs of grasshoppers and bush-crickets can be amplified in the field with a bat detector, set to a frequency of 35–40 kHz. Song is very important in courtship; mating sometimes taking many hours. A wide selection of species is illustrated, some being also found well outside Europe, or with a cosmopolitan distribution.

**HABITAT** Habitats are varied and details provided under each family.

**HOTSPOTS** There are various localities across the Mediterranean where numerous endemic species occur, particularly grassy alpine sites: some species are restricted to one mountain or hill. The South Balkans (parts of Greece and Former Yugoslav Republic of Macedonia) have a particularly rich fauna, also Crete has interesting endemic rarities. A third of the 300 species found in the Iberian Peninsula are endemic. Of 83 species recorded in Sicily, 20 species are endemic.

**Spain: Sierra Nevada**. Harsh, rocky conditions at c.2,500 m or so, provide suitable habitat for the bush-crickets *Baetica ustulata* and *Pycnogaster inermis*.

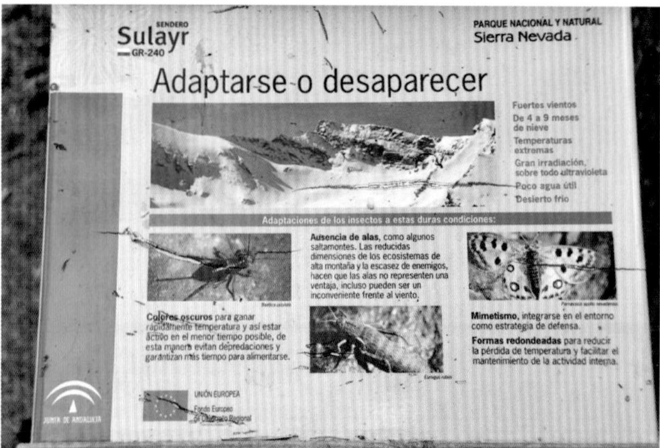


**Spain: Puerto de la Ragua, Sierra Nevada, 2,000 m**. A noticeboard discussing wildlife further up the slopes highlights two rare bush-crickets likely to be observed: *Baetica ustulata* and *Eumigus rubioi*, endemic insects only found at high altitude.

*Roesellana roeselii* (Tettigoniidae) mating pair

*Steropleurus andalusius* with spermatophore

*Gryllus campestris* ♂ (Gryllidae) singing

*Anacridium aegyptium* (Acrididae) feeding

*Oedipoda charpentieri* (Acrididae) mating pair

Lizard eating an *Oedipoda* species

## Family Tettigoniidae – BUSH-CRICKETS

Often large, recognised by a bulky appearance, with antennae often exceeding body length. ♀s have a blade-like ovipositor for egglaying, in some species as long as the body. The length given below is from head to end of abdomen, so ♀s are much longer if the ovipositor is included. Whilst some species are nocturnal, many sing by day and night. A courtship display is part of a premating process in which song (stridulation) plays an important role. Eggs of some species may take one, two or more years to hatch.

### *Amphiestris baetica* Betico Bush-cricket

Body length: 32–39 mm. Spectacular brown or green, stout-bodied species, with white and brown markings. Forewings short. **HABITAT** Rocky areas, including mountainous and coastal sites. **SEASON** May to July.

### *Baetica ustulata* Sierra Nevadan Saddle Bush-cricket

Body length: 18–26 mm. Brown head and thorax (legs paler). Bright glossy black on upper part of abdomen, with yellowish sides and edge of pronotum. Ovipositor long, curved. **HABITAT** Mountainous country 2,300 to 3,400 m (often near the snow line), only in the Sierra Nevada, almost devoid of vegetation but with *Genista baetica* present; usually seen on vegetation, hiding in rocks, or crawling on rocks or tracks. **SEASON** July to September.

### *Bradyporus dasypus* Bronze Glandular Bush-cricket

Body length: 41–60 mm. Stocky, large black wingless species with a metallic copper sheen. **HABITAT** Partly open habitats, including woodland edge, tall grasslands and mountainous sites up to 1,300 m. **SEASON** May to September.

### *Bradyporus oniscus* Woodlouse Glandular Bush-cricket

Body length: 43–68 mm. Stocky, black and brown wingless species with green markings. **HABITAT** Grasslands, often by agricultural sites with supply of shrubs and herbs; up to 1,100 m. **SEASON** May to August.

### *Ephippiger diurnas* Western Saddle Bush-cricket

Body length: 22–30 mm. Pale to olive green, sometimes yellowish or bluish-green. Back of the head black. Forewings short, one of a number of rather humped species. ♀ ovipositor almost as long as body. **HABITAT** Grasslands with bushes, where they fed on leaves, as well as other insects. Often found resting on vegetation. **SEASON** July to October.

### *Pycnogaster inermis* Unarmed Saddle Bush-cricket

Body length: c.35 mm. Brown wingless species with black bands and markings. Two whitish longitudinal stripes on abdomen and border to pronotum. Long ovipositor. **HABITAT** Rocky mountainous slopes with little vegetation in Sierra Nevada, Spain at 1,800 to 2,500 m. **SEASON** May to September.

### *Steropleurus andalusius* Andalusian Saddle Bush-cricket

Body length: 20–35 mm. Robust brown or green with typical 'saddle' for this genus. Yellowish lateral line on abdomen. Long ovipositor. **HABITAT** Grasslands or scrub, including mountainous areas. **SEASON** July to October.

*Steropleurus andalusius* ♂

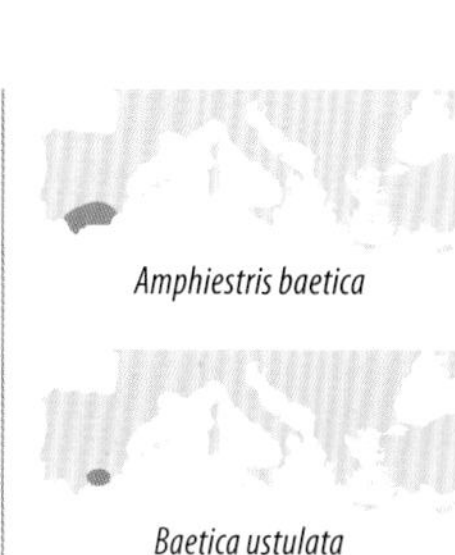

*Amphiestris baetica*

*Baetica ustulata*

*Bradyporus dasypus*

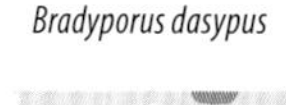

*Bradyporus oniscus*

*Ephippiger diurnus*

*Pycnogaster inermis*

*Steropleurus andalusius*

*Amphiestris baetica* ♂ [MRo]

*Bradyporus dasypus* ♂ [TN]

*Baetica ustulata* ♂ (top), ♀ (bottom)

*Bradyporus oniscus* ♂ [KB]

*Ephippiger diurnus* ♂ [PC]

*Pycnogaster inermis* ♂ [MR]

*Steropleurus andalusius* ♀

**_Conocephalus dorsalis_ Short-winged Cone-head**
Body length: 11–18 mm. Slender green (rarely brown) short-winged species, with a brown dorsal stripe. The wings only reach half length of the abdomen, (except rare long-winged form *burri*). However, the ♀ of *C. dorsalis* can then be distinguished by the long, upward curved ovipositor. **HABITAT** Wetlands, where they feed on seed heads, buds and flowers of rushes, sedges and grasses. **SEASON** June to October.

**_Conocephalus fuscus_ Long-winged Cone-head**
Body length: 16–22 mm. Slender green or occasionally brown long-winged species, with a brown dorsal stripe (formerly known as *C. discolor*). The ♀ ovipositor is long and almost straight. An extra-long winged form exists, with wings reaching the end of the ovipositor or beyond in the ♀. **HABITAT** Wetlands and dry grasslands. ♀s bite a hole in hollow stems of grass, reed or rush, inserting an egg with their long ovipositor. **SEASON** July to October.

**_Phaneroptera falcata_ Common Sickle Bush-cricket**
Body length: 24–36 mm. A long green, very long-winged insect covered with dark speckles. Small sickle-shaped ovipositor (♀ pictured left). **HABITAT** Dry grasslands and scrub. **SEASON** July to October.

**_Phaneroptera nana_ Southern Sickle Bush-cricket**
Body length: 12–18 mm. A green, long-winged insect similar to *P. falcata*, but distinguished by the form of the cerci (not broadened at the base). **HABITAT** Dry grasslands and scrub. **SEASON** July to October.

**_Ruspolia nitidula_ Large Cone-head**
Body length: 25–45 mm. Large green species, with a white line across the tip of the head. Wings long, reaching beyond the end of the long, straight ovipositor in the ♀. **HABITAT** Dry and damp grasslands. **SEASON** July to October.

**_Meconema meridionale_ Southern Oak Bush-cricket**
Body length: 11–17 mm. Small, delicate looking short-winged insect, pale green with a yellowish stripe along the back hence very similar to *M. thalassinum* except for the wings. **HABITAT** Woodlands, parks and gardens where they feed on small insects in oak *Quercus* and other trees. **SEASON** July to November.

**_Meconema thalassinum_ Oak Bush-cricket**
Body length: 12–17 mm. Small, delicate looking long-winged insect, pale green with a yellowish stripe along the back. **HABITAT** Woodlands, shrubby sites, gardens and parks where they feed on small insects. Mainly nocturnal, often resting on oak *Quercus* and many deciduous tree trunks, or fences. **SEASON** May to November.

**_Ancistrura nigrovittata_ Blackwinged Saw Bush-cricket**
Body length: c.25 mm. Green and partly brown (head and longitudinal band on abdomen), with speckled areas. Short forewings with two black longitudinal bands. **HABITAT** Shrublands, grasslands and others where bramble *Rubus* is present. Restricted to the southern Balkan peninsula. **SEASON** May to August.

*Conocephalus dorsalis*

*Conocephalus fuscus*

*Phaneroptera falcata*

*Phaneroptera nana*

*Ruspolia nitidula*

*Meconema meridionale*

*Meconema thalassinum*

*Ancistrura nigrovittata*

*Conocephalus dorsalis* ♂

*Conocephalus fuscus* ♀

*Phaneroptera falcata* ♂

*Phaneroptera nana* ♀

*Ruspolia nitidula* ♂ [MS]

*Meconema meridionale* ♀

*Meconema thalassinum* ♀ egglaying

*Ancistrura nigrovittata* ♂ [MS]

Grasshoppers such as *Oedipoda* species are frequently seen on the flat rocks in the **Gorges de Lavall, Alberes, Roussillon, France**, along with rare species such as the bush-cricket *Barbitistes fischeri*. [PC]

### *Barbitistes fischeri* Iberian Saw Bush-cricket
Body length: 20–25 mm. Green, ♂ with black speckled areas and white spotted lines on the abdomen. Short, partly brownish wings; legs often brownish. The head can be green or flushed with brown. **HABITAT** Woodlands and grasslands. Coastal in areas such as Languedoc, France. **SEASON** June to September.

*Barbitistes fischeri*

### *Isophya pyrenaea* Pyrenean Plump Speckled Bush-cricket
Body length: 16–26 mm. Green with darker dots and a yellowish stripe (reddish brown above) runs from the eye to forewings (hindwings absent). **HABITAT** Grasslands and woodland edge, where they feed on leaves, often near the ground. **SEASON** June to September.

*Isophya pyrenaea*

### *Leptophyes punctatissima* Common Speckled Bush-cricket
Body length: 9–18 mm. A stout, small green, reduced-winged species with a brown stripe on the back and conspicuous dark speckles over the whole body. The ovipositor is broadened and upturned. **HABITAT** Various bushy grasslands, parks and gardens where they feed on bramble *Rubus* and others. **SEASON** July to October.

*Leptophyes punctatissima*

### *Odontura aspericauda* Iberian Striped Bush-cricket
Body length: 10–18 mm. Green, heavily speckled species over the whole body. The ovipositor stout and upturned. **HABITAT** Bushy slopes including mountainous areas to 2,000 m., restricted to Iberia. **SEASON** April to August.

*Odontura aspericauda*

### *Poecilimon jonicus* Tiled Bright Bush-cricket
Body length: 14–25 mm. Unmistakeable colourful species, the subspecies illustrated is *tesselatus*. **HABITAT** Grasslands including mountainous areas, sometimes near woodlands. **SEASON** May to August.

*Poecilimon jonicus*

### *Saga hellenica* Greek Predatory Bush Cricket
Body length: 48–78 mm. Similar to *S. pedo*, but both sexes present in this and other *Saga* species. **HABITAT** Various grasslands with bushes, up to 1,500 m. A mainly nocturnal stalk hunter. **SEASON** June to September.

*Saga hellenica*

### *Saga pedo* Common Predatory Bush Cricket
Body length: 34–67 mm, ovipositor up to a further 45 mm, making it the largest bush-cricket in Europe and one of Europe's largest insects. A green wingless insect, with whitish or yellow lateral stripe and sometimes black marking on whole body. Reproduces parthenogenetically i.e. ♀s only. Spiny legs. **HABITAT** Grasslands to 1,500 m., often in dense vegetation, where they feed on other grasshoppers and bush-crickets. **SEASON** July to October.

*Saga pedo*

*Leptophyes punctatissima* ♂

*Odontura aspericauda* ♂

*Barbitistes fischeri* ♂ [PC]

*Poecilimon jonicus* ♂ [MS]

*Isophya pyrenaea* ♀

*Saga hellenica* ♀ [PF]

*Saga pedo* ♀ [PF]

***Decticus verrucivorus*** **Common Wart-biter**
Body length: 24–44 mm. A large, robust, dark green long-winged but flightless insect, with black marks on the pronotum and wings. **HABITAT** Mainly dry grasslands to c.2,500 m, including the short grass of alpine meadows and in the lowlands, the sites include Venice lagoon. They feed on insects, including grasshoppers, and vegetation. **SEASON** June to October.

*Decticus verrucivorus*

***Drymadusa dorsalis*** **Ocellated Tonged Bush-cricket**
Body length: 37–48 mm. A large, robust, brown, slightly mottled species. **HABITAT** Rocky grasslands, with bushes present. **SEASON** May to September.

*Drymadusa dorsalis*

***Eupholidoptera megastyla*** **Greek Marbled Bush-cricket**
Body length: 22–25 mm. Pale brown, broad black band on outer part of pronotum, bordered by orange (sometimes head also orange). 1st abdominal segment black and most of legs. Long ovipositor. **HABITAT** Rocky grasslands, with bushes present. **SEASON** May to September.

*Eupholidoptera megastyla*

***Metrioptera brachyptera*** **Bog Meadow Bush-cricket**
Body length: 11–21 mm. Green or brown short-winged species (♂ pictured left) (occasional fully winged form *marginata*), with bright green underside. Hind part of pronotum with a cream side band. **HABITAT** Wetlands and sometimes dry grasslands with long grass, including mountainous areas. They mainly feed on buds, seeds and flowers and on small insects. The song is difficult to hear. **SEASON** July to October.

*Metrioptera brachyptera*

***Pholidoptera griseoaptera*** **Common Dark Bush-cricket**
Body length: 11–21 mm. Almost wingless, dark brown with yellow underside. **HABITAT** Woodland edges and clearings, thickets and others, where they feed on vegetation (often bramble *Rubus*) and on small insects. Eggs are laid into rotting wood or bark crevices. In a role reversal, ♀s can be rejected by ♂s during courtship. **SEASON** June to November.

*Pholidoptera griseoaptera*

***Platycleis albopunctata*** **Common Grey Bush-cricket**
Body length: 18–28 mm. Usually greyish brown but variable; long-winged. **HABITAT** Sparsely vegetated grasslands to c.2,000 m., where they feed on herbs, grasses and flowers and on small insects. **SEASON** June to September.

*Platycleis albopunctata*

***Roeseliana roeselii***
**Roesel's Bush-cricket**
Body length: 13–26 mm. Dark brown and yellow or green markings on the thorax, usually short-winged (less common is the fully winged form *diluta* pictured left). **HABITAT** Various grasslands (often damper areas), feeding on grass and other vegetation, but will eat small insects. The song is loud and although often hidden, they sometimes sit on the top of bramble *Rubus* or other vegetation. **SEASON** May to October.

*Roeseliana roeselii*

Drymadusa dorsalis ♀ [MS]

Decticus verrucivorus ♂ (top) [MS], ♀ (bottom) [TB]

Eupholidoptera megastyla ♂ [MS]

Metrioptera brachyptera ♀

Pholidoptera griseoaptera ♂

Platycleis albopunctata ♂

Roeseliana roeselii ♀

***Tettigonia cantans*** **Upland Green Bush-cricket**
Body length: 20–33 mm. Green, with partly brown on the head, pronotum and forewings, which are much shorter than in *T. viridissima*. **HABITAT** Mountainous areas. **SEASON** Late June to October.

***Tettigonia viridissima*** **Great Green Bush-cricket**
Body length: 28–55 mm. Stunning large green long-winged species with a brown stripe along the back. **HABITAT** Grasslands up to 1,800 m, gardens and waste ground, mainly feeding on insects, occasionally vegetation. The long rattling song is easily recognisable from afternoon to evening. **SEASON** June to October.

***Thyreonotus corsicus*** **Moroccan Bush-cricket**
Body length: 20–29 mm. Greyish brown with conspicuously shaped large pronotum. **HABITAT** Grasslands with bushes, where they may be hide in thickets. **SEASON** July to November.

***Zeuneriana burriana*** **Burr's Wide-winged Bush-cricket**
Body length: 16–22 mm. Greenish brown, with dark pronotum lobes; short-winged. **HABITAT** Grasslands and forest clearings in mountainous areas to 2,000 m. **SEASON** July to September.

## Family Gryllidae – TRUE CRICKETS

Antennae shorter than bush-crickets and thread-like. As they are adapted to running and burrowing, the hind legs are less proficient at jumping. True crickets take more than one year to mature after hatching, so may overwinter as nymphs and/or adults.

***Acheta domesticus*** **House Cricket**
Body length: 14–20 mm. Sandy brown with dark bars across the head. **HABITAT** Often indoors in heated buildings, such as homes, hotels and factories, but is most likely outdoors at rubbish tips and land-fill sites. These nocturnal insects feed on a wide range of animal and vegetable matter. **SEASON** All year.

***Gryllus bimaculatus*** **Southern Field Cricket**
Body length: 17–23 mm. Like *G. campestris*, but when the hindwings are folded, these extend well beyond the end of the abdomen. **HABITAT** Grasslands, dunes and others, feeding on live and dead plant parts. **SEASON** July to September.

***Gryllus campestris*** **Field Cricket**
Body length: 17–23 mm. A large, robust, shiny insect, black with a deep yellow band beneath the thorax, but lacks hindwings. Forewings much shorter than end of abdomen. **HABITAT** Grasslands including hay meadows and at high altitude. Older nymphs and adults reside in burrows, with the loud song from ♂s distinctive, even from up to 100 metres away; this extends into the night. **SEASON** May to July.

***Nemobius sylvestris*** **Wood Cricket**
Body length: 7–12 mm. Small dark brown species with lighter brown pronotum; wings short. **HABITAT** Mainly woodland clearings, edges and scrub, in leaf litter, feeding on dead leaves and fungi. A high pitched trilling noise is often heard but they often hide and should be searched for in the vicinity; night searches by torchlight are often productive. The life cycle varies, but can be about two years and they may overwinter as nymphs and/or adults. **SEASON** June to November.

***Oecanthus pellucens*** **European Tree Cricket**
Body length: 9–15 mm. Small yellowish to pale brown species. **HABITAT** Grasslands and scrub, including mountainous areas. Sings after dark. **SEASON** August to October.

*Tettigonia cantans*

*Tettigonia viridissima*

*Thyreonotus corsicus*

*Zeuneriana burriana*

*Acheta domesticus*

*Gryllus bimaculatus*

*Gryllus campestris*

*Nemobius sylvestris*

*Oecanthus pellucens*

*Tettigonia cantans* ♀ [PC]

*Tettigonia viridissima* ♀

*Thyreonotus corsicus* ♂ [KM]

*Zeuneriana burriana* ♂ [TB]

*Acheta domesticus* ♀ [SR]

*Gryllus bimaculatus* ♂

*Gryllus campestris* ♀

*Nemobius sylvestris* ♀

*Oecanthus pellucens* ♂

## Family Mogoplistidae – SCALY CRICKETS

Covered in small scales.

***Pseudomogoplistes vicentae*** **Atlantic Beach-cricket** [Scaly Cricket]
Body length: 8–13 mm. Small greyish brown wingless insect. **HABITAT** Shingle beach among shingle and under stones, these fast moving nocturnal insects scavenge on vegetable and animal matter on the seaweed strandline. Related species are found on other coastlines throughout Europe. **SEASON** Mainly August to October.

*Pseudomogoplistes vicentae*

## Family Gryllotalpidae – MOLE CRICKETS

Large forelegs, modified for digging. The antennae are shorter than in the Gryllidae.

***Gryllotalpa gryllotalpa*** **European Mole Cricket**
Body length: 35–46 mm. Brown with patches of golden brown velvet-like hair on the thorax and abdomen; wings full length. Several species are similar, mostly difficult to identify, but some have shorter wings. **HABITAT** Damp grasslands with short grass, and vegetable gardens. Nocturnal; ♂s stridulate from underground burrows and should be searched for on warm nights. The life cycle is about three years and they mainly feed on insect larvae and earthworms. ♀s guard and care for small nymphs. **SEASON** April to June.

*Gryllotalpa gryllotalpa*

## Family Acrididae – GRASSHOPPERS

Grasshoppers have large hind legs for jumping. The short antennae readily distinguish grasshoppers from bush-crickets. They are found in grassy areas, often heard, not seen – unless walking through the grass. The similarity of some species may make them difficult to identify in the wild, without close examination, a situation not helped by the range of colour forms sported by most species. Grasshoppers hatch in spring, develop and mature in the same year, lay eggs, die.

***Acrida ungarica*** **Common Cone-headed Grasshopper**
Body length: 25–73 mm. Conical head, distinctively shaped green or brown species, sometimes with darker markings. **HABITAT** Grasslands with sparse vegetation, often low elevation. **SEASON** July to November.

*Acrida ungarica*

***Truxalis nasuta*** **Nosey Cone-headed Grasshopper**
Body length: c.70 mm. Conical head, green or brown species, wings are violet-tinged (transparent in *Acrida*) and ♀s of *T. nasuta* are usually larger. **HABITAT** Grasslands including river beds and sand dunes; rather restricted in range in the southern Mediterranean. **SEASON** April to June and perhaps later.

*Truxalis nasuta*

***Calliptamus barbarus*** **Eurasian Pincer Grasshopper**
Body length: 15–23 mm. Variable greyish or brown species, with large eyes and pink to burgundy wings. Hind femora banded. **HABITAT** Steep stony slopes, mainly feeding on grasses and herbs. **SEASON** July to October.

*Calliptamus barbarus*

***Calliptamus italicus*** **Common Pincer Grasshopper**
Body length: 15–34 mm. Robust often mottled species, with pink wings and orange hindlegs. **HABITAT** Grasslands to 2,000 m. **SEASON** Late June to October.

*Calliptamus italicus*

***Paracaloptenus caloptenoides*** **Balkan Pincer Grasshopper**
Body length: 15–34 mm. Various shades of brown with black marking; very shortened wings. Hind tibiae bright red. **HABITAT** Stony mountain slopes with low vegetation, mainly 800 to 1,600 m. **SEASON** July to October.

*Paracaloptenus caloptenoides*

*Pseudomogoplistes vicentae* ♀

*Gryllotalpa gryllotalpa* ♀ [MR]

*Acrida ungarica* ♀ [SR]

*Truxalis nasuta* ♀

*Calliptamus barbarus* ♀ colour forms [both PC]

*Calliptamus italicus* ♂ [WW]

*Paracaloptenus caloptenoides* ♀ [MS]

***Stenobothrus lineatus* Stripe-winged Toothed Grasshopper**
Body length: 15–26 mm. Brightly coloured, often green and brown with red on the abdomen (red on hind abdominal segments is absent in *Omocestus viridulus*, which often occurs with *S. lineatus*). Gently incurved side keels on the pronotum. White line and elongated spot on the forewing. **HABITAT** Grasslands, including mountainous areas and heathlands. Prefers shorter turf. **SEASON** July to October.

*Stenobothrus lineatus*

***Stenobothrus rubicundulus* Wing-buzzing Toothed Grasshopper**
Body length: 18–26 mm. ♂ forewings very dark. **HABITAT** Grasslands, including mountains up to 2,000 m. **SEASON** July to September.

*Stenobothrus rubicundulus*

***Omocestus bolivari* Iberian Grasshopper**
Body length: 10–18 mm. ♀ forewings smaller than those of closely related species. **HABITAT** Restricted range of grasslands in mountains 1,700 to 2,900 m in south-eastern Spain. **SEASON** July to October.

*Omocestus bolivari*

***Omocestus rufipes* Woodland Grasshopper**
Body length: 12–21 mm. Dark greyish brown species; underside of the abdomen and sometimes top is red in the ♂ (pictured below). The tips of the palps (mouthparts) are almost white. ♀s are brown or sometimes with green forewings, head and pronotum. **HABITAT** Rocky, barren grasslands (including mountainous and other areas, such as short-cropped sheep pasture). **SEASON** July to November.

*Omocestus rufipes*

***Omocestus viridulus* Common Green Grasshopper**
Body length: 13–24 mm. Usually green or green and brown or purple sides, mature adults never having red abdomens, with gently incurved side keels on the pronotum. **HABITAT** Damp grasslands, or sometimes drier tall grasslands, including mountainous areas often at 1,500 to 2,000 m. **SEASON** Mid June to September.

*Omocestus viridulus*

***Eyprepocnemis plorans* Lamenting Grasshopper**
Body length: 25–40 mm. Greyish brown, pronotum with dark band bordered by yellowish streaks, extended to head. Eyes with longitudinal lines. Hind femora with green or yellow streaks, hind tibiae partly reddish or blue, with white, black-tipped spines. **HABITAT** Open places often coastal and damper areas, near rivers. **SEASON** All year.

*Eyprepocnemis plorans*

***Arcyptera fusca* Large Banded Grasshopper**
Body length: 23–40 mm. Yellowish to olive, with yellow and black markings. Hind legs with red lower border on hind femora and mostly red hind tibiae. **HABITAT** Open places, often mountainous meadows to 2,500 m. **SEASON** Late June to October.

*Arcyptera fusca*

***Arcyptera labiata* Turkish Banded Grasshopper**
Body length: 22–35 mm. Various shades of brown or yellowish, with diagonal black abdominal markings. Hind femora banded black and white and mostly red hind tibiae. **HABITAT** Mountainous stony areas from 400 to 1,400 m. **SEASON** May to August.

*Arcyptera labiata*

*Stenobothrus lineatus* ♂ [PC]

*Stenobothrus rubicundulus* ♂ [MS]

*Omocestus bolivari* ♀

*Omocestus rufipes* ♀

*Omocestus viridulus* ♀

*Eyprepocnemis plorans* ♀

*Arcyptera fusca* ♀

*Arcyptera labiata* ♂ [MS]

***Chorthippus albomarginatus* Lesser Marsh Grasshopper**
Body length: 13–23 mm. Pale brown or green, less brightly coloured than *Pseudochorthippus parallelus* which it resembles because of the relatively short wings (in both sexes). The side keels on the pronotum are almost parallel. **HABITAT** Moist and dry grasslands, often with sedges. In coastal areas typically saltmarshes. **SEASON** July to October.

*Chorthippus albomarginatus*

***Chorthippus bornhalmi* Balkan Field Grasshopper**
Body length: 15–21 mm. Variable and rather like *C. brunneus* (but the song and distribution range differs). **HABITAT** Mountainous areas and bare rocky ground open forests. The Balkan counterpart of *C. brunneus*. **SEASON** May to October.

*Chorthippus bornhalmi*

***Chorthippus brunneus* Field Grasshopper**
Body length: 14–25 mm. Often brown, but variable, striped and mottled forms with parts of the body varying from buff through orange and even purple; the underside of the body is very hairy. Sharply incurved side keels on the pronotum; dark wedge-shaped markings not reaching hind edge. **HABITAT** Various grasslands with short turf or stony ground, including sand dunes and woodland clearings. **SEASON** July to October.

*Chorthippus brunneus*

***Chorthippus dorsatus* Steppe Grasshopper**
Body length: 14–25 mm. Often brown or olive green. **HABITAT** Damp meadows, sometimes drier sites. **SEASON** July to September.

*Chorthippus dorsatus*

***Chorthippus jacobsi* Iberian Field Grasshopper**
Body length: 15–19 mm. Variable and rather like *C. brunneus* (but the song and distribution range differs, as well as number of pegs on hind femora of ♂s). **HABITAT** Grasslands. The Iberian counterpart of *C. brunneus*. **SEASON** May to October.

*Chorthippus jacobsi*

***Chorthippus jucundus* Large Green Grasshopper**
Body length: 20–31 mm. Fairly plain green species with orange hind tibiae and end of hind femora. **HABITAT** Grasslands up to 500 m., including slightly damp sites i.e. by ponds. **SEASON** March to October.

*Chorthippus jucundus*

***Chorthippus vagans* Penumbra Grasshopper** [Heath Grasshopper]
Body length: 12–22 mm. Dark greyish brown. The pronotum has incurved side keels and dark wedge-shaped markings reaching hind edge. The end of abdomen may be orange or tinged with that colour, also the hind femora, which otherwise have two dark bands. Likely to be confused with the *C. brunneus*, but the underside of the thorax is only slightly hairy (very hairy in *C. brunneus*) although it is straightforward to see the pronotum difference in the field. **HABITAT** Stony sites, sand dunes and open coniferous woodlands, typically with bare ground. **SEASON** July to October.

*Chorthippus vagans*

***Dociostaurus maroccanus* Moroccan Cross-backed Grasshopper**
Body length: 16–38 mm. Yellowish grey with dark markings. The pronotum has a white cross-shaped marking. Forewings large and sometimes brown speckled, hindwings colourless. **HABITAT** Various with undisturbed soil for breeding, but numbers migrating in swarms from North Africa have diminished, resulting in a less serious threat to agriculture than formerly, at least in Europe. **SEASON** May to September.

*Dociostaurus maroccanus*

*Chorthippus bornhalmi* ♂ [MS]

*Chorthippus albomarginatus* ♂

*Chorthippus brunneus* ♀

*Chorthippus dorsatus* ♂ [MS]

*Chorthippus vagans* ♀

*Chorthippus jacobsi* ♂

*Chorthippus jucundus* ♀

*Dociostaurus maroccanus* ♀ [MS]

***Euchorthippus elegantulus*** **Elegant Straw Grasshopper**
[Jersey Grasshopper]
Body length: 10–22 mm. Yellowish brown, wings not quite reaching end of the abdomen. **HABITAT** Various tall grasslands. **SEASON** June to October.

*Euchorthippus elegantulus*

***Euthystira brachyptera*** **Small Gold Grasshopper**
Body length: 13–26 mm. Glossy yellowish-green. Wings in the ♂ reach half length of abdomen, but are very short and purple in ♀. **HABITAT** Grasslands. Found mainly in mountains and subalpine areas. **SEASON** July to September.

*Euthystira brachyptera*

***Pseudochorthippus parallelus*** **Meadow Grasshopper**
Body length: 10–23 mm. Green, sometimes with brown wings, although a striking pinkish form occurs. The usually short-winged ♀ is easily recognised (long-winged form *explicatus* also occurs). Slightly incurved side keels on the pronotum. The ♂ is long-winged, but these do not reach the end of the abdomen (mating pair pictured left). **HABITAT** Various grasslands, including mountainous areas. **SEASON** June to November.

*Pseudochorthippus parallelus*

***Gomphocerippus rufus*** **White-clubbed Grasshopper**
[Rufous Grasshopper]
Body length: 14–23 mm. Variable in colour but readily distinguished by the clubbed, white-tipped antennae. **HABITAT** Coarse grasslands, including hills and mountainous areas to 2,000 m., also woodland edge and scrub. **SEASON** July to November.

*Gomphocerippus rufus*

***Myrmeleotettix maculatus*** **Common Club Grasshopper**
[Mottled Grasshopper]
Body length: 10–19 mm. Variably mottled with several colour forms. Clubbed antennae in the ♂ and the thickened antennal tips of the ♀ help to distinguish them. The side keels on the pronotum are deeply Indented. **HABITAT** Open grasslands with short turf and some bare ground, including mountains up to 2,550 m., heathlands and sand dunes. **SEASON** Mid June to October.

*Myrmeleotettix maculatus*

***Cophopodisma pyrenaea*** **Pyrenean Mountain Grasshopper**
Body length: 15–21 mm. Conspicuously coloured, pinkish head, hind margin of pronotum and legs. Yellow banded abdomen, black and yellow markings, with much green on top of thorax and abdomen. **HABITAT** Grazed mountainous slopes, mainly 2,000 m to 2,600 m, often on the ground. **SEASON** July to October.

*Cophopodisma pyrenaea*

***Podisma pedestris*** **Common Mountain Grasshopper**
Body length: 17–30 mm. Reddish brown with yellow and black markings. Underside of hind femora reddish and hind tibiae blue. **HABITAT** Woodland clearings and alpine meadows, typically from 1,300 to 2,600 m. **SEASON** June to October.

*Podisma pedestris*

***Miramella alpina*** **Green Mountain Grasshopper**
Body length: 16–31 mm. Green and black-marked flightless species, with very short wings. **HABITAT** Sub-alpine mountains only, 1,000 to 2,800 m. In meadows, clearings and open woodlands. **SEASON** Late June to September.

*Miramella alpina*

***Pezotettix giornae*** **Common Maquis Grasshopper**
Body length: 11–18 mm. Brown, sometimes with black and whitish markings. **HABITAT** Grasslands and others with some tall vegetation to c.1,400 m. Overwinters as an adult. **SEASON** July to November, also spring.

*Pezotettix giornae*

*Euchorthippus elegantulus* ♀ [PC]

*Euthystira brachyptera* ♀ [PC]

*seudochorthippus parallelus* ♀ pink form

*Gomphocerippus rufus* ♂

*Myrmeleotettix maculatus* ♀ [PC]

*Cophopodisma pyrenaea* ♀ [PC]

*Miramella alpina* ♂ [PC]

*Podisma pedestris* ♂ (left), ♀ (right) [both MS]

*Pezotettix giornae* pair [PC]

### *Aiolopus strepens* Broad Green-winged Grasshopper

Body length: 18–32 mm. Variable, greyish brown or possibly some green, with distinctive black and whitish forewing markings. Hind tibiae red, hind femora particularly thickened compared with *A. thalassinus*. **HABITAT** Grasslands, river banks, woodland edge up to 2,000 m. **SEASON** All year.

*Aiolopus strepens*

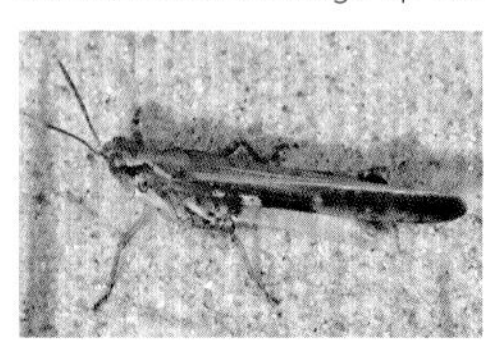

### *Aiolopus thalassinus* Slender Green-winged Grasshopper

Body length: 15–29 mm. Green, sometimes brown (♂ pictured left), with distinctive black and whitish forewing markings. **HABITAT** Prefers damp areas, such as river banks. **SEASON** August to October, also in spring.

*Aiolopus thalassinus*

### *Anacridium aegyptium* Egyptian Grasshopper

Body length: 32–66 mm. Robust grey, brown, yellowish or olive species (one of Europe's largest), easily recognisable by several vertical black lines down the eyes. Nymphs (pictured left) are often green, with developing wings. **HABITAT** Various, including scrub, agricultural land (orchards, olive groves) and gardens, where they feed on various leaves, often in bushes and trees. **SEASON** All year, but most likely May to September.

*Anacridium aegyptium*

### *Schistocerca gregaria* Desert Locust

Body length: 60–90 mm. Similar to *Locusta migratoria*, but easily recognisable by several lines down the eyes. **HABITAT** Open areas, mainly grasslands, usually migrating from North Africa. **SEASON** April to October.

*Schistocerca gregaria*

### *Locusta migratoria* Migratory Locust

Body length: 32–80 mm. Solitary phase largely green, hind tibiae reddish. When abundant the migratory phase develops. Locusts are sold as reptile or amphibian food in pet shops. **HABITAT** Open areas, including damper areas and sandy soil, where they feed on grasses and cereal crops. Well known for flying in swarms and used to be common in the Mediterranean, less so today. **SEASON** April to October.

*Locusta migratoria*

### *Mecostethus parapleurus* Leek Grasshopper

Body length: 17–32 mm. Often bright green, sometimes olive or brown; bold black lateral stripes on head and pronotum. **HABITAT** Grasslands, typically fens and lake shores. **SEASON** July to October.

*Mecostethus parapleurus*

### *Oedipoda caerulescens* Blue Band-winged Grasshopper

Body length: 15–28 mm. Variable, as they tend to blend in with their background. The forewings have two or three dark bands; hindwings pale blue with dark cross-band (pictured left). **HABITAT** Open stony areas, including mountains with sparse vegetation. **SEASON** July to October.

*Oedipoda caerulescens*

### *Oedipoda charpentieri* Western Band-winged Grasshopper

Body length: c.24 mm. Similar to *O. caerulescens*. The forewing bands in *O. charpentieri* usually narrower; wings blue or pink. **HABITAT** Arid places on bare ground. **SEASON** August to November.

*Oedipoda charpentieri*

*Aiolopus strepens* ♀

*Aiolopus thalassinus* ♀ [PC]

*Anacridium aegyptium* ♀

*Schistocerca gregaria* ♀ [KB]

*Locusta migratoria* ♀

*Mecostethus parapleurus* ♂ [PC]

*Oedipoda caerulescens* ♀ (left) [PF], ♀ unusual colour form (right)

*Oedipoda charpentieri* ♀ [FR]

***Oedipoda germanica* Red Band-winged Grasshopper**
Body length: 15–28 mm. Variable, as in the similar *O. caerulescens*, however hindwings are red with dark cross-band (pictured left). If photographing *Oedipoda* species, one needs to remember the wing colour! **HABITAT** Open barren, stony or rocky areas. **SEASON** July to October.

***Psophus stridulus* Rattle Grasshopper**
Body length: 23–40 mm. ♂ black, ♀ brownish or grey. Prominent keel, hindwings red with black tip. **HABITAT** Stony grasslands, up to 2,000 m. ♂s fly with a loud rattling sound. **SEASON** July to October.

***Stethophyma grossum* Large Marsh Grasshopper**
Body length: 12–39 mm. Yellowish green to olive brown. Lower margin of hind femora vivid red. A plum coloured form is sometimes observed in ♀s, which are considerably larger than ♂s. **HABITAT** Wetlands including bogs. When disturbed, they can fly some distance. **SEASON** July to October.

## Family Tetrigidae – GROUND-HOPPERS

Small grasshopper-like insects with short antennae, with the pronotum extending backwards over the top of the abdomen, sometimes beyond. The forewings are reduced to small scales. These well-camouflaged insects are variable in colour and are active in the day, where they can be found in damp areas with bare ground, where they feed on algae, lichen and mosses. They are good swimmers, even underwater. Ground-hoppers take more than one year to mature after hatching, so nymphs and/or adults may overwinter, hence may be found all year round. Unlike grasshoppers, the ground-hoppers do not sing.

***Paratettix meridionalis* Mediterranean Ground-hopper**
Body length: 7–12 mm. Variably coloured, one of the long winged ground-hoppers, which can be plain, but often has whitish patches. **HABITAT** Sandy, stony or muddy places near salt water, often coastal. **SEASON** April to October, most likely in spring when out of hibernation, or autumn.

***Tetrix undulata* Common Ground-hopper**
Body length: 8–11 mm. Distinguished by its short pronotum and short wings about reaching or just exceeding the end of the abdomen (a rare long-winged form occurs). **HABITAT** Wetlands or sometimes dry bare earth in woodlands and open areas with sparse vegetation. Well camouflaged, search on bare ground in damp areas and soon enough, one will jump out of the way. **SEASON** All year.

## Family Pamphagidae – STONE GRASSHOPPERS

Robust, often large, understudied mountainous grasshoppers living at high altitude, with shortened wings, most with a rather restricted distribution and found on the ground, or hiding under stones.

***Acinipe hesperica* Western Stone Grasshopper**
Body length: 43–78 mm. Large greenish brown species with yellowish, reddish and black markings. Pronotum arched, rough with raised tubercles, extending to mesonotum. Wings very short. **HABITAT** Rocky areas, including mountainous areas and gardens in Spain. **SEASON** March to December.

***Asiotmethis limbatus* Bordered Stone Grasshopper**
Body length: 25–35 mm. Greyish or brown species with black markings. Orange at back of head, deep blue when head is extended. Wings shorter than end of abdomen. **HABITAT** Rocky areas, in grazed grasslands. **SEASON** Mid May to July.

*Oedipoda germanica*

*Psophus stridulus*

*Stethophyma grossum*

*Paratettix meridionalis*

*Tetrix undulata*

*Acinipe hesperica*

*Asiotmethis limbatus*

*Oedipoda germanica* ♀ [MS]

*Psophus stridulus* ♀ [PC]

*Paratettix meridionalis* ♀

*Tetrix undulata* ♀

*Acinipe hesperica* ♀

*Stethophyma grossum* ♀ purple form (top), ♀ (bottom)

*Asiotmethis limbatus* ♀ [MS]

***Eumigus monticolus* Mountain Stone Grasshopper**
Body length: 26–50 mm. ♂ brownish, ♀ greyish brown. Distinctively shaped pronotum. **HABITAT** Rocky mountainous slopes in Sierra Nevada and surrounds, Spain at 1,000–3,100 m. **SEASON** June to September.

*Eumigus monticolus*

***Eumigus rubioi* Rubio's Stone Grasshopper**
Body length: 25–48 mm. Brown, similar to *E. monticolus* but pronotum normal and vestigial wings even shorter. **HABITAT** Dry, rocky mountainous slopes with little vegetation in Sierra Nevada, Spain at 2,000 to 3,000 m. **SEASON** May to September.

*Eumigus rubioi*

***Euryparyphes terrulentus* Earthling Stone Grasshopper**
Body length: 25–47 mm. Pale to dark, sometimes green with whitish markings. ♂ slender. Laterally compressed pronotum. Inner spines of hind tibiae yellow, tip with black ring. **HABITAT** Rocky areas. **SEASON** April to August.

*Euryparyphes terrulentus*

***Pamphagus marmoratus* Marbled Stone Grasshopper**
Body length: 48–87 mm. Greenish yellow, some purple streaks and white border to pronotum, forewings and other markings. **HABITAT** Maquis in Sicily, otherwise in Algeria and Tunisia; overwinters as a nymph. **SEASON** April to August. **SIMILAR SPECIES** *P. sardeus* [not illustrated] from Sardinia.

*Pamphagus marmoratus*

***Paranocaracris bulgaricus* Bulgarian Stone Grasshopper**
Body length: 22–40 mm. Uniform brown. **HABITAT** Dry, rocky limestone mountainous areas with little vegetation in parts of southern Bulgaria and northern Greece, up to 2,000 m. **SEASON** May to August.

*Paranocaracris bulgaricus*

# Order EMBIOPTERA – WEBSPINNERS

**Southern Europe & Mediterranean: some of Europe's 13 species**
A small, poorly known order with long, cylindrical bodies and two-segmented cerci. ♀s are wingless, but the ♂s of some species have soft wings. The legs are short and stout, the base of the fore tarsi have a silk gland used to create galleries in leaf litter or on rocks, tree trunks and others. This provides a retreat, where they live gregariously on the food source within such as leaf litter or bark, extending the galleries as necessary and tending to the offspring. ♀s sometimes eat ♂s.
**HABITAT** Woodlands and others, typically around silken galleries on bark or rocks.

## Family Embiidae

***Embia amadorae***
Body length: c.11 mm. Dark brown winged ♂ (forewing length 5.5 mm) with red thorax and reddish abdomen; ♀ paler. **HABITAT** Typically under stones in rocky areas in Iberia. **SEASON** All year.

*Embia amadorae*

## Family Oligotomidae

***Haploembia solieri***
Body length: 10–14 mm. Reddish to dark brown or black (head darker), legs paler. Wingless in both sexes. **HABITAT** Various. **SEASON** All year. Note: This successful species has even become established in parts of United States and Mexico. In the Mediterranean it reproduces bisexually, but there are also parthenogenetic populations (♀s only) in parts of Italy, Sardinia, Elba, Capri and Corsica [assuming all belong to the same species].

*Haploembia solieri*

*Eumigus monticolus* mating pair (left), ♀ (right)

*Eumigus rubioi* ♀

*Euryparyphes terrulentus* ♀ [DRo]

*Pamphagus marmoratus* ♂ [DW]

*Paranocaracris bulgaricus* ♀ [MS]

*Embia amadorae* ♂ [FR]

*Haploembia solieri* ♀ (left), inside silk gallery (right) [both SO]

# Order PHASMIDA – STICK INSECTS

**Southern Europe & Mediterranean: 18 species**

Stick insects are often large insects resembling sticks, with c.3,200 worldwide species, mainly in the tropics (the order includes 65 leaf insect species). The life cycle is incomplete metamorphosis: egg, nymph and adult. Many species are able to reproduce parthenogenetically i.e. ♀s lay fertilised eggs which hatch into ♀s only. European species are all wingless and although both sexes occur in some species, others are parthenogenetic, resulting in populations of ♀s only. Species belong to distinct groups of lookalike insects, only reliably distinguished by molecular work, in several cases. These insects rely on camouflage for protection against predators and are nocturnal, feeding on leaves and sometimes flowers. Adults may be found most months in good weather, but they are generally commoner in May to November, leaving the eggs to overwinter and the nymphs to hatch in spring. The seed-like eggs are dropped to the ground, the structure helping to identify species. *Bacillus rossius* or *Clonopsis gallica* are the species most likely to be seen. The majority of species have been described since 1990, following molecular work and are unlikely to be encountered unless searched for. However, few species are well studied, so they can easily be found in unreported localities – including new species to science. Several of the species most likely to be seen are illustrated.

**HABITAT** Typically open areas with shrubs where foodplants occur, often coastal sites.

**HOTSPOTS** One of best areas for the phasmid specialist is the Syracuse district, south-east Sicily; with determined effort, it should be possible to find at least three species during a week's trip. However, much of the Mediterranean is a good searching area, concentrating on bramble *Rubus* spp., Lentisk *Pistacia lentiscus*, broom *Cytisus* and related plants. Large round bites often indicate the presence of these insects, which are, however, much easier to find at night by torch-light.

## Family Phasmatidae

One non-native species with medium length antennae.

### *Carausius morosus* Laboratory Stick-insect

Body length: 70–84 mm. ♀ dull green or brown, with small tubercles (knobs) on the thorax (end of abdomen pictured left). The inside base of the leg is red. ♂s are known but extremely rare in culture stocks, possibly genetic ♀s, incapable of reproduction. This species was first used in a laboratory culture and is widely kept in schools. **HABITAT** Gardens, hedgerows or other areas where they feed on bramble *Rubus* spp., ivy *Hedera* and other vegetation. Notes: Discarded culture stocks have occasionally been recorded in various parts of southern Europe including France, Portugal, Spain and Madeira. A native of southern India, they have been introduced to various countries, including Australia, Madagascar, South Africa and the USA.

## Family Bacillidae

Short antennae with 19–25 segments in *Bacillus*, 12–18 segments in *Clonopsis*.

### *Bacillus atticus* Greek Stick-insect

Body length: 64–105 mm. ♀ brown, occasionally green, conspicuously granulated, more so in some subspecies. Cerci short and stout. **HABITAT** Mainly coastal sites with Lentisk *Pistacia lentiscus* shrubs. Interestingly these mastic feeders rarely accept bramble *Rubus* in culture. Notes: There are three subspecies in Greece, Croatia, Italy (including Sardinia and Sicily), Crete, Cyprus, Rhodes, Turkey, Israel and Libya.

### *Bacillus rossius* Mediterranean Stick-insect

Body length: 64–105 mm. ♀ brown, reddish or green, rather plain except for red inner base of fore legs and cream or red side stripe (end of abdomen pictured left). Cerci slender (longer than in *atticus*). The slender plain brown ♂ occurs in some populations. **HABITAT** Mainly coastal shrublands where they feed on *Rubus* and other plants. Notes: ♀s only extend as far north as Britain (likely escapees from culture), but mainly Mediterranean. **SIMILAR SPECIES** Other *Bacillus* species [not illustrated or mapped] some of which are virtually identical: ***B. grandii*** (three bisexual subspecies in Sicily feeding on bramble *Rubus* or Lentisk *Pistacia lentiscus* depending on population), ***B. lynceorum*** and ***B. whitei*** (Sicily, bramble feeders). Sometimes confused with *Clonopsis gallica*.

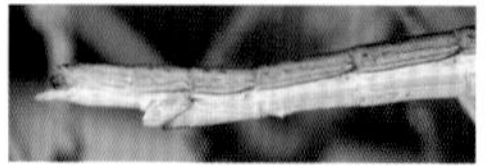

*Carausius morosus*

*Bacillus atticus*

*Bacillus rossius*

*Carausius morosus* ♀

*Bacillus atticus* ♀ [CM]

*Bacillus rossius* ♂ (left) [PV], ♀ green form (right)

**Hoya de Pedraza, Sierra Nevada, Spain** – habitat near the botanical gardens for *Pijnackeria recondita* and *P. hispanica.*

### *Clonopsis gallica* French Stick-insect

Body length: 59–79 mm. ♀ brown or green, rather plain but the moderately granulated thorax and usually smaller size distinguish it from *Bacillus rossius*, as well as number of antennal segments (only 12–13). ♂s recorded in the literature appear to be intersexes, unable to fertilise ♀s. **HABITAT** Shrublands, hedges and woodland edges or rides where they usually feed on bramble *Rubus* and other Rosaceae, even broom *Cytisus* in the Iberian Peninsula. Notes: Extends as far north as Normandy in France, but well represented in Mediterranean countries, and the Azores, Madeira and Tenerife. Much more likely well inland than *Bacillus*. **SIMILAR SPECIES** Only *C. gallica* occurs in Europe. Sometimes confused with *Bacillus rossius*.

Other *Clonopsis* species [not illustrated] reproducing bisexually or parthenogenetically are outside the region covered in this book: ***C. algerica*** (Algeria), ***C. felicitatis***, ***C. maroccana*** and ***C. soumiae*** (all Morocco).

## Family Diapheromeridae

11 species with long or short antennae.

### *Leptynia attenuata* Portugese Stick-insect

Body length: 34–57 mm. Small species, antennae short with 13–18 segments. ♀ green or brown, longitudinal stripes running along body, two by eyes. End of abdomen rounded. ♂ brown, cerci long, incurved. **HABITAT** Shrublands often in mountains in Iberia, where they feed on broom *Cytisus*, *Genista* and others. **SIMILAR SPECIES** Other recently described *Leptynia* species: ***L. annapaulae***, ***L. caprai*** and ***L. montana*** (all Spain), also *Pijnackeria* species.

### *Pijnackeria hispanica* Spanish Stick-insect

Body length: 35–58 mm. Small species, antennae short with 10–11 segments. ♀ green or brown, longitudinal stripes running along body. Thorax granulated. End of abdomen with a pointed tip. ♂ brown, cerci long, incurved. **HABITAT** Shrublands, often in mountains, where they feed on broom *Cytisus*, *Dorycnium*, *Rosa* and others, sometimes in company with other phasmid species. **SIMILAR SPECIES** Other *Pijnackeria* species, also *Leptynia* species.

### *Pijnackeria recondita* Sierra Nevada Stick-insect

Body length: 41–59 mm. Differs from *P. hispanica* by smooth thorax in ♀s. **HABITAT** Shrublands in mountains (only known at present from Sierra Nevada, Spain), feeding on broom *Cytisus scoparius*. **SIMILAR SPECIES** Other *Pijnackeria* and *Leptynia* species.

Other recently described *Pijnackeria* species [not illustrated or mapped]: ***P. barbarae***, ***P. lelongi***, ***P. lucianae***, ***P. originis*** (all Spain) and ***P. masettii*** (southern France and Spain). Further afield, elongate thin *Clonaria* species [not illustrated] may also be found: ***C. eitami*** (Israel). ***C. libanica*** (Israel, Syria, Turkey) appears to belong to a genus more closely related to *Bacillus*.

There is always a possibility that escapees of phasmids kept in culture could become established, hence rearers must not release specimens in the wild.

*Clonopsis gallica*

*Leptynia attenuata*

*Pijnackeria hispanica*

*Pijnackeria recondita*

*Clonopsis gallica* ♀ (inset: ♀ head and thorax)

*Leptynia attenuata* ♂ (left) [NC], ♀ (right) [AG]

*Pijnackeria hispanica* ♀ [PV]

*Pijnackeria recondita* ♂ (left), ♀ (right)

# Order MANTODEA – MANTIDS

**Southern Europe & Mediterranean: c.26 species**

These well camouflaged insects are recognised by the usually elongate body and forelegs held in 'praying' position, although they are sometimes confused with stick insects. However, mantids (variably known as mantises or praying mantids) have large, well separated eyes and spiny forelegs designed for catching prey. The life cycle shows incomplete metamorphosis (development), so plump-bodied ♀s lay eggs in a spongy eggcase, known as an ootheca, which may overwinter. The nymphs hatch out *en masse* and quickly disperse to find hunting grounds, although some may eat other nymphs. Food includes insects (including other mantid species) and some other invertebrates, often taken by day. Many people are aware that the ♀s have a reputation for eating the ♂ during mating (commonplace in captivity, presumably to provide nourishment whilst the eggs are growing in the abdomen) and that mantids are popular in horror films. Several representative species are illustrated.

**HOTSPOTS** Try searching on sunny days low down in vegetation such as garrigue with sparse bushes, but these insects are well camouflaged on grasses or on the bushes. It is therefore rarely easy to find many; even common species such as the Praying Mantis *Mantis religiosa* may present a challenge. Moving leaves or branches may cause them to reveal themselves. They can also sometimes be found at night by torch-light; some ♂s fly to lights and rest on walls, finding rich pickings. If handled, they may have a painful bite! Spain is arguably the hotspot for mantids, with 14 species, Andalucia being particularly good. Greece, Italy and Turkey are also species-rich countries with less than 15 species, but a week's intensive searching in peak season may only reveal a few species.

**Casares area, Andalucia, Spain.** Habitat for several species of mantids. The spot shown is good for *Empusa*, *Iris*, *Mantis*, *Apteromantis* and *Sphodromantis*.

## Family Tarachodidae

### *Iris oratoria* Mediterranean Mantis

Body length: 27–46 mm. Green, brown or yellowish, ♀s wings shorter than abdomen. ♂ with translucent forewings, when revealed the hindwings are colourful, with a large purple basal spot, readily distinguishing this sex from *Mantis religiosa*. **HABITAT** Open habitats. **SEASON** Mainly July to November.

*Iris oratoria*

*Mantis religiosa* ♀ head

*Empusa pennata* ♂ head

*Sphodromantis viridis* eggcase and nymph

*Sphodromantis viridis* nymph

*Empusa fasciata* nymph [PG]

*Iris oratoria* ♂ (left), ♂ defence display (right)

## Family Mantidae

### *Ameles spallanzania* European Dwarf Mantis

Body length: 18–40 mm. Stout, green or brown, abdomen held curled up in ♀, which has short wings. ♂ slender with long wings. **HABITAT** Sparse low vegetation. **SEASON** May to September.

*Ameles spallanzania* ♂ [SO]

### *Apteromantis aptera*

Body length: 27–36 mm. Mostly green species with angular eyes, more pointed in the ♂; wings absent. **HABITAT** Grasslands, sometimes seen on the ground, but nymphs in particular are able to jump well. This protected species is the only endemic mantid in Iberia. **SEASON** All year.

### *Mantis religiosa* Praying Mantis

Body length: 43–88 mm. Green, brown or yellowish; dark stripe on front edge of forewing. Conspicuous bold all black or black-ringed spot at base of fore coxae. **HABITAT** Open habitats, this is Europe's most widespread species. **SEASON** All year.

*Mantis religiosa* ♀ well camouflaged in dry grass.

### *Sphodromantis viridis*

Body length: 53–75 mm. Similar to *Mantis religiosa* but this African species is easily recognised by the bold white forewing spot. **HABITAT** Open habitats in southern Iberia only. **SEASON** All year.

## Family Empusidae

### *Empusa fasciata*

Body length: 60–72 mm. Edge of forewings whitish or yellow; tip of fore and hindwings brownish. **HABITAT** Dry grasslands, often on bushes. **SEASON** May to August.

### *Empusa pennata* Conehead Mantis

Body length: 50–67 mm. Edge of forewings whitish or pink; tip of forewings pinkish marked. **HABITAT** Dry grasslands and scrub, often on bushes. **SEASON** May to early August.

*Ameles spallanzania*

*Apteromantis aptera*

*Mantis religiosa*

*Sphodromantis viridis*

*Empusa fasciata*

*Empusa pennata*

*Ameles spallanzania* ♀ [PH]

*Apteromantis aptera* ♂ (left), ♀ (right)

*Mantis religiosa* ♂

*Sphodromantis viridis* ♂ [ARP]

*Empusa fasciata* ♂ (left) [KB], ♀ (right)

*Empusa pennata* ♂ (left), ♀ (right)

# Order BLATTODEA – COCKROACHES & TERMITES

**Southern Europe & Mediterranean: most of Europe's c.150 species**

Generally regarded as pests by many, but that only applies to the larger, introduced species. Europe's smaller native species are never pests. These flat-bodied insects have long antennae and are equipped to run fast. The forewings are leathery and cover the membranous hindwings. After mating, ♀s are sometimes seen with an ootheca (egg pod) protruding from the end of the abdomen, until it is released in leaf litter after a few days. Whilst sometimes observed on flowers or vegetation by day and often on tree trunks at night, they are nervous, and winged species can fly well or move rapidly. Termites have a worse reputation than cockroaches due to the damage they can cause by eating through wood in buildings, but they are not common in Europe, although Spain has three established species.

**HABITAT** The native species live among low vegetation, scavenging on decaying plants or eating dead insects.

**NOTE ON CLASSIFICATION** Blattodea, together with the closely related Mantodea (mantids) are placed together in the superorder Dictyoptera. Blattodea also includes the termites (Termitoidae), which used to be treated as a separate order, Isoptera.

## Family Ectobiidae

### *Ectobius lucidus*

Body length: 8–11 mm. Pronotum with pale border. **HABITAT** Woodlands and others, often seen on tree trunks. **SEASON** May to September.

### *Capraiellus panzeri* Lesser Cockroach

Body length: 5–8 mm. Small, dark brown. The flightless ♀ is easily recognised by its short, truncate forewings. **HABITAT** Various, the life cycle takes one year (two in some other native species). **SEASON** July to October.

### *Phyllodromica marginata*

Body length: 5–8 mm. Black; thorax rather glossy. Pronotum and forewings with bold white border. **HABITAT** Various. **SEASON** May to September.

Other cockroach species are occasionally recorded including infestations in the kitchen, most likely ***Blattella germanica* German Cockroach** (10–15 mm, Family Ectobiidae) and ***Blatta orientalis* Common or Oriental Cockroach** (17–30 mm, Family Blattidae). Found indoors, pest cockroaches are likely in bakeries, basements, bathrooms, kitchens, greenhouses and heating ducts, often in commercial premises but also residential houses. Some other species periodically seen on the European list are: Blaberidae: ***Pycnoscelus surinamensis* Surinam Cockroach** (16–25 mm), usually in greenhouses. Blattidae: ***Periplaneta americana* American Cockroach** (27–43 mm) and ***P. australasiae* Australian Cockroach** (25–35 mm).

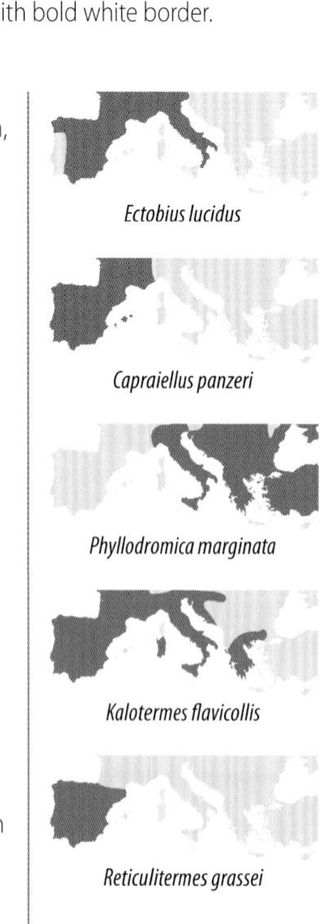

*Ectobius lucidus*

*Capraiellus panzeri*

*Phyllodromica marginata*

*Kalotermes flavicollis*

*Reticulitermes grassei*

## Family Kalotermitidae

### *Kalotermes flavicollis*

Body length: soldiers 8 mm, winged adults 8–10 mm. Pale yellow to dark brown. The pronotum is yellow in the dark-winged caste. **HABITAT** A mainly coastal drywood species infesting the roots or trunks of living trees, or occasionally wood structures, with an average colony size c.600. Hosts include fruit trees and this species is regarded as a serious pest in parts of Spain and mainland Portugal. **SEASON** All year.

## Family Rhinotermitidae

### *Reticulitermes grassei*

Body length: workers and soldiers c.5 mm, winged adults 9 mm. Heads of soldiers are larger than workers, as is typical in termites. Wings clear. **HABITAT** A subterranean termite species. These insects attack wood, although this species nest in the ground, not in wood. They do, however, visit the wood to gnaw, feeding the colony, but tend to be difficult to eradicate. *Reticulitermes* species are the major termite pests in Europe. **SEASON** All year.

*Ectobius lucidus* ♀

*Capraiellus panzeri* ♂ (left), ♀ (right)

*Phyllodromica marginata* ♀ [TB]

*Blattella germanica* ♂ (left), ♀ (right)

*Pycnoscelus surinamensis* ♀ [DR]

*Blatta orientalis* ♂ (left), ♀ (right)

*Periplaneta australasiae* ♂ [DR]

*Periplaneta americana* ♀

*Kalotermes flavicollis* [SO]

*Reticulitermes grassei* with soldier at bottom

# Order PSOCODEA – LICE, BARKLICE & BOOKLICE

**Southern Europe & Mediterranean: many of Europe's c.1,000 species**

This group of small insects comprises book/barklice (Order Psocoptera) and flattened, wingless parasitic lice (Order Phthiraptera). The crab-like parasitic lice are attached to birds and some mammal species, feeding on feathers, hair or blood. ***Pediculus humanus capitis*** **Head Louse** (pictured left [GSM]) [family Pediculidae] is associated with humans, particularly young children. Some lice can transmit diseases. The booklice and barklice (or barkflies) are small, soft-bodied with large eyes. The antennae are long, forewings are larger than hindwings, but wings are absent in some species. The life cycle is incomplete metamorphosis: egg, larva and adult.

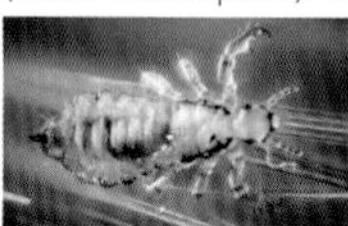

## Family Caeciliusidae

### *Valenzuela flavidus*

Body length: 3 mm. Pale with strongly marked veins on wings. **HABITAT** Gardens and woodlands, on various trees and shrubs. **SEASON** May to December.

*Valenzuela flavidus*

## Family Stenopsocidae

### *Graphopsocus cruciatus*

Body length: c.3 mm. Bold dark brown blotches on wings. **HABITAT** Woodlands and others, on various trees and shrubs. **SEASON** All year.

*Graphopsocus cruciatus*

### *Stenopsocus stigmaticus*

Body length: c.4 mm. Black bumps on thorax; usually with a green abdomen with white markings and band. Forewing with distinctive black stigma. **HABITAT** Woodlands on trees and shrubs. **SEASON** May to November.

*Stenopsocus stigmaticus*

## Family Mesopsocidae

### *Mesopsocus immunis*

Body length: 4–5 mm. ♂ black, mottled with green and brown mottled areas. ♀ mottled yellowish and brown, with tiny wings. **HABITAT** Woodlands, on various trees; often on tree trunks. **SEASON** April to August.

*Mesopsocus immunis*

## Family Psocidae

### *Loensia fasciata*

Body length: c.4 mm. Spotted wings strongly marked with dark brown bands. **HABITAT** Woodlands, on various trees. **SEASON** May to July.

*Loensia fasciata*

### *Psococerastis gibbosa*

Body length: 5.5–7 mm. Yellowish and black with boldly marked veins on wings. **HABITAT** Woodlands, on various trees. **SEASON** July to October.

*Psococerastis gibbosa*

# Order THYSANOPTERA – THRIPS

**Southern Europe & Mediterranean: many of Europe's c.570 species**

This order of small insects are nearly all winged (with fringes); most European species are only 1–3 mm long. Some are considered pests of ornamental flowers and crops. The life cycle is incomplete metamorphosis: egg, larva and adult.

## Family Thripidae

### *Odontothrips ulicis*

Body length: c.2 mm. Dark species, hairy, with yellow-banded abdominal segments; also part of antennae and legs paler. **HABITAT** Grasslands with bushes, on Gorse *Ulex europeus* flowers. **SEASON** All year.

*Odontothrips ulicis*

### *Thrips flavus* Honeysuckle Thrips

Body length: c.2 mm. Yellow. **HABITAT** Grasslands and agricultural areas. A pest on citrus, causing sterility and fruit distortion. **SEASON** February to October.

*Thrips flavus*

*Valenzuela flavidus*

*Graphopsocus cruciatus*

*Stenopsocus stigmaticus*

*Mesopsocus immunis*

*Loensia fasciata*

*Psococerastis gibbosa*

*Odontothrips ulicis*

*Thrips flavus* [BV]

# Order HEMIPTERA – BUGS

**Southern Europe & Mediterranean: many of Europe's c.8,000 species**

Even entomologists tend to call insects 'bugs', but Hemiptera are the 'true' bugs. Whilst different in appearance, the groups all have piercing beak-like mouthparts (the rostrum), designed for sucking juices from plants or sometimes animals; they vary in size from under 1 mm to large cicadas, or Water Stick-insect *Ranatra linearis*, c.50 mm including its tail. The familiar aphids are serious agricultural pests, damaging crops and some transmit viral diseases. However, most bugs are harmless and often rather colourful; they are divided into three main groups, suborder Heteroptera, meaning 'different wings' (forewings tough and leathery; hindwings membranous, all wings folded flat over their backs, except for flight) and the suborders Auchenorrhyncha and Sternorrhyncha [these two suborders were formerly known as the Homoptera, meaning 'uniform wings' (forewings (where present) held like a roof over the body; toughened area absent]. The Heteroptera include land and water bugs. Amongst the larger species, the shieldbugs (stinkbugs) and leatherbugs (also known as squashbugs) are most popular with naturalists, plant bugs less so. The unmistakeable Striped Shieldbug *Graphosoma lineatum* is very likely to be observed on flowers sporting its bright warning colours. Assassin bugs feed on other invertebrates, but bed bugs prefer animals, including humans. Water bugs are often seen on ponds. Auchenorrhyncha are bugs with short antennae: cicadas (when abundant, the ♂ song is familiar to many people on warm, sunny days), froghoppers and leafhoppers (infraorder Cicadomorpha) and planthoppers and relatives (infraorder Fulgoromorpha). The Sternorrhyncha have long antennae: aphids, scale insects and the like. The life cycle is one of incomplete metamorphosis (development), adults laying eggs which hatch into nymphs, which develop into winged or occasionally wingless adults. A selection of species is shown from some of the families likely to be encountered.

**HABITAT** Many habitats are suitable; whilst some bugs are easily observed on flowers or in sunny weather by just keeping an eye on vegetation and on the ground, keen hemipterists (people who study bugs) collect by sweeping or beating vegetation for them, or grub around on bare, dry ground. Water bugs can be examined in a tray and returned to the water via a small net.

**HOTSPOTS** Good general sites include coastal areas, one of the best being sand dunes in the Tarifa surrounds, southern Spain (at times, a very windy site). A wide range of bugs can be found on the boardwalks and surrounding vegetation, also resting on nearby walls.

**Spain: Tarifa**. Sandy areas are easily explored in this area via a boardwalk. Bare patches of ground support a rich diversity of bugs and numerous species rest on the boardwalk, as well as on low-growing vegetation and even on the graffiti-covered walls! These include various *Eurydema*, *Odontoscelis* and *Emblethis* species.

*Graphosoma lineatum* (Pentatomidae) on an umbellifer [PC]

*Carpocoris mediterraneus* (Pentatomidae) with eggs

*rona caerulea* (Pentatomidae) with prey [SR]

*Gonocerus acuteangulatus* mating pair (Coreidae)

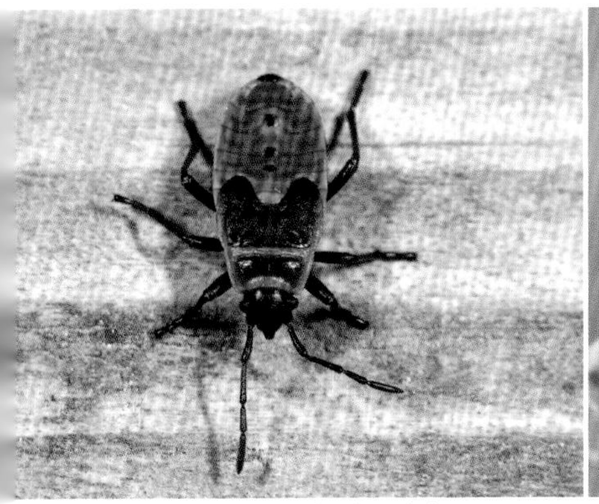

*Pyrrhocoris apterus* nymph (Pyrrhocoridae)

*Cicadetta montana* (Cicadidae) freshly emerged from its exuvia [GSM]

**SHIELDBUGS** or stinkbugs (families Acanthosomatidae, Cydnidae, Thyreocoridae, Scutelleridae and Pentatomidae) have a conspicuous shield-like shape when adult, with a triangular plate (scutellum) between the wing-cases. They look something like beetles, except for sucking mouthparts. Many species feed on vegetation, whilst others are predatory; most overwinter as adults with some changing colour then; the variability within species and similarity between some may confuse. As a defensive reaction, shieldbugs have glands in their thorax between the first and second pair of legs which produce a foul-smelling liquid. In the field specimens may be spotted on vegetation, including flowers (umbellifers are popular) or on the ground, particularly in sandy areas. These insects tend to peak at certain times of the year and may then be abundant. See 'season' for most likely time to see adults, which usually includes at least one generation of new adults before hibernation. A fairly wide selection of this popular group is illustrated.

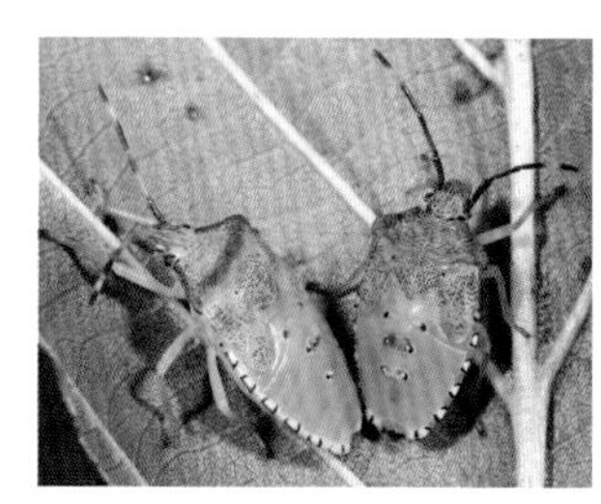

## Family Acanthosomatidae – KEELED SHIELDBUGS

Tarsi two-segmented. The species featured are more widespread in central Europe.

### *Acanthosoma haemorrhoidale* Hawthorn Shieldbug

Body length: 12–18 mm. Mostly apple green covered with dark punctures. Broad lateral extensions of the pronotum, marked with red; the pronotum and scutellum have a broad, reddish brown border. The abdomen is red-tipped (nymphs pictured left). **HABITAT** Various, often on hawthorn *Crataegus* spp., but scarcer in the Mediterranean climate than more northerly. **SEASON** March to November.

### *Cyphostethus tristriatus* Juniper Shieldbug

Body length: 7–11 mm. Green with curved and conspicuous pinkish red markings. **HABITAT** Woodlands and others, feeding on juniper *Juniperus* and *Chamaecyparis* spp. **SEASON** March to October

### *Elasmostethus interstinctus* Birch Shieldbug

Body length: 8–12 mm. Green covered with dark punctures whilst the pronotum and scutellum have a broad reddish brown and blackish border. **HABITAT** Woodlands and others on birch *Betula*, oak *Quercus* spp. and others. **SEASON** March to November.

### *Elasmucha grisea* Parent Shieldbug

Body length: 7–9 mm. Variably coloured, often reddish with black and white lateral edges to the abdomen and scutellum with black patches. **HABITAT** Woodlands, gardens and others on birch *Betula* and alder *Alnus* spp. The ♀ affords her offspring protection by sitting over the eggs for two to three weeks before they hatch, in addition to guarding the young nymphs. **SEASON** March to November.

## Family Cydnidae – BURROWING SHIELDBUGS

Tarsi three-segmented; tibiae with strong spines

### *Cydnus aterrimus*

Body length: 8–12 mm. Large black species, the corium with a distinctive wavy edge. **HABITAT** Sandy and calcareous sites and garrigue on or beneath the foodplant spurge *Euphorbia* spp. or other low vegetation. **SEASON** April to September.

### *Geotomus punctulatus* [Cornish Shieldbug]

Body length: 3.5–5 mm. Oval, small black species with long hairs. Reddish margins including at hind part of pronotum. **HABITAT** Often coastal, sandy sites on or beneath plants of various families, including spurge *Euphorbia*, bedstraw *Galium*, *Lavandula* and *Satureja* spp. **SEASON** April to August.

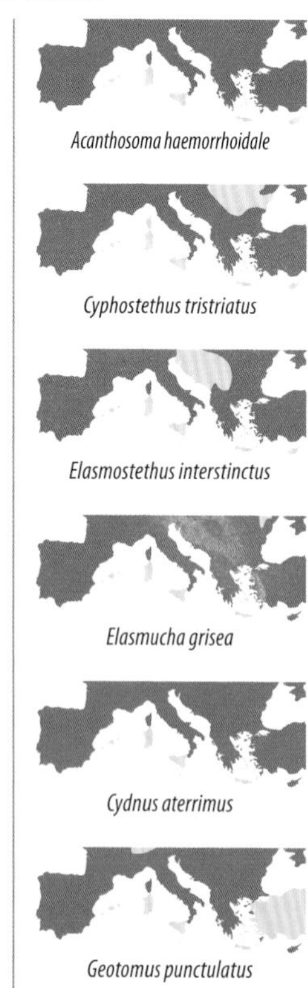

*Acanthosoma haemorrhoidale*

*Cyphostethus tristriatus*

*Elasmostethus interstinctus*

*Elasmucha grisea*

*Cydnus aterrimus*

*Geotomus punctulatus*

*Acanthosoma haemorrhoidale*

*Elasmostethus interstinctus*

*Cyphostethus tristriatus* (left), nymph (right) [both PC]

*Elasmucha grisea* (top), nymphs (bottom)

*Cydnus aterrimus*

*Geotomus punctulatus*

***Macroscytus brunneus***
Body length: 6–9 mm. Oval, black or brownish species, with corium paler than pronotum and scutellum. **HABITAT** Sandy sites such as dunes, on or beneath grasses or other low vegetation; sometimes under stones. **SEASON** April to October.

***Adomerus biguttatus* Cow-wheat Shieldbug**
Body length: 5–8 mm. Black or bluish black with a pale border and white dot in the centre of the wing-cases. The tibiae are spiny. **HABITAT** Sunny woodland rides, edges or clearings, on or beneath the foodplants, often Betony *Betonica officinalis* and cow-wheat *Melanpyrum* spp. **SEASON** April to August.

***Canthophorus impressus* [Down Shieldbug]**
Body length: 6–7 mm. Oval, blue or bluish-black species with a white border along lateral margin of the wing-cases. Abdominal margins black and white. **HABITAT** Grasslands including mountains on or beneath foodplants including bastard-toadflaxes *Comandra umbellata* and *Thesium alpinum*. **SEASON** May to June.

***Canthophorus melanopterus***
Body length: 6–8 mm. Oval, blue or bluish-black species with a white border along lateral margin of the wing-cases. Membrane black and unlike *C. impressus*, black and white markings on border of abdominal margins equal in length. **HABITAT** Grasslands, gardens and others on vegetation, including *Osyris* and bastard-toadflax *Thesium* spp., where adults and the brightly coloured nymphs (pictured left) are sometimes in abundance. **SEASON** March to October.

***Legnotus limbosus* Bordered Shieldbug**
Body length: 3.5–5 mm. Small round black species with a whitish lateral abdominal border; wing membrane brown. **HABITAT** Dry grassy areas or young woodlands on or beneath various bedstraw *Galium* spp. **SEASON** April to June.

***Legnotus picipes* Heath Shieldbug**
Body length: 3–4.5 mm. Small round black species, similar to the Bordered Shieldbug but with a reduced whitish lateral abdominal border. **HABITAT** Sandy soils such as coastal dunes, mountains to 2,300 m., on or beneath various bedstraw *Galium* spp. **SEASON** April to June.

***Sehirus luctuosus* Forget-me-not Shieldbug**
Body length: 5.5–9 mm. Larger all black species, sometimes with a bronze sheen. **HABITAT** Sparse vegetation on or beneath the foodplants forget-me-not *Myosotis* spp., and others. They are found in mountains to 1,800 m and can occur in vast numbers in gardens, as reported in Salerno province, Campania, Italy in 2005. **SEASON** April to August.

***Tritomegas bicolor* Pied Shieldbug**
Body length: 5–8 mm. Black with white patches on the wing-cases. White margin on pronotum reaching about half length of segment. Wing membrane brown. **HABITAT** Various in lowlands, on or beneath foodplants including *Lamium* and *Ballota* spp. **SEASON** April to August.

***Tritomegas sexmaculatus* Rambur's Pied Shieldbug**
Body length: 5–8 mm. Black with white patches on the wing-cases. Pronotum with extensive white margin. Wing membrane black. **HABITAT** Various, often on or beneath the main foodplant *Ballota* spp. **SEASON** April to August.

*Macroscytus brunneus*

*Adomerus biguttatus*

*Canthophorus impressus*

*Canthophorus melanopterus*

*Legnotus limbosus*

*Legnotus picipes*

*Sehirus luctuosus*

*Tritomegas bicolor*

*Tritomegas sexmaculatus*

*Macroscytus brunneus*

*Adomerus biguttatus* [PC]

*Canthophorus impressus*

*Canthophorus melanopterus* [PC]

*Legnotus limbosus*

*Legnotus picipes*

*Sehirus luctuosus*

*Tritomegas bicolor*

*Tritomegas sexmaculatus* [TB]

## Family Thyreocoridae – SCARAB SHIELDBUGS

Scutellum covering much of abdomen.

### *Thyreocoris scarabaeoides* Scarab Shieldbug

Body length: 3–4 mm. Small black rounded beetle-like species, with a slightly metallic blue sheen. **HABITAT** Grasslands and open areas with bare ground to 1,600 m., where they feed on buttercup *Ranunculus* and violet *Viola* spp., and can be found in moss and litter on the ground, or on tracks. **SEASON** April to September.

*Thyreocoris scarabaeoides*

## Family Scutelleridae – TORTOISE SHIELDBUGS

Tarsi three-segmented; smaller, usually triangular, plate behind pronotum (scutellum) extends to end of abdomen.

### *Solenosthedium bilunatum*

Body length: 12–17 mm. Large, easily recognised species from the speckled appearance and large whitish spot on each wingcase. **HABITAT** Bushy grasslands, feeding on the fruits of *Arbutus* and *Pistacia*. **SEASON** April to November.

*Solenosthedium bilunatum*

### *Eurygaster austriaca*

Body length: 11–14 mm. Pale or reddish brown, often plainer than related species. Antennae black-tipped. **HABITAT** Grasslands up to c.1,400 m., on the foodplants, grasses, cereals and other plants. Considered a pest in some areas. **SEASON** April to October.

*Eurygaster austriaca*

### *Eurygaster hottentotta*

Body length: 11–13 mm. Rather broad, particularly the connexivum; rugged appearance. **HABITAT** Grasslands, on grasses and cereals. **SEASON** May to October.

*Eurygaster hottentotta*

### *Eurygaster maura* [Scarce Tortoise Shieldbug]

Body length: 8–11 mm. Distinguished from *E. testudinaria* by the smoothly rounded head (pictured left) lacking a central depression. **HABITAT** Grasslands, on the foodplants, grasses and cereals. Regarded as a pest and in many areas, by far the commonest *Eurygaster* species. **SEASON** April to October.

*Eurygaster maura*

### *Eurygaster testudinaria* Tortoise Shieldbug

Body length: 9–11 mm. Often brownish but variable in shade, also spots and markings. Distinguished from *E. maura* and other related species by the slight central depression at the front of the head. **HABITAT** Tall grasslands, often on the tips of foodplants, grasses, sedges and rushes. **SEASON** May to October.

*Eurygaster testudinaria*

### *Psacasta exanthematica*

Body length: 9–12 mm. Dark brown with numerous white spots and flecks. **HABITAT** Grasslands, on *Echium* spp. and many other plants. **SEASON** May to October.

*Psacasta exanthematica*

### *Psacasta tuberculata*

Body length: 6–7 mm. Dark brown, robust and rugged. **HABITAT** Grasslands, on *Echium* spp. **SEASON** May to October.

*Psacasta tuberculata*

### *Odontoscelis fuliginosa* Greater-streaked Shieldbug

Body length: 6–8 mm. Rounded bug with dense dark brown hairs. **HABITAT** Sandy areas, in sparsely vegetated areas such as coastal sand dunes, under the foodplant stork's-bill *Erodium* spp. or on the ground; nymphs overwinter. Also occurs in mountainous areas to 2,500 m. **SEASON** April to August.

*Odontoscelis fuliginosa*

*Thyreocoris scarabaeoides*

*Solenosthedium bilunatum* [SO]

*Eurygaster austriaca*

*Eurygaster hottentotta*

*Eurygaster maura*

*Eurygaster testudinaria*

*Psacasta exanthematica*

*Psacasta tuberculata*

*Odontoscelis fuliginosa*

***Odontoscelis lineola*** **Lesser-streaked Shieldbug**
Body length: 4–6 mm. Smaller than *O. fuliginosa*, with silver as well as darker hairs. **HABITAT** Sandy areas under the foodplant stork's-bill *Erodium* spp.; nymphs overwinter. **SEASON** June to August.

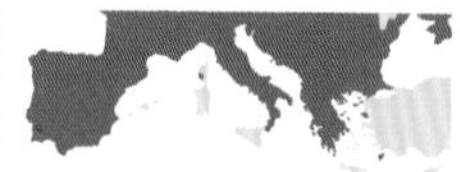
*Odontoscelis lineola*

***Odontotarsus purpureolineatus***
Body length: 8–12 mm. Characteristic shape and streaks with varying degree of purple. **HABITAT** Grasslands, to 1,100 m mainly on Salad Burnet *Poterium sanguisorba*, also *Centaurea* spp. and others. **SEASON** May to October.

*Odontotarsus purpureolineatus*

***Odontotarsus robustus***
Body length: 9–11 mm. Characteristic pattern of streaks. **HABITAT** Grasslands, on *Centaurea*, thistles *Cirsium* and *Carduus* spp. and others. **SEASON** May to October.

*Odontotarsus robustus*

## Family Pentatomidae – TYPICAL SHIELDBUGS
Tarsi three-segmented; tibiae lacking strong spines.

***Picromerus bidens*** **Spiked Shieldbug**
Body length: 10–14 mm. Large brown species with characteristic thorn-like extensions to the pronotum. **HABITAT** Various up to 1,650 m. Adults are predators of caterpillars, particularly butterflies, moths and sawflies, but also suck sap. **SEASON** July to October.

*Picromerus bidens*

***Rhacognathus punctatus*** **Heather Shieldbug**
Body length: 7–10 mm. Heavily mottled metallic brownish-bronze over a pale orange or reddish background, often with a pale central line on the pronotum. The legs are conspicuously banded pale to orange or red. **HABITAT** Heathlands and others, where they are predators of leaf beetle larvae. **SEASON** April to September.

*Rhacognathus punctatus*

***Troilus luridus*** **Bronze Shieldbug**
Body length: 10–13 mm. Similar to *Pentatoma rufipes*, except easily recognised by the lack of an orange tip to the scutellum, in addition to an orange band on the penultimate antennal segment and mottled brown legs. **HABITAT** Mixed woodlands where prey is usually caterpillars. **SEASON** March to November.

*Troilus luridus*

***Zicrona caerulea*** **Blue Shieldbug**
Body length: 6–8 mm. Dark metallic bluish-green species, with dark wing membrane. **HABITAT** Low vegetation in damp grasslands, woodland rides and heathlands where they are predators, mainly on metallic blue leaf beetles of the genus *Altica*, but also other species. **SEASON** March to September.

*Zicrona caerulea*

***Aelia acuminata*** **Bishop's Mitre Shieldbug**
Body length: 7–10 mm. Large brown striped species, with a pointed head and ridged pronotum. Mid and hind femora with two black spots. **HABITAT** Tall grasslands including in mountains to 2,000 m., on fine grasses. **SEASON** April to September.

*Aelia acuminata*

***Aelia rostrata***
Body length: 8–12 mm. As for *A. acuminata*, but often with bold pale or vibrant orange blotches. Mid and hind femora without black spots. **HABITAT** Tall grasslands including in mountains to 1,000 m., on grasses including crops such as wheat, barley and rye, hence is sometimes regarded as a pest. **SEASON** May to September.

*Aelia rostrata*

*Odontoscelis lineola* [SR]

*Odontotarsus purpureolineatus*

*Odontotarsus robustus*

*Picromerus bidens*

*Rhacognathus punctatus*

*Troilus luridus*

*Zicrona caerulea*

*Aelia acuminata*

*Aelia rostrata* [TB]

***Neottiglossa pusilla*** **Small Grass Shieldbug**
Body length: 4–6 mm. Small, shiny pale brown species, with paler margins to the pronotum and abdomen, also a pale central stripe from the head to scutellum, which has two whitish spots at the front margin. **HABITAT** Dry or damp grasslands with fine grasses. Found in mountains to 1,800 m. **SEASON** May to September.

*Neottiglossa pusilla*

***Halyomorpha halys*** **Brown Marmorated Shieldbug**
Body length: 12–17 mm. Large brown and whitish mottled species with dense punctuation. **HABITAT** Woodlands and agricultural areas. Since reaching the USA and many other countries from its native Asia, this invasive species is regarded as a severe agricultural pest in some areas, feeding on fruit trees, ornamentals, hardwoods, shrubs and crops. It reached Europe in 2004 and is spreading. **SEASON** April to October.

*Halyomorpha halys*

***Brachynema germarii***
Body length: 10–15 mm. Green with blue-edged wing-cases. Yellow border to pronotum, upper part of wing-cases and abdomen. **HABITAT** Bushy areas in hot, arid places feeding on seeds of *Ephedra distachya* and others. **SEASON** March to October.

*Brachynema germarii*

***Brachynema purpureomarginatum***
Body length: 8–12 mm. Similar to *B. germarii*, but more yellow markings and often with a stunning reddish-edged border to pronotum and upper part of wing-cases. Abdomen black-banded. **HABITAT** Bushy areas, including wetlands feeding on *Salsola* and others. **SEASON** March to September.

*Brachynema purpureomarginatum*

***Carpocoris mediterraneus***
Body length: 10–14 mm. Variable in colour but often bright, Angles of pronotum acute, with extensive black tip. **HABITAT** Open places to 1,000 m., occasionally considerably higher elevations, feeding on many plants. **SEASON** April to October. **SIMILAR SPECIES** Originally thought to be a synonym of the very similar *C. fuscispinus* (differs slightly in shape of pronotum), but the latter has a Continental European distribution.

*Carpocoris mediterraneus*

***Carpocoris pudicus***
Body length: 10–14 mm. Variable in colour. Angles of pronotum rounded; smallish black tip. **HABITAT** Open places to 1,600 m., feeding on many plants. **SEASON** April to October.

*Carpocoris pucidus*

***Carpocoris purpureipennis***
**Black-shouldered Shieldbug**
Body length: 10–13 mm. Variable, purple to yellowish brown (nymph pictured left). Angles of pronotum with smaller black tip than *C. mediterraneus*. **HABITAT** Grasslands and others. **SEASON** April to October.

*Carpocoris purpureipennis*

***Chlorochroa juniperina***
Body length: 10–13 mm. Green with yellow margin and yellow tip to scutellum. **HABITAT** Various to 2,200 m feeding mainly on juniper *Juniperus*. **SEASON** April to September.

*Chlorochroa juniperina*

***Codophila varia***
Body length: 9–14 mm. Bright, orange to brown, often reddish. Pronotum and scutellum with conspicuous markings. **HABITAT** Open places to 1,100 m., feeding on many plants, particularly Asteraceae. **SEASON** April to October.

*Codophila varia*

*Neottiglossa pusilla*

*Brachynema purpureomarginatum* [FR]

*Brachynema germarii* with nymph on left [FR]

*Halyomorpha halys*

*Carpocoris mediterraneus*

*Carpocoris pucidus* [TB]

*Carpocoris purpureipennis*

*Chlorochroa juniperina* [TB]

*Codophila varia*

***Dolycoris baccarum*** **Hairy Shieldbug**
Body length: 10–13 mm. Large, distinctive purplish brown and greenish bug, covered in long hairs. The antennae are black and white, also margins of abdomen. **HABITAT** Woodlands and others to 2,400 m., feeding on trees and shrubs, including Rosaceae. **SEASON** March to November.

*Dolycoris baccarum*

***Holcostethus albipes***
Body length: 8–10 mm. The thick white margins to the thorax distinguishes it from related species. **HABITAT** Grasslands and shrublands to 1,000 m, on a wide range of foodplants. **SEASON** April to October.

*Holcostethus albipes*

***Holcostethus sphacelatus***
Body length: 8–10 mm. Brown or reddish, similar shape but often darker than *Peribalus strictus*, with black antennae with white bands and black and white connexivum [abdominal margin]. **HABITAT** Woodlands to 1,850 m., mainly feeding on mullein *Verbascum*. **SEASON** April to October.

*Holcostethus sphacelatus*

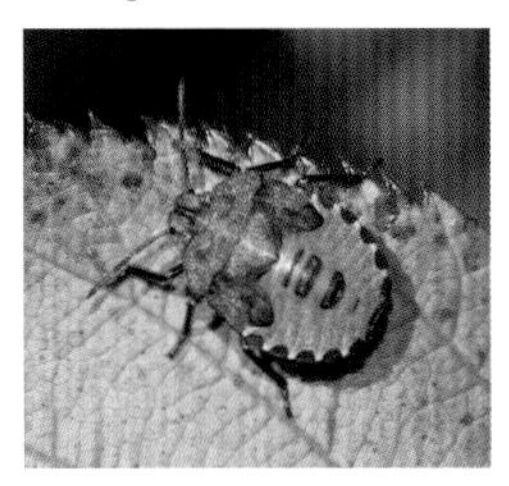

***Palomena prasina*** **Green Shieldbug**
Body length: 12–15 mm. Large green bug in spring and summer; finely punctured with dark marks (nymph pictured left [PC]). They become darker, often brown prior to hibernation in winter. The 4th and 5th antennal segments are often reddish. **HABITAT** Woodlands and others to 1,900 m., on various trees and shrubs. **SEASON** March to November.

*Palomena prasina*

***Peribalus strictus*** **Vernal Shieldbug**
Body length: 8–11 mm. The concave sides on the pronotum in this yellowish-brown species have a narrow white border; antennae reddish. **HABITAT** Sheltered woodland rides and others to 1,850 m., on bushes and trees. **SEASON** April to September.

*Peribalus strictus*

***Staria lunata***
Body length: 6–8 mm. Small, mottled yellowish brown and heavily punctured species; scutellum angles and base yellow. Legs pale. **HABITAT** Open places to 1,650 m., feeding on many plants. **SEASON** April to October.

*Staria lunata*

***Eysarcoris aeneus*** [New Forest Shieldbug]
Body length: 4–6 mm. Variable, often yellowish brown or greyish, always with a white spot at the basal angles of the scutellum. **HABITAT** Heathlands, grasslands or woodland rides; foodplants include various Lamiaceae. **SEASON** April to September.

*Eysarcoris aeneus*

***Eysarcoris ventralis*** **White-spotted Shieldbug**
Body length: 5–6 mm. Front margin of eyes with yellowish pit, which is absent in related species. **HABITAT** Woodlands and other habitats below 1,000 m, feeding on grasses Bulbous Meadow-grass *Poa bulbosa* and *Glyceria aquatica* aand others. **SEASON** April to September.

*Eysarcoris ventralis*

***Eysarcoris venustissimus*** **Woundwort Shieldbug**
Body length: 5–7 mm. Shiny, with the head, front of pronotum and much of the scutellum metallic copper, with a variable amount of white. The edge of the lateral abdominal margins is black and white. **HABITAT** Various to 1,500 m., feeding on Lamiaceae such as *Lamium*, woundwort *Stachys* and *Ballota* spp. **SEASON** April to October.

*Eysarcoris venustissimus*

*Dolycoris baccarum* [PC]

*Holcostethus albipes* [SO]

*Holcostethus sphacelatus*

*Palomena prasina*

*Peribalus strictus*

*Staria lunata*

*Eysarcoris aeneus*

*Eysarcoris ventralis* [TB]

*Eysarcoris venustissimus*

### *Stagonomus amoenus*
Body length: 6–8 mm. Brown to reddish brown, with tapered abdomen; scutellum with face-like markings. **HABITAT** Open places to 1,500 m., feeding on *Salvia* spp. **SEASON** April to September.

*Stagonomus amoenus*

### *Mustha spinosula*
Body length: 20–25 mm. Unmistakeable large dark brown species, with spiny lateral margins to pronotum and abdomen. **HABITAT** In association with Cupressaceae, oak *Quercus*, hawthorn *Crataegus* spp. and others, in eastern Europe. **SEASON** May to August.

*Mustha spinulosa*

### *Acrosternum heegeri*
Body length: 9–13 mm. Attractive green species, with yellow lateral border and partly reddish antennae. **HABITAT** Various, feeding on a range of trees and shrubs, including juniper *Juniperus*, cypress *Cupressus*, oak *Quercus* and spurge *Euphorbia* spp. **SEASON** May to September.

*Acrosternum heegeri*

### *Nezara viridula* Southern Green Shieldbug
Body length: 11–18 mm. Similar to the Green Shieldbug, except for the three to five white spots at the front of the scutellum and by the two dark marks at the corners. The wing membrane is pale. Small nymphs are dark (below left) with red and white spots, usually becoming greener from the 3rd moult (below right).

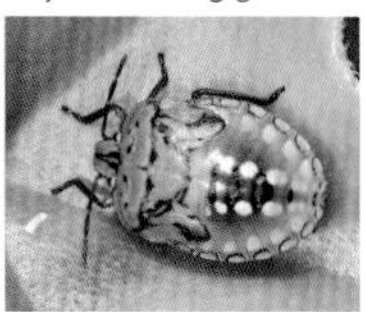

**HABITAT** Various, feeding on numerous plants including crops such as Fabaceae, hence regarded as a pest. Present worldwide. **SEASON** All year, but mainly May to September.

*Nezara viridula*

### *Pentatoma rufipes* Red-legged Shieldbug
Body length: 12–16 mm. Large brown species with orange legs and slightly hooked projection at the front of the pronotum. Pale spot at tip of the scutellum. The legs can be dull or bright red. **HABITAT** Woodlands and others, including some mountains to 1,850 m.; mainly on deciduous trees. However, adults are also predators of caterpillars and other insects. **SEASON** July to November; nymphs overwinter.

*Pentatoma rufipes*

### *Rhaphigaster nebulosa* Mottled Shieldbug
Body length: 14–17 mm. Large brown mottled species, lacking hairs. **HABITAT** Woodlands to 1,200 m., feeding on various trees. **SEASON** April to October.

*Rhaphigaster nebulosa*

### *Piezodorus lituratus* Gorse Shieldbug
Body length: 10–13 mm. Green with blue-edged wing-cases or purplish-red markings on the pronotum and blue-edged wing-cases; in both colour forms the pronotum and upper parts of the wing-cases have a narrow yellow border. **HABITAT** Various to 1,700 m on gorse *Ulex*, broom *Cytisus* and many others. **SEASON** March to October.

*Piezodorus lituratus*

### *Dyroderes umbraculatus*
Body length: 7–9 mm. Characteristic shape with large white patches on the pronotum and tip of scutellum. **HABITAT** Open places, feeding on bedstraw *Galium*. **SEASON** April to September.

*Dyroderes umbraculatus*

### *Sciocoris cursitans* Sandrunner
Body length: 4–6 mm. Distinctive brown variably marked species, with a rounded head. **HABITAT** Sandy areas with sparse vegetation, where they feed on various low-growing plants. Sometimes at higher elevations, to 2,000 m. In defence, ♂s can stridulate loudly. **SEASON** May to September.

*Sciocoris cursitans*

*Stagonomus amoenus*

*Mustha spinulosa* [MS]

*Acrosternum heegeri*

*Nezara viridula*

*Pentatoma rufipes*

*Rhaphigaster nebulosa*

*Piezodorus lituratus*

*Dyroderes umbraculatus*

*Sciocoris cursitans*

### *Sciocoris macrocephalus*
Body length: 5–8 mm. Various dark markings on upperside. **HABITAT** Exposed hillsides, mountains and river terraces up to 1,850 m, feeding on various plants including scabious *Knautia* and *Scabiosa* spp. **SEASON** May to October.

*Sciocoris macrocephalus*

### *Sciocoris microphthalmus*
Body length: 4.5–7 mm. Tip of chorion more rounded than in related species. **HABITAT** Mountainous areas up to 2,000 m, feeding on various plants. **SEASON** May to October.

*Sciocoris microphthalmus*

### *Eurydema dominulus* Scarlet Shieldbug
Body length: 5–7 mm. Red or orange and black species; the edge of the corium plain. Smaller than related species. **HABITAT** Most likely in woodland edges in hilly or mountainous areas feeding on Brassicaceae. **SEASON** April to September.

*Eurydema dominulus*

### *Eurydema oleracea* Crucifer Shieldbug
Body length: 5–7 mm. Often bluish-black but can be metallic green, blue or violet, usually with red or white spots and markings; the latter change from red to orange following overwintering as adults and are reversed once adults feed in spring. **HABITAT** Various up to 2,000 m feeding on Brassicaceae. **SEASON** April to October.

*Eurydema oleracea*

### *Eurydema ornata* Ornate Shieldbug
Body length: 7–9 mm. Red or orange and black species (pictured left [PC], sometimes with a whitish yellow background, the distinctive dark marking along the edge of the corium readily distinguishes it from related species. **HABITAT** Open areas and scrublands to 1,700 m., feeding on Brassicaceae. **SEASON** April to October.

*Eurydema ornata*

### *Eurydema rugulosa*
Body length: 8 mm. Mainly black with red markings. **HABITAT** Open areas feeding on Brassicaceae in eastern Mediterranean, likely in Greece, Cyprus and Turkey. **SEASON** April to August.

*Eurydema rugulosa*

### *Eurydema spectabilis*
Body length: 9–11 mm. Red and black, distinctive shape black mark on thorax. **HABITAT** Open areas feeding on Brassicaceae in north-eastern and eastern Mediterranean. **SEASON** April to September.

*Eurydema spectabilis*

### *Eurydema ventralis*
Body length: 8–11 mm. Variable, usually red or orange and black species; edge of the corium near centre with large black blotch (nymphs pictured left). **HABITAT** Grasslands, scrublands and others to 2,100 m., feeding on Brassicaceae. **SEASON** April to October.

*Eurydema ventralis*

### *Ancyrosoma leucogrammes*
Body length: 6–7 mm. Brown with distinctive cream stripes, some curved and darker streaks; lateral angles of pronotum acute. **HABITAT** Open areas on umbellifers (Apiaceae), including Hartwort *Tordylium maximum*, Spreading Hedge-parsley *Torilis arvensis* and Wild Carrot *Daucus carota*. **SEASON** April to September.

*Ancyrosoma leucogrammes*

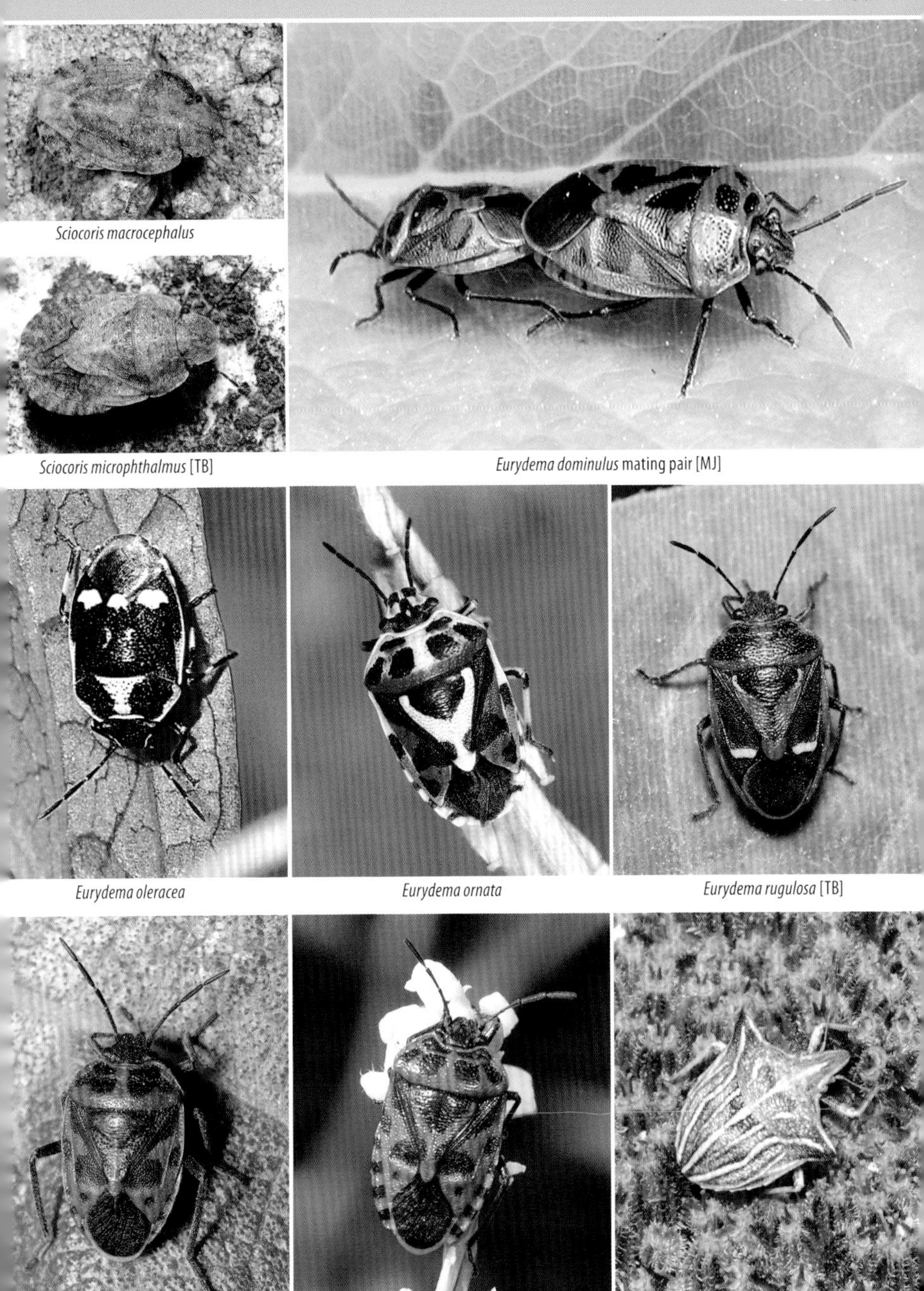

*Sciocoris macrocephalus*

*Sciocoris microphthalmus* [TB]

*Eurydema dominulus* mating pair [MJ]

*Eurydema oleracea*

*Eurydema ornata*

*Eurydema rugulosa* [TB]

*Eurydema spectabilis* [TB]

*Eurydema ventralis* [PC]

*Ancyrosoma leucogrammes* [PC]

***Graphosoma lineatum* Striped Shieldbug**
Body length: 8–11 mm. Red with bold black stripes. There is some variation in width of stripes and the ground colour is orange rather than red in Sicily. Some authors regard *G. lineatum* and *G. italicum* as two different species, others regard them as subspecies of *lineatum*, as in this book. Subspecies *lineatum* has orange legs and is restricted to Corsica and Sardinia; most observers would notice the widespread subspecies *italicum*, with mainly black legs. **HABITAT** Open areas and woodland edge to 1,900 m., feeding on umbellifers (Apiaceae) Wild Carrot *Daucus carota*, Cow Parsley *Anthriscus sylvestris* and others. **SEASON** April to October.

*Graphosoma lineatum*

***Graphosoma semipunctatum***
Body length: 10–13 mm. Red or orange with bold black stripes, but often only with black spots or blotches on pronotum. **HABITAT** Open areas feeding on umbellifers (Apiaceae). More strictly Mediterranean range than *G. lineatum*; also often seen on umbellifer flowers such as Wild Carrot *Daucus carota* up to c.2,000 m. **SEASON** April to September.

*Graphosoma semipunctatum*

***Ventocoris falcatus***
Body length: 7–9 mm. Brown, unmistakeable from the shape. **HABITAT** Various uncultivated grasslands, verges and others, feeding on fruits of Brassicaceae, including Pale Cabbage *Brassica tournefortii*. **SEASON** May to October.

*Ventrocoris falcatus*

***Ventocoris rusticus***
Body length: 8–10 mm. Conspicuous two colours, blackish brown on much of upperside, otherwise yellow. **HABITAT** Open areas to 1,000 m., feeding on love-in-a-mist *Nigella* spp. **SEASON** April to July.

*Ventrocoris rusticus*

***Podops inunctus* Knobbed Shieldbug**
Body length: 5–6 mm. This brown species has a large scutellum reaching the end of the abdomen in addition to projections on the side the pronotum. **HABITAT** Grasslands, dunes and others where they feed on various grasses. **SEASON** May to September.

*Podops inunctus*

***Tarisa flavescens***
Body length: 4 mm. Green, unusual hump-shaped. **HABITAT** Grasslands with bare ground, feeding on *Artemisia*, *Salsola* and others. **SEASON** All year.

*Tarisa flavescens*

## Family Coreidae – LEATHERBUGS

The leatherbugs or squashbugs are similar to shieldbugs, but are generally narrower in body shape with the abdomen expanded laterally. They mainly feed on fruit and seeds some species sometimes require specialised searching for on bare dry ground, others on vegetation.

***Gonocerus acuteangulatus* Box Bug**
Body length: 11–14 mm. Brown with a narrow abdomen and pale legs; Pronotum narrower than the abdomen; edge pointed. **HABITAT** Various, where the foodplants grow, berried shrubs including box *Buxus*, rose *Rosa*, bramble *Rubus*, hawthorn *Crataegus* spp. and others. **SEASON** April to October.

*Gonocerus acuteangulatus*

***Gonocerus insidiator***
Body length: 14–15 mm. Pronotum wider than the abdomen, usually reddish brown. **HABITAT** Various, where the foodplants grow: *Arbutus*, *Cistus*, oak *Quercus*, *Pistacia* and others. **SEASON** April to September.

*Gonocerus insidiator*

***Gonocerus juniperi***
Body length: 11–14 mm. Various shades of brown to purple; slenderer than closely related species. Black spot on scutellum. **HABITAT** Various, feeding on conifers including cypress *Cupressus* and juniper *Juniperus*. **SEASON** April to September.

*Gonocerus juniperi*

*Graphosoma lineatum* subsp. *italicum*

*Graphosoma semipunctatum*

*Ventrocoris falcatus* [FR]

*Ventrocoris rusticus*

*Podops inunctus*

*Tarisa flavescens* [FR]

*Gonocerus acuteangulatus*

*Gonocerus insidiator* [TB]

*Gonocerus juniperi* [TB]

### *Plinachtus imitator*
Body length: 12–14 mm. Brown, but abdomen and much of legs, green. **HABITAT** Open areas where the only foodplant, Lentisk *Pistacia lentiscus* grows. **SEASON** March to September.

*Plinachtus imitator*

### *Coreus marginatus* Dock Bug
Body length: 10–14 mm. Mottled brown, with a broad, oval abdomen. The second and third antennal segments are reddish. **HABITAT** Various, where they feed on dock *Rumex* and others. This species is often seen on vegetation, including bramble *Rubus*, sometimes congregating in numbers. **SEASON** April to November.

*Coreus marginatus*

### *Enoplops scapha* Boat Bug
Body length: 10–13 mm. Brown or grey with cream markings on abdominal margins (underside of head and pronotum whitish). **HABITAT** Sparsely vegetated areas, feeding on mayweed *Tripleurospermum* spp. and others. **SEASON** April to September.

*Enoplops scapha*

### *Syromastus rhombeus* Rhombic Leatherbug
Body length: 9–12 mm. Mottled brown, similar to *Coreus marginatus*, but recognised by its broad, diamond-shaped abdomen, and narrow lateral whitish margin of the pronotum. **HABITAT** Grasslands, feeding on plants from several families. **SEASON** April to October.

*Syromastus rhombeus*

### *Haploprocta sulcicornis*
Body length: 11–13 mm. Brown, usually with a pinkish tinge. Pronotum edge pointed, but unlike *Gonocerus* spp., the abdomen is broad. **HABITAT** Grasslands and others, feeding on dock *Rumex*, juniper *Juniperus* and oak *Quercus*. **SEASON** April to September.

*Haploprocta sulcicornis*

### *Centrocoris variegatus*
Body length: 10–13 mm. Conspicuously shaped variable species, brown or black mottled with white. **HABITAT** Grasslands. **SEASON** April to September.

*Centrocoris variegatus*

### *Spathocera dalmanii* Dalman's Leatherbug
Body length: 5–6.5 mm. Long pale margined pronotum; distinct black marks on upper part of scutellum. **HABITAT** Sites with sparse vegetation, feeding on Sheep's Sorrel *Rumex acetosella*. Rare in the Mediterranean subregion and usually in mountains. **SEASON** May to October.

*Spathocera dalmanii*

### *Spathocera lobata*
Body length: 6–6.5 mm. Rather like *S. dalmanii* except for the shape of the pronotum; hind part edges with sloping angles. **HABITAT** Sites with sparse vegetation, feeding on dock *Rumex*. **SEASON** May to October.

*Spathocera lobata*

### *Arenocoris falleni* Fallén's Leatherbug
Body length: 6–8 mm. Variable shades of brown, pronotum with inverted V-shaped spiny ridge. **HABITAT** Sandy sites under stork's-bill *Erodium* or other foodplants. **SEASON** April to October.

*Arenocoris falleni*

### *Arenocoris waltlii* [Breckland Leatherbug]
Body length: 7–8 mm. Resembles *A. falleni*, but pronotum lacking inverted 'V'-shaped spined ridge. Also the 3rd antennal segment is thickened towards the tip. **HABITAT** Sandy sites under stork's-bill *Erodium* or other foodplants. **SEASON** March to October.

*Arenocoris waltlii*

*Plinachtus imitator*

*Coreus marginatus*

*Enoplops scapha*

*Syromastus rhombeus*

*Haploprocta sulcicornis*

*Centrocoris variegatus* colour forms (left & right)

*Spathocera dalmanii*

*Spathocera lobata* [TB]

*Arenocoris falleni*

*Arenocoris waltlii*

***Leptoglossus occidentalis*** **Western Conifer Seed Bug**
Body length: 15–24 mm. Large, unmistakable species, with white zigzag pattern on the forewings. Hind tibiae with leaf-like expansions. **HABITAT** Wherever there are conifers, where they feed on flowers, developing cones and seeds of several species. This strong flier may sometimes be attracted to lights or far away from suitable habitat looking for suitable hibernation sites. Since reaching Italy in 1999 this native of USA has spread throughout Europe. **SEASON** Mainly September to November.

*Leptoglossus occidentalis*

***Phyllomorpha lacerata***
Body length: c.10 mm. Pale with similar spiky lobes to *P. laciniata*, but easily distinguished by very long spines on 2nd antennal segment and mid tibiae. **HABITAT** Near the foodplants *Paronychia* spp. **SEASON** March to August.

*Phyllomorpha lacerata*

***Phyllomorpha laciniata*** **Golden Egg Bug**
Body length: 7–11 mm. Translucent white, with brown and reddish areas; easily recognised by the extraordinary lateral leaf-like spiky lobes on the pronotum and abdomen. **HABITAT** Dry, open places, often rocky mountainous areas (as an example, Sierra Nevada, Spain c.2,200 m.) with little vegetation near the foodplants *Paronychia* spp. The ♀ lays eggs on mainly ♂ or some ♀ carriers of the same species, which transport eggs in an attempt to reduce parasitoid attack [losses are up to 10 times higher with eggs laid directly on foodplants]. ♂s carry up to 28 eggs. **SEASON** March to August.

*Phyllomorpha laciniata*

*Phyllomorpha laciniata* well camouflaged amongst its foodplant *Paronychia argentata* [PC]

***Bathysolen nubilus*** **Cryptic Leatherbug**
Body length: 6–7 mm. Brown, short and broad spineless pronotum. **HABITAT** Various sites with sparse vegetation near the foodplants such as medick *Medicago*. **SEASON** May to September.

*Bathysolen nubilus*

***Ceraleptus gracilicornis***
Body length: 10–12 mm. Dark brown; head with cream central and side stripes, running behind eyes. Edge of abdomen bold black and white. Membrane dark. **HABITAT** Grasslands, on or under clover *Trifolium* spp. **SEASON** May to September.

*Ceraleptus gracilicornis*

***Ceraleptus lividus*** **Slender-horned Leatherbug**
Body length: 10–12 mm. Brown, slender species similar to the *Coriomeris denticulatus* but with a dark eye-stripe and forewings with a pale margin, in addition to lacking spines. Plain compared to *C. gracilicornis*. **HABITAT** Grasslands, on or under clover *Trifolium* spp. **SEASON** May to September.

*Ceraleptus lividus*

***Loxocnemis dentator***
Body length: 8–10 mm. Dark brown and hairy; short antennae. **HABITAT** Grasslands, on restharrow *Ononis* and other Fabaceae. **SEASON** May to September.

*Loxocnemis dentator*

***Coriomeris denticulatus*** **Denticulate Leatherbug**
Body length: 7–10 mm. Brown, slender species with a clear white spiny margin to the pronotum. **HABITAT** Grasslands, on or under various foodplants, including medick *Medicago* and clover *Trifolium* spp. **SEASON** April to September.

*Coriomeris denticulatus*

*Leptoglossus occidentalis*

*Phyllomorpha laciniata* with eggs

*Phyllomorpha lacerata* [TB]

*Bathysolen nubilus* [TB]

*Loxocnemis dentator* [TB]

*Ceraleptus gracilicornis*

*Ceraleptus lividus*

*Coriomeris denticulatus*

### *Coriomeris hirticornis*
Body length: 8–11 mm. Like *C. denticulatus* but with very long antennal hairs. **HABITAT** Grasslands, on or under various foodplants. **SEASON** April to September.

*Coriomeris hirticornis*

### *Strobilotoma typhaecornis*
Body length: 7–8 mm. Conspicuously shaped antennal tips. **HABITAT** Grasslands, foodplants include *Calendula persica*. **SEASON** April to September.

*Strobilotoma typhaecornis*

## Family Alydidae – BROAD-HEADED BUGS
Elongate, broad-headed bugs similar to the closely related Coreidae.

### *Alydus calcaratus*
Body length: 10–12 mm. Dark brown, bright orange patch on abdomen (visible in flight). Hind femora with several spines. Tibiae straight. **HABITAT** Open areas including heathlands, mainly feeding on seeds of various plants. Nymphs resemble ants. **SEASON** May to September.

*Alydus calcaratus*

### *Camptopus lateralis*
Body length: 12–15 mm. Brown, narrow white lateral margin on pronotum and wings and central whitish line on head and upper part of pronotum. Abdomen orange. Hind femora with several spines. Tibiae curved. **HABITAT** Open areas where they are an Alfalfa *Medicago sativa* seed pest. **SEASON** May to September.

*Camptopus lateralis*

## Family Rhopalidae – RHOPALID BUGS
Mainly seed or fruit feeders with conspicuously shaped antennae, sometimes known as scentless plant bugs.

### *Corizus hyoscyami*
Body length: 9–11 mm. Conspicuously marked red and black species. **HABITAT** Open areas and woodlands, feeding on various plants. **SEASON** May to September.

*Corizus hyoscyami*

### *Liorhyssus hyalinus* Hyaline Grassbug
Body length: 6–7 mm. Smaller brown species; membrane transparent. **HABITAT** Open areas, feeding on various plants. **SEASON** April to September.

*Liorhyssus hyalinus*

## Family Pyrrhocoridae – FIREBUGS
There are five European species in this family, sporting bright warning colours and with enlarged front femora.

### *Pyrrhocoris apterus* Fire Bug
Body length: 9–10 mm. Unmistakeable red and black species; particularly bold black spots on corium, including hind tip. There are several described forms. **HABITAT** Open areas often on bare ground. They feed on various plants, including seeds and stems of mallow *Malva*. Sometimes occurs in large aggregations, including mating pairs, also nymphs. **SEASON** April to October.

*Pyrrhocoris apterus*

### *Scantius aegyptius*
Body length: 7–9 mm. Smaller species; black spots smaller than in *P. apterus*. **HABITAT** Open areas, feeding on various plants. **SEASON** March to November.

*Scantius aegyptius*

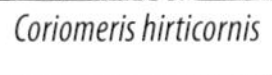

*Coriomeris hirticornis*

*Strobilotoma typhaecornis*

*Alydus calcaratus*

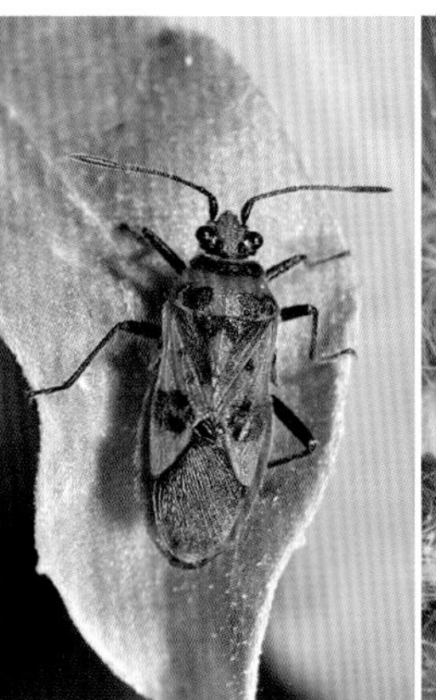

*Camptopus lateralis*

*Corizus hyoscyami*

*Liorhyssus hyalinus*

*Pyrrhocoris apterus* mating pair

*Scantius aegyptius* [TB]

## Family Stenocephalidae – SPURGEBUGS

As the name implies, colourful bugs with black and white banded antennae, feeding on spurges *Euphorbia* spp..

### *Dicranocephalus agilis*

Body length: 11–14 mm. slightly longer and more elongate than *D. medius*. **HABITAT** Open areas. **SEASON** May to September.

### *Dicranocephalus albipes*

Body length: 11–14 mm. Elongate, easily distinguished by differences in the antennae banding, 2nd segments mainly whitish. **HABITAT** Open areas. **SEASON** May to September.

### *Dicranocephalus medius*

Body length: 8–11 mm. slightly longer and more elongate than *D. agilis*. **HABITAT** Open areas, including in woodlands. **SEASON** May to September.

## Family Lygaeidae – GROUNDBUGS

A group of mainly dark brown or black species which are mostly terrestrial, plant feeding bugs. Some species, however, show conspicuous red and black warning colours and around the world are pests on cereals. A small selection of ground bugs is shown, with many overwintering as adults and more conspicuous in spring when they breed.

### *Lygaeus creticus*

Body length: 11–13 mm. Red and black, corium lacking transverse black band. **HABITAT** Various, feeding on *Sorbus* spp and Oleander *Nerium oleander*.

### *Lygaeus equestris* Black and Red Bug

Body length: 8–14 mm. Red and black with characteristic white spots or markings on wing membrane. **HABITAT** Open areas, feeding on many plants, a particular favourite are ripe seeds of Swallow-wort *Vincetoxicum hirundinaria*.

### *Spilostethus pandurus*

Body length: 12–15 mm. Black and red, with dominant red areas. Similar to *L. equestris* with white spots on wing membrane, but black markings distinct. **HABITAT** Various, on many plants and trees, often on flowers.

### *Spilostethus saxatilis*

Body length: 9–13 mm. Black and red, with dominant black areas; wing membrane black. **HABITAT** Open areas, mainly on Apiaceae, Asteraceae and Rosaceae.

### *Melanocoryphus albomaculatus*

Body length: 7–10 mm. Red, with black head, pronotum with conspicuous black arch, spots on corium and tip of abdomen. Membrane also black, but with white spots. **HABITAT** Various including slopes, feeding on seeds of many plants.

### *Horvathiolus superbus*

Body length: 4–5 mm. Small colourful red and black species. Two variably sized black blotches on pronotum [classification of similar species unclear]. **HABITAT** Various, feeding on plants from various families, including Foxglove *Digitalis purpurea* and stonecrop *Sedum* spp.

*Dicranocephalus agilis*

*Dicranocephalus albipes*

*Dicranocephalus medius*

*Lygaeus creticus*

*Lygaeus equestris*

*Spilostethus pandurus*

*Spilostethus saxatilis*

*Melanocoryphus albomaculatus*

*Horvathiolus superbus*

*Dicranocephalus agilis*

*Dicranocephalus albipes*

*Dicranocephalus medius*

*Lygaeus equestris* [PC]

*Lygaeus creticus* [TB]

*Spilostethus pandurus* (left), nymph (right)

*Spilostethus saxatilis*

*Melanocoryphus albomaculatus* mating pair

*Horvathiolus superbus*

### *Caenocoris nerii*
Body length: 7–10 mm. Black with red areas. **HABITAT** Often near water, where the foodplants Oleander *Nerium oleander* and *Cynanchum acutum* grow.

*Caenocoris nerii*

### *Graptostethus servus*
Body length: 8–10 mm. Black and red, body and legs slightly hairy. **HABITAT** Various, feeding on many low-growing plants.

*Graptostethus servus*

### *Ischnodemus sabuleti* European Cinchbug
Body length: 4–6 mm. Long and short winged forms. **HABITAT** Often wetlands but also dry habitats, feeding on grasses, including cereals, also reeds. Sometimes in thousands.

*Ischnodemus sabuleti*

### *Heterogaster urticae* Nettle Groundbug
Body length: 5–8 mm. Dark and light coloured; long hairs on head and pronotum. **HABITAT** Open places, feeding on nettle *Urtica* spp., often in large congregations of nymphs and adults (pictured below).

*Heterogaster urticae*

*Heterogaster urticae* group

### *Oxycarenus lavaterae*
Body length: 5–6 mm. Black densely punctured head and thorax, with reddish or pink corium. **HABITAT** Various, feeding on Malvaceae, including limes *Tilia*, mallows *Lavatera* and *Malva* spp.

*Oxycarenus lavaterae*

### *Gastrodes grossipes* Pine-cone Bug
Body length: 5–7 mm. Rather broad-bodied and flattened. **HABITAT** Coniferous woodlands.

*Gastrodes grossipes*

### *Emblethis griseus*
Body length: 5–7 mm. Rather oval straw coloured bug, densely dotted in darker shades. **HABITAT** Sandy or stony ground, including disturbed ground, feeding on stork's-bill *Erodium* spp.

*Emblethis griseus*

### *Trapezonotus ullrichi*
Body length: 5–6 mm. Two coloured pronotum and black scutellum; more oval than other *Trapezonotus* spp. **HABITAT** Open areas including woodland edges and clearings, associated with *Anthemis*, *Leucanthemum*, thyme *Thymus* and others, often found on flowers.

*Trapezonotus ullrichi*

### *Beosus maritimus*
Body length: 6–8 mm. Attractive pale and dark bug, with large white blotch on hind part of corium. **HABITAT** Sandy areas, often coastal, but also heathlands where they feed on seeds of various plants.

*Beosus maritimus*

*Caenocoris nerii*

*Graptostethus servus* [PC]

*Ischnodemus sabuleti* long-winged form (left), short-winged form and nymphs (right) [PC]

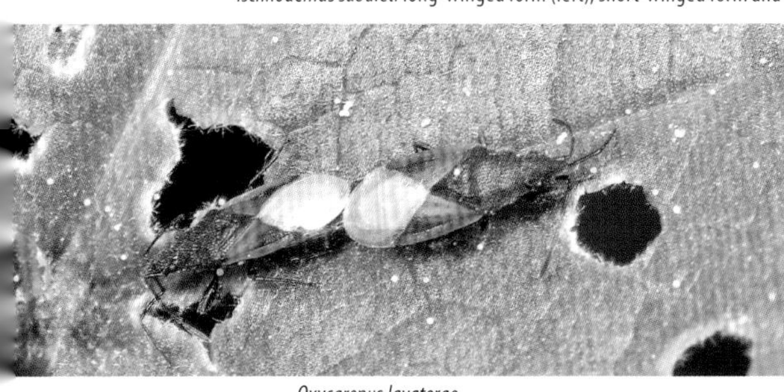

*Oxycarenus lavaterae*

*Gastrodes grossipes*

*Emblethis griseus*

*Trapezonotus ullrichi*

*Beosus maritimus*

***Beosus quadripunctatus***
Body length: 6–7 mm. Part reddish, name derived from four black blotches. **HABITAT** Sandy areas, often coastal, but also heathlands where they feed on seeds of various plants.

*Beosus quadripunctatus*

***Aellopus atratus***
Body length: 8–9 mm. Oval, black species. **HABITAT** Typically limestone slopes up to 1,000 m, often feeding on *Echium* spp.

*Aellopus atratus*

***Xanthochilus saturnius* Mediterranean Seed Bug**
Body length: 7–8 mm. Clear black markings, otherwise cream with brown spots. **HABITAT** Dry areas, but has been found in wetlands in Corsica.

*Xanthochilus saturnius*

***Ragliodes delineatus***
Body length: 7 mm. Black, with distinctive pale borders and streaks, also antennal bands. **HABITAT** Open areas, little known about this attractive endemic Spanish species.

*Ragliodes delineatus*

***Rhyparochromus vulgaris***
Body length: 7–8 mm. Oval, long-legged, markings include white triangular area on pronotum; wing membrane dark. **HABITAT** Woodland edges and clearings, feeding on seeds of many species; often observed moving quickly on the ground.

*Rhyparochromus vulgaris*

## Family Berytidae – STILTBUGS
A small group of elongate bugs with stilt-like legs.

***Metatropis rufescens***
Body length: 9–11 mm. **HABITAT** Woodlands, feeding on mainly reproductive organs of Enchanter's-nightshade *Circaea lutetiana*. In the Alps on Alpine Enchanter's-nightshade *C. alpina*. **SEASON** May to October.

*Metatropis rufescens*

## Family Tingidae – LACEBUGS
A group of attractive, small plant-feeding bugs with lace-like edges to the pronotum and wings.

***Kalama tricornis***
Body length: 3–3.5 mm. Black, long-haired antennae. Two rows of meshes at the lateral edges of the forewings. **HABITAT** Open areas to 1,500 m., on various plants. **SEASON** May to October.

*Kalama tricornis*

***Stephanitis takeyai* Andromeda Lacebug**
Body length: c.4 mm. Distinctive black markings, including on wings. Antennae and legs pale. **HABITAT** Gardens, parks and others, feeding on Ericaeae *Pieris*, *Rhododendron* and *Azalea*. Introduced to Europe from Japan along with related species and considered a pest on ornamental plants. **SEASON** June to November.

*Stephanitis takeyai*

## Family Cimicidae – BED BUGS
Closely related to flower bugs, the oval, flattened blood-sucking bed bugs have only reduced forewings and no hindwings.

***Cimex lectularius* Bed Bug**
Body length: 4–5 mm. Rather broad-bodied and flattened. **HABITAT** On or near birds or mammals, where they feed at night. Some hotels still have problems with these insects, but bites do not transmit diseases, although they can cause rashes and other conditions. Following an old tradition, several early modern Italian writers recommended eating bed bugs as a cure for quartan fever! **SEASON** All year.

*Cimex lectularius*

*Beosus quadripunctatus* [TB]

*Aellopus atratus*

*Xanthochilus saturnius* [TB]

*Ragliodes delineatus* [TB]

*Rhyparochromus vulgaris*

*Metatropis rufescens*

*Stephanitis takeyai*

*Kalama tricornis* [TB]

*Cimex lectularius*

## Family Reduviidae – ASSASSIN BUGS

The assassin bugs are mainly predators on various insects, often waiting for or hunting them on flowers. They have a three-segmented beak; the 1st antennal segment being the longest. Some *Rhynocoris* species provide parental care of offspring, guarding eggs.

### *Empicoris vagabundus*

Body length: 4–5 mm. Rather slender and mottled, a type of thread-legged bug with curved rostrum, unlike the similar stiltbugs. **HABITAT** Woodlands. **SEASON** All year.

### *Coranus griseus*

Body length: 8–12 mm. Robust, medium-sized, dark mottled species. **HABITAT** Bare ground. **SEASON** March to August.

### *Phymata crassipes*

Body length: 7–9 mm. Dark brown; broadened abdomen with paler lower part and legs. Whitish patches on upper part of abdomen **HABITAT** Open areas. **SEASON** May to September.

### *Oncocephalus pilicornis*

Body length: 12–18 mm. Elongate brown species with black markings. **HABITAT** Various, hiding under stones or soil, but readily attracted to lights. **SEASON** May to September.

### *Peirates hybridus*

Body length: 12–15 mm. Distinctive red and black markings. **HABITAT** Various, often hiding under stones. **SEASON** April to October.

### *Reduvius personatus* Fly Bug

Body length: 16–19 mm. Large black species. **HABITAT** Often inside buildings, seeking prey, also in rocky areas. The larvae cover themselves with sand or dust after each moult, providing effective camouflage. **SEASON** May to September.

### *Rhynocoris cuspidatus*

Body length: c.11 mm. Margins of abdomen yellow and black. Pronotum with more black than related species; legs banded, but mainly black. **HABITAT** Open areas. **SEASON** May to September.

### *Rhynocoris erythropus*

Body length: 12–15 mm. Margins of abdomen yellowish orange and black. **HABITAT** Open areas. **SEASON** May to September.

### *Rhynocoris iracundus*

Body length: 14–18 mm. Vivid red and black species, including abdominal margin. Front lobe of pronotum mainly black. **HABITAT** Open areas. **SEASON** May to September.

*Rhynocoris iracundus* showing underside

*Empicoris vagabundus*

*Coranus griseus*

*Phymata crassipes*

*Oncocephalus pilicornis*

*Peirates hybridus*

*Reduvius personatus*

*Rhynocoris cuspidatus*

*Rhynocoris erythropus*

*Rhynocoris iracundus*

Empicoris vagabundus

Coranus griseus [SO]

Phymata crassipes

Oncocephalus pilicornis

Peirates hybridus

Reduvius personatus [SR]

Rhynocoris cuspidatus

Rhynocoris erythropus

Rhynocoris iracundus

## Family Nabidae – DAMSEL BUGS

These predatory brown bugs differ from assassin bugs by having a four-segmented beak; the 2nd antennal segment is always the longest. Two example species are illustrated, most species frequent low vegetation.

### *Himacerus apterus* Tree Damsel Bug

Body length: 8–12 mm. Black connexivum. Short winged species with long antennae. **HABITAT** Woodlands, gardens and others, one of few damsel bugs to live mainly in trees. **SEASON** July to October.

*Himacerus apterus*

### *Prostemma guttula*

Body length: 7–10 mm. Distinctive black with red wing-cases and legs. **HABITAT** Grasslands. **SEASON** June to September.

*Prostemma guttula*

## Family Anthocoridae – FLOWER BUGS

These predatory bugs feed on aphids for much of the year. Various species similar in appearance.

### *Anthocoris nemorum*

Body length: 3–4 mm. Head and pronotum black. Forewings reflective. Attractively marked but delicate-looking. **HABITAT** Various, feeding on small prey and sometimes leaves; it can pierce human flesh.

*Anthocoris nemorum*

## Family Miridae – PLANT OR CAPSID BUGS

Where wings are present, these bugs have soft forewings, with a prominent triangular area, often a different colour than the rest of the body. This is a large family of often attractive bugs, mainly feeding on fruits, leaves and seeds, although some eat aphids and other prey. A few species are illustrated.

### *Deraeocoris ruber*

Body length: 6–8 mm. Variable in colour but with two bold red or orange blotches. **HABITAT** Various plants, feeding on small insects. **SEASON** May to October.

*Deraeocoris ruber*

### *Calocoris nemoralis*

Body length: 8–10 mm. Various colour forms. **HABITAT** Grasslands, feeding on various thistles, including *Cirsium* and *Carduus* spp. **SEASON** June to September.

*Calocoris nemoralis*

### *Hadrodemus m-flavum*

Body length: 6–8 mm. Red or yellow with large black spots blotches and markings. **HABITAT** Grasslands and woodlands, feeding on herbs, including *Salvia* spp. **SEASON** June to September.

*Hadrodemus m-flavum*

### *Adelphocoris lineolatus* Lucerne Bug

Body length: 8–10 mm. Pale green or brown. Elongate with spiny hind tibiae. **HABITAT** Grasslands, on legumes. It is regarded as an agricultural pest on Lucerne, also known as Alfalfa *Medicago sativa* crops worldwide. **SEASON** July to October.

*Adelphocoris lineolatus*

### *Lygus maritimus*

Body length: 8–10 mm. Various colour forms and to confuse matters, closely related species. **HABITAT** Grasslands, mainly in coastal areas, feeding on various herbs in the Asteraceae and others. **SEASON** All year.

*Lygus maritimus*

## Family Veliidae – WATER CRICKETS

Colourful, robust looking water bugs. There are sometimes aggregations of colourful water crickets in calmer parts of swift streams, waiting for ripples caused by insects landing on the surface, which they eat.

### *Velia caprai* Water Cricket

Body length: 5–6 mm. Red spotted abdomen. Usually wingless, but sometimes fully winged. It has the ability to travel at twice its normal speed by spitting on the water surface i.e. thereby lowering the water tension.

*Velia caprai*

*Himacerus apterus*

*Prostemma guttula* [SO]

*Anthocoris nemorum*

*Deraeocoris ruber* (left), (right) [PC]

*Calocoris nemoralis* [TB]

*Hadrodemus m-flavum* [PC]

*Adelphocoris lineolatus*

*Lygus maritimus*

*Velia caprai* (left), group (right) [RW]

## Family Hydrometridae – WATER MEASURERS

Elongate, remarkably thin stick-like water bugs. These slender stick-like insects slowly tred the margins of ponds and streams or are found in damp areas.

**_Hydrometra stagnorum_ Water Measurer**
Body length: 9–12 mm. Elongate. Sensitive to underwater vibrations, spearing water fleas with the rostrum.

## Family Gerridae – PONDSKATERS

Elongate water bugs, legs adapted for rowing on water surface. The pondskaters have long legs adapted in order to detect vibrations and therefore obtain prey. The middle pair of legs are rather like oars which provide propulsion on the surface. Pondskaters sometimes fly to lights at night.

**_Gerris lacustris_ Common Pondskater**
Body length: 8–10 mm. One of many similar brown species. **HABITAT** Ponds, streams and other waters.

## Family Nepidae – WATERSCORPIONS

Characterised by an abdomen with a stiff, elongate tail, used for breathing. Body shape can be broad or elongate. The water scorpions have a long tail to distinguish them from other families.

**_Nepa cinerea_ Waterscorpion**
Body length: 17–23 mm. Brown; flattened leaf-shaped abdomen. **HABITAT** Shallow muddy slow or still waters, often eating tadpoles and small fish. Also known to hunt out of water.

**_Ranatra linearis_ Water Stick-insect**
Body length: 30–35 mm [plus a breathing tube up to 20 mm]. Brown, elongate species. **HABITAT** Ponds and waters with emergent vegetation, where they catch prey such as small fish and insects, although they occasionally exit the water to hunt. They feign death when handled i.e. remain motionless, like a stick.

## Family Naucoridae – SAUCER BUGS

Fore femora thickened; forewings may be present. Saucer-shaped.

**_Ilyocoris cimicoides_ Saucer Bug**
Body length: 11–16 mm. **HABITAT** Bottom of muddy ponds and stagnant canals. Although winged, they are incapable of flight, although they can walk rapidly and bite in defence. They are predators of water fleas and insect larvae.

## Family Notonectidae – WATER BOATMEN

Boat-shaped, back-swimming bugs. The predatory water boatmen, sometimes known as backswimmers, swim upside down on the water surface.

**_Notonecta glauca_ Common Backswimmer**
Body length: 14–16 mm. Light brown with darker markings; eyes red. **HABITAT** Ponds, lakes and canals as well as animal troughs and others.

## Family Corixidae – LESSER WATER BOATMEN

Elongate, flattened water bugs with fine striations marking the wings; long hindlegs covered in hairs shaped like oars adapted for swimming. Beak (rostrum) short, broad and blunt. The lesser water boatmen swim right-side up near the bottom of ponds or streams and mainly feed on vegetation. They communicate by stridulating.

**_Corixa punctata_ Common Water Boatman**
Body length: 5–14 mm. Black with numerous yellowish markings; eyes brown. **HABITAT** On the water surface of ponds.

*Hydrometra stagnorum*

*Gerris lacustris*

*Nepa cinerea*

*Ranatra linearis*

*Ilyocoris cimicoides*

*Notonecta glauca*

*Corixa punctata*

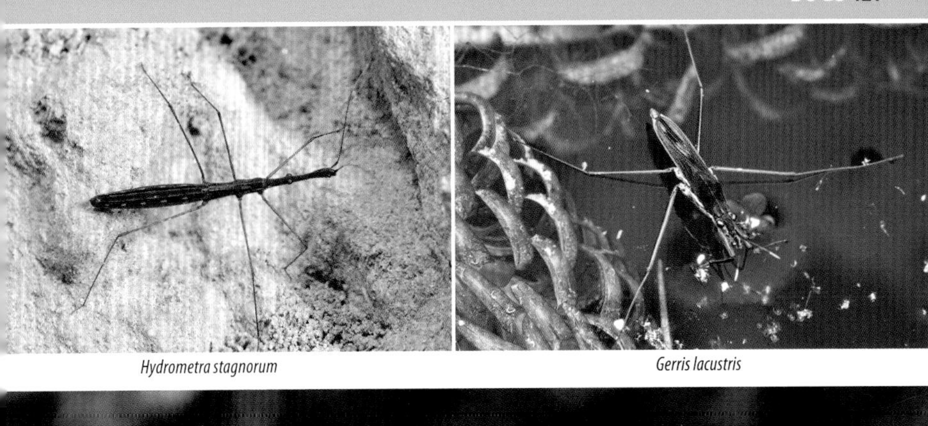

*Hydrometra stagnorum*

*Gerris lacustris*

*Ranatra linearis* [PG]

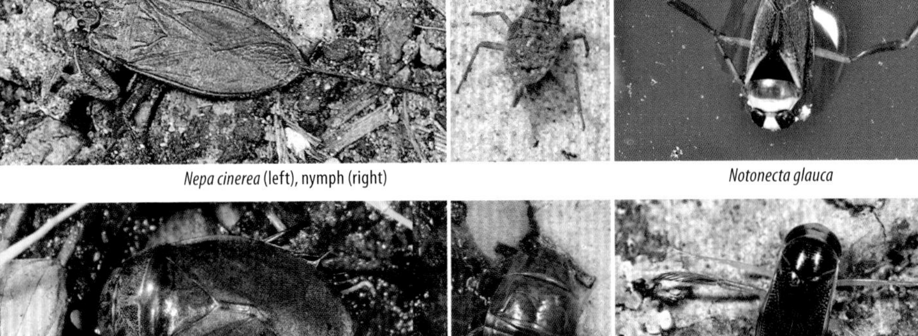

*Nepa cinerea* (left), nymph (right)

*Notonecta glauca*

*Ilyocoris cimicoides* (left), nymph (right)

*Corixa punctata*

# Suborder Auchenorrhyncha

## Family Cicadidae – CICADAS

There are about 2,500 worldwide species of cicada (popular as food for humans in some countries), bugs with large eyes wide apart on the head and often transparent, well-veined wings. Many visitors taking trips to the Mediterranean often wonder where the constant shrill noise originates from. Cicadas are well known by the long life cycle of some species, the larvae living underground on roots of trees or shrubs for several years; when adults do hatch, ♂s are heard and sometimes both sexes seen in vast numbers on tees, fences and vegetation, along with shed skins. Song is important and can help distinguish between species.

The shed skins of Cicada species are sometimes visible on vegetation and tree trunks across the Mediterranean. Adults often emerge under cover of darkness [TN]

*Cicada barbara*

*Cicada orni*

*Cicadatra atra*

*Lyristes plebejus*

*Tettigettula pygmea*

*Tibicina haematodes*

### *Cicada barbara*

Body length: c.28 mm. Brownish, rather like *C. orni*, with two well defined black spots on forewings. **HABITAT** Open woodlands and garrigue. Unlike *C. orni*, the calling song is a continuous buzzing; ♂s call from *Eucalyptus globulus*, Olive *Olea europaea*, pine *Pinus* spp., Lentisk *Pistacia lentiscus* and others. The species overlap in Iberia. **SEASON** Late June to October.

### *Cicada orni*

Body length: c.28 mm. Olive-greenish with four distinctive black spots on forewings. **HABITAT** Open woodlands, the ♂s calling from various trees, including pine *Pinus* spp. The calling song includes intervals of silence. The ♀ lays eggs in branches of *Fraxinus ornus* and others. **SEASON** June to October.

### *Cicadatra atra*

Body length: c.19 mm. Blackish brown, with orange markings. **HABITAT** Various, including more open areas with suitable vegetation, such as scrub and wastelands. **SEASON** June to July.

### *Lyristes plebejus*

Body length: 30–37 mm. One of Europe's largest cicadas, conspicuously marked. **HABITAT** Open woodlands, ♂s calling from trees such as Olive *Olea europaea* and Maritime Pine *Pinus pinaster*. This species occurs up to 1,000 m in France. **SEASON** Late May to October.

### *Tettigettula pygmea*

Body length: up to 20 mm. Black with various orange markings. As the species name implies, rather small and could be confused with other species. **HABITAT** Deciduous and coniferous woodlands. **SEASON** June to September.

### *Tibicina haematodes*

Body length: c.30 mm. Basal veins on forewings and abdominal segments conspicuously reddish. **HABITAT** Found in deciduous and coniferous trees and more open hot, dry sites including parks, gardens and even vineyards; occurs up to 500 m in France. **SEASON** Mid May to mid August.

*Cicada barbara*

*Cicada orni* [MR]

*Cicadatra atra* [SP]

*Lyristes plebejus* [SP]

*Tettigettula pygmea*

*Tibicina haematodes* [SP]

**FROGHOPPERS** – The plant feeding froghoppers (named after the frog-like shape of their heads) in the families Cercopidae and Aphrophoridae, have leathery wings folded back over the body, with short bristly antennae; they can jump well and the so called 'cuckoo-spit' or white froth surrounding a nymph is a familiar sight on stems, including in gardens. The hind tibiae are rounded with few spines.

## Family Cercopidae

***Cercopis intermedia***
Body length: 8–10 mm. Black with small red markings; also red band on legs. **HABITAT** Open areas. **SEASON** April to June.

*Cercopis intermedia*

***Cercopis vulnerata* Red-and-black Froghopper**
Body length: 9–11 mm. Black with vivid, large red markings. **HABITAT** Open areas, the nymphs feeding on roots underground. **SEASON** April to August.

*Cercopis vulnerata*

## Family Aphrophoridae

***Philaenus spumarius* Common Froghopper**
Body length: 5–7 mm. Brown, with remarkably variable colour forms. **HABITAT** Various. **SEASON** June to September.

*Philaenus spumarius*

***Aphrophora alni* Alder Spittelbug**
Body length: 9–10 mm. Brown, with distinctive white patches on wing margins. **HABITAT** Various trees and bushes. **SEASON** May to October.

*Aphrophora alni*

## Family Membracidae – TREEHOPPERS

The pronotum extends horn-like, back over the body.

***Centrotus cornutus* Horned Treehopper**
Body length: c.10 mm. Brown, horn on pronotum curved, narrow towards hind part. **HABITAT** Woodland clearings on various herbs and shrubs. **SEASON** April to August.

*Centrotus cornutus*

***Stictocephala bisonia* Buffalo Treehopper**
Body length: 6–8 mm. Green, horn on hind part of pronotum very broad, the hump-backed appearance resembling the shape of a buffalo. **HABITAT** Woodlands and grasslands, on many plants and known to cause damage in orchards to fruit trees, laying eggs in bark of twigs. It was probably introduced from USA with fruit tree cuttings, first reported in Europe in 1912. **SEASON** July to September.

*Stictocephala bisonia*

## Family Cicadellidae – LEAFHOPPERS

A large family of often slender, jumping plant-feeding bugs, which can also fly well. They suck sap from grasses, shrubs and trees. The forewings are often softer than those of froghoppers; hind legs have a series of bristles. A small selection of species is shown.

***Cicadella viridis***
Body length: 6–8 mm. ♀ green, ♂ bluish mauve or sometimes black. Pronotum yellow at front, hind part green. **HABITAT** Damp grasslands and marshes. **SEASON** July to October.

*Cicadella viridis*

***Evacanthus interruptus***
Body length: c.6 mm. Yellow and black. **HABITAT** Grasslands and scrub. **SEASON** June to October.

*Evacanthus interruptus*

***Graphocephala fennahi* Rhododendron Leafhopper**
Body length: 8–10 mm. Unmistakeable colours. **HABITAT** Wherever *Rhododendron* spp. grows, sometimes several congregate on one leaf. This species was introduced first to the UK from the USA in 1930s, eventually spreading south from the Netherlands after 1960. **SEASON** June to November.

*Graphocephala fennahi*

*Cercopis intermedia*

*Cercopis vulnerata*

*Philaenus spumarius*

*Aphrophora alni* mating pair

*Centrotus cornutus*

*Stictocephala bisonia* [PC]

*Graphocephala fennahi*

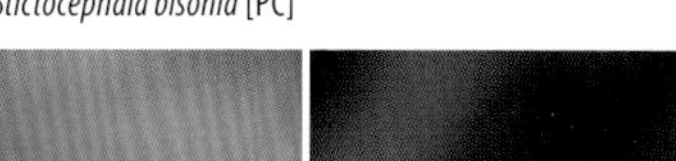

*Cicadella viridis* ♀ (left), ♂ (right)

*Evacanthus interruptus* [PC]

***Eupelix cuspidata***
Body length: 5–7 mm. Distinctive large, flattened head. **HABITAT** Grasslands. **SEASON** March to October.

*Eupelix cuspidata*

***Ledra aurita* Eared Leafhopper**
Body length: 13–18 mm. Large greyish with ear-like lobe. **HABITAT** Woodlands, particularly oak *Quercus*. As well as playing dead, it can stridulate loudly. **SEASON** May to September.

*Ledra aurita*

***Iassus lanio***
Body length: 6.5–8 mm. Large, conspicuous green and brown. **HABITAT** Oak *Quercus* woodlands. **SEASON** June to October.

*Iassus lanio*

### Family Cixiidae – LACEHOPPERS
Foewings with at least partly transparent wings.

***Cixius nervosus***
Body length: 6–8 mm. Transparent wings with dark band bands, spots and markings. **HABITAT** Woodlands, hedgerows, scrublands and others, on various plants. **SEASON** May to October.

*Cixius nervosus*

### Family Delphacidae – PLANTHOPPERS
Small hopping bugs with a moveable spur at tip of hind tibiae. Antennae pointing out from base of eyes; broad base. Species often with short and long-winged forms.

***Conomelus anceps***
Body length: 4 mm. Abdomen often darker than head, thorax and forewings. **HABITAT** Damp areas on rushes *Juncus* spp. **SEASON** June to November.

*Conomelus anceps*

### Family Issidae – ISSID PLANTHOPPERS
Robust, rather beetle-like, distinctively shaped planthoppers.

***Issus coleoptratus***
Body length: c.9 mm. Forewings usually a similar colour; numerous cross-veins. **HABITAT** Various, on bushes and trees. **SEASON** June to November.

*Issus coleoptratus*

***Issus muscaeformis***
Body length: c.9 mm. Forewings usually mottled, often with bold whitish markings. **HABITAT** Various, on bushes and trees. **SEASON** June to October.

*Issus muscaeformis*

## Suborder Sternorrhyncha

### Family Aphididae – APHIDS
A large family of small insects feeding on the phloem sap of plants and often tended by ants; some species are well known agricultural pests so gardeners are usually keen to see ladybirds eating them. Two examples are illustrated.

***Macrosiphum rosae* Rose Aphid**
Body length: c.3 mm. Green or pink, in winged and wingless forms; dark antennae, also tips to ends of femora and tibiae. **HABITAT** Various, on rose *Rosa* spp. often tended by ants. **SEASON** April to October.

*Macrosiphum rosae*

***Eucallipterus tiliae* Lime Aphid**
Body length: 2–3 mm. Pale yellow winged species, with black markings. **HABITAT** Various, feeding on the underside of limes *Tilia* spp. No known association with ants. **SEASON** May to September.

*Eucallipterus tiliae*

***Tuberolachnus salignus* Giant Willow Aphid**
Body length: 5–6 mm. Large, conspicously marked long-legged species, reproducing parthenogenetically. Nymphs can develop into wingless or winged adults. **HABITAT** Often on willow *Salix* spp. **SEASON** Late June to March.

*Tuberolachnus salignus*

*Eupelix cuspidata*

*Ledra aurita* (left) [PC], face (right)

*Iassus lanio*

*Cixius nervosus*

*Conomelus anceps*

*Issus coleoptratus* (left), nymph (right)

*Issus muscaeformis*

*Macrosiphum rosae* pink form [PC]

*Eucallipterus tiliae*

*Tuberolachnus salignus*

# Order NEUROPTERA – LACEWINGS, ANTLIONS & OWLFLIES

**Southern Europe & Mediterranean: many of Europe's 313 species**

Graceful, fluttering, delicate-looking soft-bodied insects; the adults mainly have two pairs of wings, often with cross-veins, giving a lace-like appearance. The wings are held roof-like over the body at rest. The antennae are often long and threadlike, mouthparts are designed for biting or chewing. Many adults are predators on small insects such as aphids (or ants in the case of antlions), as are the fierce-looking larvae, of which a few species are aquatic. The mouthparts of spoonwings are adapted to enable them to collect pollen and nectar from flowers. The life cycle is one of complete metamorphosis: egg, larva, pupa and adult. Lacewings are often small , the antlions and stunning owlflies much larger, the order ranging from c.3 mm to 100 mm. in wingspan. Many lacewing species are similar in appearance and require examination of genitalia. However, in many cases, they can be divided into green and brown species. Eggs of Chrysopidae can sometimes be seen on vegetation hanging onto threads (those of Mantspidae onto very short threads), but other lacewings do not attach eggs to threads.

**HABITAT** Some of the lacewings and their allies are attracted to light and are common in gardens, in addition to woodlands, hedgerows and grasslands. Allies often like open areas in full sun.

**HOTSPOTS** If new to the world of Neuroptera, try searching for owlflies in alpine meadows on sunny days. Spain has a diverse fauna, with 176 recorded species of Neuroptera, including 9 species of owlflies. Almost 100 of these species are recorded in the Sierra Nevada.

## Family Osmylidae – OSMYLIDS

Small to medium-sized, resembling green lacewings, but often with spotted wings.

### *Osmylus fulvicephalus* Giant Lacewing

Forewing length: 20–26 mm (body c.13 mm). Large, black with a reddish head, boldly mottled wings. **HABITAT** Open woodland, often near shaded streams. **SEASON** April to August.

*Osmylus fulvicephalus*

## Family Mantispidae – MANTIDFLIES

Similar in appearance to mantids, hence the common name for this small family of similar-looking species.

### *Mantispa styriaca*

Forewing length: 7–17 mm. Brown, resembling a mantis but with flimsy wings. **HABITAT** Woodland edges and open sites, hunting insects such as small flies, often waiting for prey to move within reach of the forelegs; the larvae penetrate spider egg sacs and feed on eggs. The adults are active by day and night. **SEASON** May to August.

*Mantispa styriaca*

## Family Berothidae – BEADED LACEWINGS

Similar in general appearance to lacewings, the larvae may be associated with termites.

### *Isoscelipteron glaserellum*

Forewing length 9–12 mm. Brown, leaf-like. **HABITAT** Scrublands. **SEASON** June to August.

*Isoscelipteron glaserellum*

## Family Chrysopidae – GREEN LACEWINGS

Often green, bluish-green or yellowish-green.

### *Chrysopa perla*

Forewing length c.15 mm. Bluish-green with extensive black marks and spots on head and thorax. **HABITAT** Shrubby grasslands and woodland edge. **SEASON** April to September.

*Chrysopa perla*

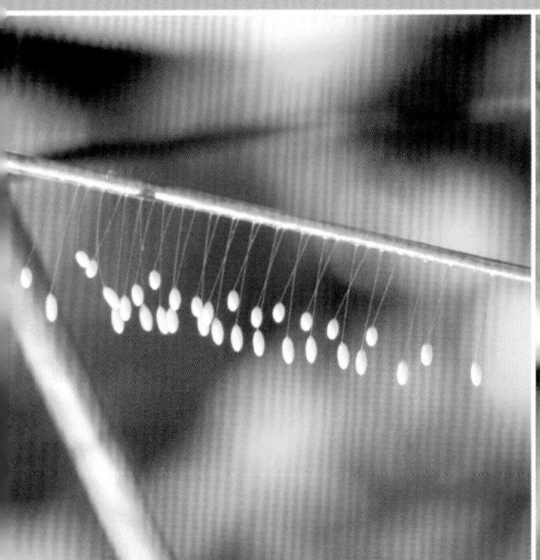
Lacewing eggs (Chrysopidae) [SO]

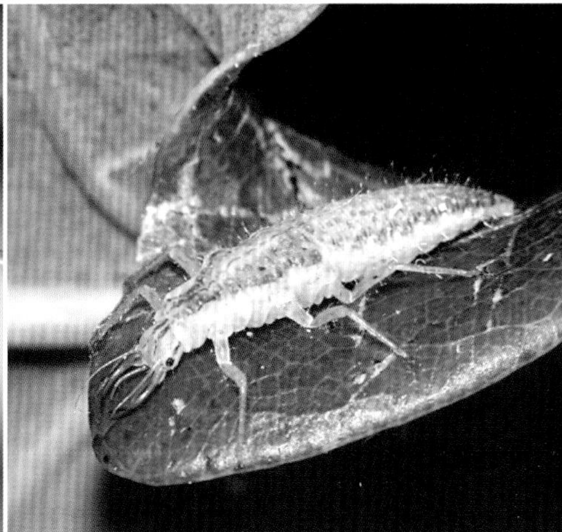
Lacewing larva (Chrysopidae)

*Osmylus fulvicephalus*

*Mantispa styriaca*

*Isoscelipteron glaserellum* [FR]

*Chrysopa perla*

***Chrysoperla carnea***
Forewing length c.15 mm. Green with yellow central stripe. **HABITAT** Woodlands and open areas, one of Europe's commonest lacewing (56 species of Neuroptera were recorded during a comprehensive study in south-western Europe (2006); over 41% of the total were *C. carnea*). **SEASON** April to September.

*Chrysoperla carnea*

***Italochrysa stigmatica***
Forewing length 22–25 mm. Brightly coloured yellowish body with several bold black spots on abdomen and wings. **HABITAT** Woodlands and grasslands with *Genista* spp. **SEASON** June to September.

*Italochrysa stigmatica*

## Family Hemerobiidae – BROWN LACEWINGS
Mainly brown insects; occasionally with hooked wing tips.

***Drepanepteryx phalaenoides***
Forewing length: 12–15 mm. A brown leaf mimic with tip of forewings hooked. **HABITAT** Woodlands and others. **SEASON** August to October.

*Drepanepteryx phalaenoides*

***Hemerobius humulinus***
Forewing length: c.9 mm. **HABITAT** Woodlands and others. **SEASON** March to November.

*Hemerobius humulinus*

## Family Nemopteridae – SPOONWINGS
Delicate fliers, the hindwings of this family (sometimes known as Thread-winged Antlions) are remarkably elongate.

***Nemoptera bipennis***
Forewing length: 25–33 mm. Black and white wings. **HABITAT** Open areas, including rocky sites; often visiting flowers. **SEASON** April to July.

*Nemoptera bipennis*

***Nemoptera sinuata* Larger Balkan Spoon-winged Lacewing**
Forewing length: 25–35 mm. Similar to *N. bipennis*, but note distinct wing markings, including less extensive black lines on upper margin of forewings. **HABITAT** Open areas. **SEASON** May to July.

*Nemoptera sinuata*

**The Taygetos mountains** in the **Peloponnese, Greece** contain a great diversity of landscapes, ranging from coastal areas to alpine habitats above 2,000m in elevation. Insects proliferate, and the rich fauna includes many endemic species of the Peloponnese. [CG]

*Chrysoperla carnea*

*Italochrysa stigmatica* [SO]

*Drepanepteryx phalaenoides* [GSM]

*Hemerobius humulinus*

*Nemoptera bipennis*

*Nemoptera sinuata* [TB]

## Family Myrmeleontidae – ANTLIONS

Similar in appearance to an owlfly, but easy to recognise by their short, hooked antennae. The fierce larvae have huge jaws and in many species lie in wait beneath cone-shaped pits to feed on insects which fall into the trap.

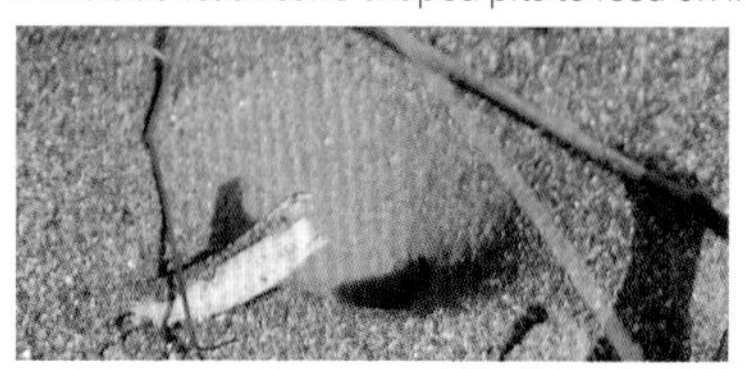
Typical antlion larval pit in sandy soil.

### *Creoleon lugdunensis*

Forewing length: 26–35 mm. Thorax yellowish with dark brown central stripe. **HABITAT** Rocky grasslands. The larvae do not make pits. **SEASON** May to August.

### *Distoleon annulatus*

Forewing length: 23–26 mm. Minimal flecks on wings. **HABITAT** Places with dry low vegetation. **SEASON** July to October.

### *Distoleon tetragrammicus*

Forewing length: 26–40 mm. Brown with spotted wings, similar to *Eureoleon nostras* but with vein differences at base of hindwings. **HABITAT** Oak *Quercus* and pine *Pinus* woodlands, where the larvae live in leaf litter and do not make pits. One of the Mediterranean's most photographed antlion species. **SEASON** June to August.

### *Euroleon nostras*

Forewing length: 25–33 mm. Large, brown species, wings with some black flecks, clubbed antennae. **HABITAT** Sandy areas often in large numbers, where the larvae make small pits in bare ground. **SEASON** June to August.

### *Macronemurus appendiculatus*

Forewing length: 21–25 mm. ♂ with distinctive long cerci. **HABITAT** Grasslands. **SEASON** May to September.

### *Myrmeleon formicarius*

Forewing length: 35–40 mm. Large, brown, wings plain, clubbed antennae. **HABITAT** Sandy soils, mainly nocturnal but can be disturbed from vegetation by day. **SEASON** May to August.

### *Palpares hispanus*

Forewing length: 50–60 mm. Similar to *P. libelluloides* but each abdominal segment is black-ringed. **HABITAT** Open sloped grasslands up to 2,000 m in Andalucía. **SEASON** May to August.

### *Palpares libelluloides*

Forewing length: 50–60 mm. Readily recognised by large dark brown or black blotches on wings. ♂s have long genital appendages. **HABITAT** Open grasslands including rocky slopes and sand dunes, adults generally fly close to the ground. **SEASON** May to September.

### *Synclisis baetica*

Forewing length: 46–50 mm. Rather hairy, large species with unspotted wings (only larva illustrated, pictured right [MRo]). **HABITAT** Often coastal sand dunes, but also sandy inland areas up to 1,000 m. The larvae live in sand and do not make pits. **SEASON** May to October.

*Creoleon lugdunensis*

*Distoleon annulatus*

*Distoleon tetragrammicus*

*Euroleon nostras*

*Macronemurus appendiculatus*

*Myrmeleon formicarius*

*Palpares hispanus*

*Palpares libelluloides*

*Synclisis baetica*

*Creoleon lugdunensis*

*Distoleon annulatus* [FR]

*Distoleon tetragrammicus* [PC]

*Euroleon nostras* [JH]

*Macronemurus appendiculatus* ♂ (left), ♀ (right)

*Myrmeleon formicarius* [DC]

*Palpares hispanus* [DRo]

*Palpares libelluloides* [KB]

## Family Ascalaphidae – OWLFLIES

Similar in appearance to antlions (or even generally to dragonflies), these aerial predators are easy to recognise by their long club-tipped antennae. The ♂s have claspers, used during mating. Species are easily distinguished by wing colour, but this can be difficult to ascertain when the wings are folded, at rest. Fortunately, they often sit with wings open. The larvae live on the ground and do not make pits.

### *Deleproctophylla bleusei*

Forewing length: 16–23 mm. Some conspicuous yellow veins on wings. Tips of hindwings with a brown patch. **HABITAT** Mainly coastal grasslands, in south-east Spain. **SEASON** May to August.

### *Libelloides baeticus*

Forewing length: 16–24 mm. Black-veined wings. Much yellow on or near basal part of wings, then white (except the outer half of forewings is transparent). **HABITAT** Grasslands. **SEASON** May to July.

### *Libelloides coccajus*

Forewing length: 20–27 mm. Distinctively shaped white or yellow patches (♂ in resting position, pictured left). Hindwings with more extensive black basal area than in related species. Forewings mostly black-veined. **HABITAT** Open woodlands and grasslands. **SEASON** April to July.

### *Libelloides hispanicus*

Forewing length: 22–27 mm. Whitish veins at base of wings, then dark. Black inverted 'Y' mark on hindwings. **HABITAT** Open pinewood. **SEASON** May to July.

### *Libelloides ictericus*

Forewing length: 17–25 mm. Yellow veins at base of wings, then whitish. Black-tipped hindwings. **HABITAT** Grasslands. **SEASON** May to June.

### *Libelloides lacteus*

Forewing length: 17–23 mm. Black-veined, wings with bluish or whitish areas. **HABITAT** Grasslands. **SEASON** May to July.

### *Libelloides longicornis*

Forewing length: 18–28 mm. Distinct yellow veins on wings (♀ at rest pictured left); tips of hindwings with black line. **HABITAT** Grasslands. **SEASON** June to August.

### *Libelloides macaronius*

Forewing length: 20–24 mm. Pale-veined, distinctly marked species. **HABITAT** Grasslands and scrublands. **SEASON** June to August.

### *Puer maculatus*

Forewing length: 17–22 mm. Various dark brown or black markings on hindwings. **HABITAT** Grasslands. **SEASON** June.

*Deleproctophylla bleusei*

*Libelloides baeticus*

*Libelloides coccajus*

*Libelloides hispanicus*

*Libelloides ictericus*

*Libelloides lacteus*

*Libelloides longicornis*

*Libelloides macaronius*

*Puer maculatus*

*Deleproctophylla bleusei* ♂ [FR]

*Libelloides macaronius* ♀ [NR]

*Libelloides hispanicus* ♂ [CT]

*Libelloides baeticus* ♂

*Libelloides coccajus* ♂

*Libelloides ictericus* ♂

*Libelloides lacteus* ♀ [ARP]

*Libelloides longicornis* ♀

*Puer maculatus* ♀ [FR]

# Order MEGALOPTERA – ALDERFLIES

**Southern Europe & Mediterranean: 4 species**

Robust-looking dark-bodied insects; two pairs of wings sculptured with a network of black veins. The antennae are thread-like. The life cycle is one of complete metamorphosis taking about two years: egg, larva, pupa and adult. Larvae are aquatic, found in lakes, ponds, large rivers and streams, where they feed on insect larvae, worms and crustaceans. The greyish egg masses are usually laid on emergent vegetation. There is no specific connection with alder, except they may settle on trees at the water's edge. Adults fly in sunny weather, often resting on waterside vegetation.

## Family Sialidae

### *Sialis lutaria*

Body length: c.20 mm, wingspan 22–34 mm. Related species are similar in size and are distinguished by genitalia of ♂s and the anal plate of ♀s. **HABITAT** Static and moving water, living for two to three days. **SEASON** March to August.

*Sialis lutaria*

# Order RAPHIDIOPTERA – SNAKEFLIES

**Southern Europe & Mediterranean: many of Europe's 74 species**

Easily recognised by the elongate pronotum, held upright to resemble a snake about to strike out. These slender insects have a blackish body and two pairs of black-veined wings; ♀s have a long ovipositor, used to deposit eggs in cracks of bark. The life cycle takes over two years: egg, larva, pupa and adult. Mouthparts are designed for biting and chewing, with both larvae and adults predatory; the larvae feed on other insect larvae under the bark of trees and adults on aphids and other small insects. Adults, 10–15 mm long, are best looked for on trunks of oak *Quercus* and pine *Pinus* trees, or nearby from May; although often high up, in sunny weather they fly around nearby low vegetation. Widespread representative species are illustrated. Species are very similar in appearance and require specialist identification. It is not often possible to clearly see wing cell differences between species in photographs.

## Family Raphidiidae

### *Dichrostigma flavipes*

Body length: 8–14 mm. Some wing veins yellowish-brown. Pale legs. **HABITAT** Various. **SEASON** May to July.

*Dichrostigma flavipes*

### *Harraphidia laufferi*

Body length: 8–14 mm. Black, the genus recently divided into further species. **HABITAT** Various in Iberia. **SEASON** March to July.

*Harraphidia laufferi*

### *Phaeostigma notata*

Body length: 10–15 mm. **HABITAT** Around oaks *Quercus* sp. **SEASON** May to July.

*Phaeostigma notata*

*Sialis lutaria* (left), eggs (right)

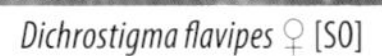

*Dichrostigma flavipes* ♀ [SO]

*Harraphidia laufferi* ♂ [FR]

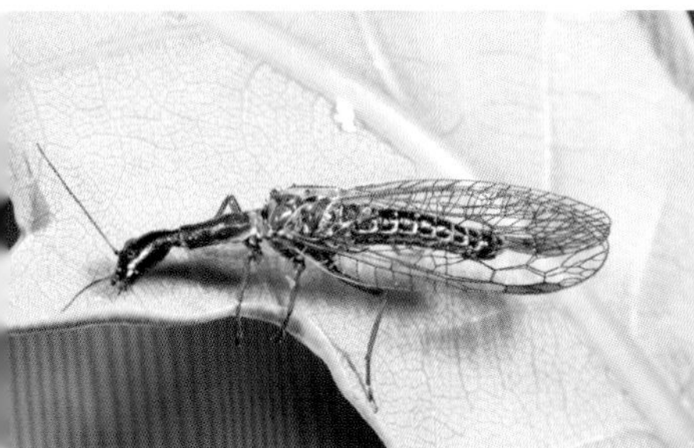

*Phaeostigma notata* ♂ (left) ♀ (right)

# Order COLEOPTERA – BEETLES

**Southern Europe & Mediterranean: most of Europe's 12,500 species**

This is by far the largest order of insects (c.400,000 species worldwide), c.40 % of all described insect species. Some species in Europe are less than 1 mm in length whereas the Stag Beetle *Lucanus cervus* reaches up to 75 mm. Coleoptera means 'sheath-winged insects' after the hardened forewings (known as wing-cases or elytra), which cover the membranous hindwings (where present) and usually the whole abdomen, although a small number of beetles completely lack hindwings. The biting jaws can tackle most food; some are predators, whilst others eat live or dead plants, live and rotting wood, dead animals and dung. Some larvae damage timber and thus are of economic importance, particularly longhorns. Other species of economic importance include the stored-product pests, such as flour beetles and grain weevils. Pests in domestic premises such as carpet beetles and spider beetles are a nuisance to householders but others such as woodworm (damage caused by wood-eating larvae of one of various species of beetles), have the potential to cause structural damage to timbers. The colourful ladybirds are well known in controlling aphid populations, hence are of economic importance. Dung beetles are well known for their ability to dispose of animal dung. In all cases the life cycle is one of complete metamorphosis, so adults lay eggs which hatch into larvae, taking the form of fast-running predators, plant feeders or grubs with or without legs, concealed in their foodplants. The larva forms a pupa, before the adult emerges. Although beetles are popular with naturalists, they are less well known than several other orders. Although many species can be identified in the field or from photographs, numerous small species require close examination and reference to specialist publications. Although many species are included in this book, a number of families have been omitted because the species in them are rare, of obscure habits, or too small to be meaningfully depicted in a book of this nature.

**HABITAT** Beetles occur in all habitats, but those that are perhaps most productive are woodlands and grasslands.

**HOTSPOTS** The best sites in Europe generally tend to be meadows or clearings with plenty of flowers, where a multitude of beetles occur. Colourful species including jewel beetles (Buprestidae) often abound and saproxylic (dead wood) species occur, particularly if dead wood is nearby. A 2010 Red List survey shows that 11% of saproxylic beetles in Europe are threatened and it is hoped that measures are taken to help conserve the increasing number of rarities.

Mid elevation submontane habitat on **Mount Olympos, Macedonia, Greece**. Beetles present include *Carabus arcadicus* (Carabidae), *Copris lunaris* (Scarabaeidae), *Trypocopris vernalis* (Geotrupidae), and many lepturine longhorn beetles, in addition to a wealth of butterflies. [CG]

Ash *Fraxinus* trees can attract numerous metallic green *Lytta vesicatoria* the well known Spanish Fly in June and July, as in this example in **Barèges (Hautes-Pyrénées), south-western France**.

*Lucanus cervus* Stag Beetle ♂s fighting

*Berberomeloe majalis* var. *laevigatus* oil beetle feeding

*Perotis lugubris* jewel beetle camouflaged at rest on tree [NR]

*Pachytodes cerambyciformis* longhorn beetles mating pair [PC]

*Silpha tristis* snail beetle larva (Silphidae)

Ground beetle, stag beetle and chafer remains from animal attack

## Family Dytiscidae – DIVING BEETLES

A popular family of small to large fast-moving, streamlined beetles, adapted for life in the water. Some are aggressive predators, whilst others feed on vegetation. They breathe by trapping air under the wing-cases. **HABITAT** Inland water habitats, including ponds and streams, where they have been reasonably well studied in Europe. However, some species are in decline due to a loss of Mediterranean wetlands.

### *Dytiscus marginalis* Great Diving Beetle

Body length: 26–32 mm. Large black beetle, with a continuous yellow margin around the pronotum; underside yellow. **HABITAT** Ponds and other aquatic habitats, often still or slow flowing waters. **SEASON** Most of the year.

*Dytiscus marginalis*

## Family Carabidae – GROUND BEETLES

Ground beetles are usually found at ground level, under stones, in leaf litter or running across a track. Large eyes help them hunt prey, often at night, but a number of brightly coloured species are often seen by day. *Carabus* eat various insects and are also often observed on tracks, eating worms.
**HABITAT** Various, particularly exposed or partly vegetated ground. Some are wetland specialists.
**HOTSPOTS** Whilst much of southern Europe is good, Italy has c.1,300 species, but Spain (1,100 species) and Turkey with c.1,200 species have a high richness and endemism (in Turkey, 41%). Greece has c.1,000 species.

The following eight species are representatives of the medium-sized tiger beetles, which have huge eyes and jaws and are active in the day. They are fast-moving hunters, usually in open dry, often sandy areas, so coastal sites tend to be particularly good. Species are usually distinguished by position and pattern of markings on the wing-cases. Larvae live in burrows where they often attack ants:

### *Calomera littoralis*

Body length: 10–14 mm. Shiny green, bronze or black. **HABITAT** Sandy soils, much wider range of habitats than other European tiger beetles. **SEASON** April to October.

*Calomera littoralis*

### *Cephalota maura*

Body length: 12–15 mm. Very dark, wing-cases black with several white spots. **HABITAT** Coastal areas, beaches, ponds and rivers. **SEASON** May to July.

*Cephalota maura*

### *Cicindela campestris* Green Tiger Beetle

Body length: 10–17 mm. Green (variable in shade) yellow and whitish spots or markings. There are several subspecies. **SEASON** March to October.

*Cicindela campestris*

### *Cicindela hybrida* [Northern Dune Tiger Beetle]

Body length: 11–16 mm. Dark brown, central markings a different shape than in related species. **SEASON** April to October.

*Cicindela hybrida*

### *Cicindela majalis*

Body length: 11–16 mm. Dark brown, markings slightly different shape than *C. hybrida*. **DISTRIBUTION** Italy, south of the River Po. **SEASON** March to June.

*Cicindela majalis*

### *Cicindela sylvatica* Heath Tiger Beetle

Body length: 14–20 mm. Dark brown, with narrow whitish markings; labrum (upper lip) black in this often local, mainly northern European species. **SEASON** April to September.

*Cicindela sylvatica*

### *Cylindera germanica* Cliff Tiger Beetle

Body length: 7–12 mm. Brown to bluish green; rarely flies. **SEASON** May to September.

*Cylindera germanica*

### *Lophyra flexuosa*

Body length: 11–14 mm. Copper (occasionally greenish) with characteristic whitish markings and spots. **SEASON** March to October.

*Lophyra flexuosa*

*Dytiscus marginalis* ♀ (left), ♀ underside (right)

*Calomera littoralis* [TB]

*Cephalota maura* [FR]

*Cicindela campestris*

*Cicindela hybrida* [NR]

*Cicindela majalis* [KB]

*Cicindela sylvatica* mating pair

*Cylindera germanica*

*Lophyra flexuosa*

***Brachinus crepitans* Bombardier Beetle**
Body length: 5–10 mm. Red with bluish wing-cases. **HABITAT** Various including quarries, under stones. This species is well known for its defence reaction when disturbed, hence the bright colours are no idle threat; it fires a volatile liquid from the anus at a potential predator (on the skin this produces a burning sensation). **SEASON** May to June.

*Brachinus crepitans*

***Omophron limbatum***
Body length: 5–7 mm. Pale yellow and green; characteristic shape and markings. **HABITAT** Sandy ground by fresh water, where this nocturnal species lives in burrows, but can be encouraged out in the daytime by splashing water near the burrows. **SEASON** May to October.

*Omophron limbatum*

***Calosoma inquisitor* Caterpillar-hunter**
Body length: 13–28 mm. Metallic bronze, abdominal margins green or bluish but has various other colour forms. **HABITAT** Oak *Quercus* woodlands. Unlike most ground beetles which are found on the ground, these climb trees and bushes at dusk in order to prey on butterfly and moth larvae. Adults can live about three years. **SEASON** April to July.

*Calosoma inquisitor*

***Calosoma sycophanta* Forest Caterpillar-hunter**
Body length: 18–35 mm. Wing-cases often metallic golden-green. **HABITAT** Woodlands. Predator of butterfly and moth larvae, including Oak Processionary Moth *Thaumetopoea processionea*. Adults can live about four years. **SEASON** March to August.

*Calosoma sycophanta*

***Carabus arcadicus***
Body length: c.25 mm. Head and thorax greenish-red (sometimes lacking red). Wing-cases bluish black, with red and/or greenish margin. **HABITAT** Woodlands. **SEASON** March to September.

*Carabus arcadicus*

***Carabus auratus* Golden Ground Beetle**
Body length: 17–30 mm. Wing-cases golden or bronze, with copper margin; sometimes bluish (several named forms). **HABITAT** Grasslands, gardens and mountains to 1,500 m., feeding on earthworms, snails, slugs and larvae. Active at night, also by day on the ground and tree trunks. **SEASON** March to September.

*Carabus auratus*

***Carabus auronitens***
Body length: 18–34 mm. Wing-cases golden-green or reddish (subspecies *punctatoauratus* pictured left [PC]), rarely blue. Wing-cases with three stout, dark veins. Femora red. **HABITAT** Woodlands up to c.2,500 m. **SEASON** May to August.

*Carabus auronitens*

***Carabus cancellatus***
Body length: 17–32 mm. Bronze, golden green (pictured left [CG]) or blue, rarely black (several named forms). Antennal base usually red. Wing-cases boldly marked. **HABITAT** Grasslands up to 1,000 m, where this species is active by day. **SEASON** May to September.

*Carabus cancellatus*

***Carabus clatratus***
Body length: 20–36 mm. Wing-cases bronze, green or black, with conspicuous gold depressions. **HABITAT** Wetlands, including bogs and saltmarshes. **SEASON** April to August.

*Carabus clatratus*

***Carabus coriaceus***
Body length: 26–42 mm. Large, black species with sculptured wing-cases. **HABITAT** Woodlands and others; various altitudes. **SEASON** May to October.

*Carabus coriaceus*

*Brachinus crepitans*

*Omophron limbatum*

*Calosoma inquisitor*

*Calosoma sycophanta* [NR]

*Carabus arcadicus* [CG]

*Carabus auratus* [CG]

*Carabus auronitens* [PC]

*Carabus cancellatus* [NR]

*Carabus clatratus* [NR]

*Carabus coriaceus*

***Carabus hispanus***
Body length: 27–35 mm. Elongate, head and thorax dark blue; wing-cases bright golden-green and reddish, margins bluish-violet and pink. **HABITAT** Woodlands often on north exposed slopes, with the Massif Central its northern boundary. **SEASON** April to September.

*Carabus hispanus*

***Carabus intricatus* Blue Ground Beetle**
Body length: 20–36 mm. Metallic blue. **HABITAT** Woodlands, often climbing tree trunks at night. **SEASON** All year, but mainly May to September.

*Carabus intricatus*

***Carabus montivagus***
Body length: 20–24 mm. Black, margins of wing-cases violet or bluish, strongly punctured. Rather similar to *C. nemoralis*. **HABITAT** Woodlands and open areas to 2,000 m., particularly calcareous. This species is frequent in the Balkans. **SEASON** May to September.

*Carabus montivagus*

***Carabus nemoralis***
Body length: 18–28 mm. Margins of pronotum purple or copper. Wing-cases black with metallic green sheen. **HABITAT** Woodland edges, gardens. **SEASON** March to October.

*Carabus nemoralis*

***Carabus problematicus***
Body length: 18–32 mm. Black with blue or violet metallic sheen on margins of wing-cases and more extensively on thorax. Wing-cases with distinctive sculpturing, otherwise could be confused with Violet Ground Beetle *C. violaceus*. One of the most distinctive southern subspecies (*inflatus*) is illustrated, found in southern France and parts of northern Italy. **HABITAT** Woodlands and grasslands, including mountains to 2,700 m. **SEASON** February to October.

*Carabus problematicus*

***Carabus scabriusculus***
Body length: 14–25 mm. Black, wing-cases densely granulated. **HABITAT** Grasslands, under stones or plant debris. **SEASON** March to September.

*Carabus scabriusculus*

***Carabus splendens***
Body length: 24–32 mm. Bright metallic copper, red or green. **HABITAT** Forests and meadows mainly in the Pyrenees and Cantabrian mountains. **SEASON** June to September.

*Carabus splendens*

***Carabus ullrichii***
Body length: 20–34 mm. Mainly bronze, but variable in colour. **HABITAT** Woodland edges and grasslands with heavy soil, in mountainous areas. **SEASON** Mid March to June, then occasionally until November.

*Carabus ullrichii*

***Carabus violaceus* Violet Ground Beetle**
Body length: 20–35 mm. Black with margins of pronotum and wing-cases violet or blue. Wing-cases with fine granulation, appearing rather smoother than *C. problematicus*. However, in much of France, subspecies *purpurascens* has regular striations on the wing-cases. Southern Balkan populations also have striations on the wing-cases. In Italy, subspecies *piceus* is smooth, but in general more brightly metallic. **HABITAT** Woodlands and gardens at various altitudes. **SEASON** April to September.

*Carabus violaceus*

***Cychrus caraboides* Snail Hunter**
Body length: 13–23 mm. **HABITAT** Woodlands to 2400 m, where they eat snails and other prey. In defence can stridulate if handled. **SEASON** April to September.

*Cychrus caraboides*

*Carabus hispanus* [CG]

*Carabus intricatus*

*Carabus montivagus* [NR]

*Carabus nemoralis*

*Carabus problematicus* subspecies *inflatus* [CG]

*Carabus scabriusculus* [NR]

*Carabus splendens*

*Carabus ullrichii* [NR]

*Carabus violaceus* (left), subspecies *purpurascens* (right) [CG]

*Cychrus caraboides*

**_Broscus cephalotes_ Strand-line Burrower**
Body length: 16–23 mm. **HABITAT** Mainly coastal beaches and dunes under tidal refuse. **SEASON** April to September.

*Broscus cephalotes*

**_Poecilus kugelanni_ Kugelann's Ground Beetle**
Body length: 12–14 mm. Coppery-red pronotum, wing-cases metallic green (rarely, black). **HABITAT** Various grasslands and sandy soils or gravel, also marshes; under stones and debris. Adults live for two years, sometimes up to four years. **SEASON** February to July.

*Poecilus kugelanni*

**_Drypta dentata_ Chine Beetle**
Body length: 7–9 mm. Metallic green or blue, with brown legs. **HABITAT** Damp areas at the foot of trees, rushes, under detritus and stones. **SEASON** All year.

*Drypta dentata*

**_Abax parallelepipedus_**
Body length: 17–22 mm. Shining black. **HABITAT** Woodlands, in mosses or under stones and dead leaves. **SEASON** April to September.

*Abax parallelepipedus*

## Family Silphidae – CARRION or BURYING BEETLES

Scavenging, carnivorous beetles with conspicuous clubbed antennae in several species.

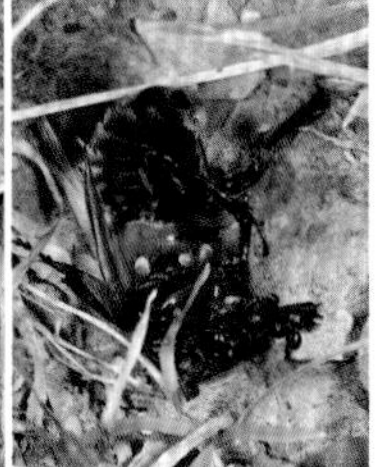
In addition to bright warning colours (left) *Nicrophorus* species have various defence mechanisms against possible predators, such as chemical secretions. In defence, this species rolled over (right) when photographs were taken with flashlight and played dead, then rapidly walked away several seconds later.

**HABITAT** Various elevations, including mountains. Typically thought to track down dead bodies of birds, mammals and reptiles by smell and fly in to bury or dispose of carcasses, laying their eggs at the site and thus providing their offspring with a food source. Others are found in fungi, feed on vegetation, or certain *Silpha* species predate snails. Some species are attracted to moth lights and are often covered in mites. Present several months of the year. **HOTSPOTS** *Silpha* species are particularly common on tracks in mountainous areas.

**_Oiceoptoma thoracicum_**
Body length: 12–16 mm. easily recognisable by its orange pronotum. **HABITAT** Carrion, but well known on fruit bodies of stinkhorn fungi, Phallaceae.

*Oiceoptoma thoracicum*

**_Thanatophilus sinuatus_**
Body length: 9–14 mm. Wing-cases with conspicuously shaped ridges.

*Thanatophilus sinuatus*

**_Silpha tyrolensis_**
Body length: 12–16 mm. Wing-cases brown or black. **HABITAT** Typically in mountain pastures.

*Silpha tyrolensis*

**_Nicrophorus humator_**
Body length: 15–30 mm. Black with orange-tipped antennae.

*Nicrophorus humator*

**_Nicrophorus vespilloides_**
Body length: 12–18 mm. Antennae club black (partly orange in most similar species, which vary by the wing-case pattern).

*Nicrophorus vespilloides*

**_Necrodes littoralis_**
Body length: 15–25 mm. Could be confused with *N. humator* but it lacks the clubbed antennae and is distinctly less convex than that species.

*Necrodes littoralis*

*Broscus cephalotes* (left), larva (right)

*Poecilus kugelanni*

*Drypta dentata*

*Abax parallelepipedus*

*Oiceoptoma thoracicum*

*Thanatophilus sinuatus*

*Silpha tyrolensis* mating pair

*Nicrophorus humator*

*Nicrophorus vespilloides*

*Necrodes littoralis*

## Family Staphylinidae – ROVE BEETLES

This is the largest family of beetles in Europe. Although often black, some of the elongate species have variable reddish and/or yellow coloration. The vast majority are easily recognised by their short wing-cases, leaving much of the abdomen visible. However, the wings are folded beneath the wing-cases, so they still fly well. They mainly prey on various invertebrates and in some cases worms and snails; others feed on fungi, dung or dead plant material. A small selection of mainly larger species is shown.

**HABITAT** Dung, carrion and litter piles are all highly productive transient habitats for rove beetles primarily because they often support vast numbers of fly larvae which the rove beetles predate. Woodchip piles and wetland litter are also productive and subterranean mammal nests have their own specific rove beetle faunas.

### *Scaphidium quadrimaculatum*

Body length: 4.5–6 mm. Black with two red marks on each wing-case. **HABITAT** Woodlands, associated with fungi of dead branches, sometimes found on or under bark of fallen logs. **SEASON** April to August.

*Scaphidium quadrimaculatum*

### *Velleius dilatatus* Hornet Rove Beetle

Body length: 15–24 mm. Large black body with glossy head and rounded pronotum. The antennae are serrate (saw-like), unlike other rove beetles. **HABITAT** Breeds in *Vespa crabro* nests in tree hollows and found at night attracted to moth lights or at the sap of trees, particularly 'Goat Moth' (*Cossus cossus*-infected trees). Both adults and larvae eat fly larvae developing at the bottom of the nest. **SEASON** Mainly June to October.

*Velleius dilatatus*

### *Emus hirtus*

Body length: 16–30 mm. Distinctive large, rarer species with yellow and black pubescence. **HABITAT** Fresh horse and cattle dung where they prey on fly and beetle larvae at low levels to mountains. It is worth checking dung heaps, but even dedicated beetle enthusiasts find this enigmatic species difficult to locate. **SEASON** April to October.

*Emus hirtus*

### *Ocypus olens* Devil's Coach-horse

Body length: 23–32 mm. Head and pronotum dull black. When disturbed, it readily initiates a startle display includes raising the abdomen, scorpion-like and both sexes open their large jaws and can emit a fluid from their mouth parts. A foul-smelling chemical is released from glands towards the end of the abdomen as well as faecal fluid from the anus. **HABITAT** Various in dry to damp soils feeding on invertebrates at night, but like other rove beetles, is sometimes conspicuous in the daytime, walking on paths. **SEASON** April to October.

*Ocypus olens*

### *Ontholestes murinus*

Body length: 8–14 mm. Black with gold and silver pubescence, appearing chequered. Legs dark except for tarsi. **HABITAT** Carrion and dung heaps. **SEASON** All year, mainly April to September.

*Ontholestes murinus*

### *Ontholestes tessellatus*

Body length: 15–22 mm. similar to *O. murinus*, but chequered pattern extending further on abdomen. This is a larger species, with the legs largely reddish. **HABITAT** Carrion and dung heaps; rather fast-moving. **SEASON** April to September.

*Ontholestes tessellatus*

### *Staphylinus dimidiaticornis*

Body length: 16–23 mm. Front of head has yellow pubescence as do other related *Staphylinus* species. Last five to six antennal segments dark. **HABITAT** Damp soils. **SEASON** April to October.

*Staphylinus dimidiaticornis*

### *Staphylinus erythropterus*

Body length: 14–18 mm. Distinguished from look-alikes by yellow scutellum (triangular area between the wing-cases) or shape of head. **HABITAT** Open sites on damp soils. **SEASON** April to October.

*Staphylinus erythropterus*

*phidium quadrimaculatum* [PC]

*Velleius dilatatus* (left), larva (right)

*Emus hirtus* (left), (right) [RP]

*Ocypus olens*

*Ontholestes tessellatus* [PC]

*Ontholestes murinus*

*Staphylinus dimidiaticornis*

*Staphylinus erythropterus*

## Family Geotrupidae – DOR BEETLES

Dor beetles are very efficient dung feeders, well known for their strength in burying food for the larvae. **HABITAT** Woodland rides and habitats with livestock in March to October. Look closely at the underside, which is often metallic blue or mauve and is most often covered in mites. The last few segments of the antennae are clubbed. Population size can vary in a long season.

**Canigou, eastern Pyrenees, France**: *Geotrupes* are often attracted to dung in large numbers, where they can attract the attention of predatory birds and mammals.

### *Typhaeus momus*

Body length: 10–21 mm. Broad, horned flightless species [some consider the genus *Chelotrupes* to be valid, rather than as a subgenus], lacking ridges on the wing-cases. ♀ (left [DRo]) with short horns. **HABITAT** Mainly sand dunes in coastal areas on dung of red deer, sheep, goats, rabbits and others. Restricted to a few scattered parts of south-west Iberia. **SEASON** All year.

*Typhaeus momus*

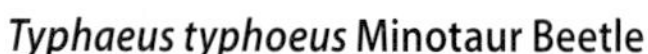

### *Typhaeus typhoeus* Minotaur Beetle

Body length: 12–20 mm. Resembles other dor beetles except for the ♂ with its fierce-looking three horns; ♀ with short horns. Capable of flight. **HABITAT** Sandy soils on sheep and rabbit dung, developing in a burrow c.1.5 metres deep. The horns are used by ♂s for fighting in order to gain access to a ♀. **SEASON** March to October.

*Typhaeus typhoeus*

### *Anoplotrupes stercorosus* Woodland Dor Beetle

Body length: 12–20 mm. Resembles other dor beetles except more rounded, very bluish, slightly smaller, with indistinct ridges on the wing-cases. **HABITAT** Woodlands and grasslands, on dung, decaying fungi and rotting plant material. **SEASON** March to October.

*Anoplotrupes stercorosus*

### *Geotrupes mutator* Violet Dor Beetle

Body length: 14–25 mm. Thorax and wing-cases often violet, with nine bold ridges inwards from the shoulder bulge. There are several similar species. **HABITAT** Well-grazed grasslands, on horse and cow dung. **SEASON** March to October.

*Geotrupes mutator*

### *Geotrupes stercorarius* Dor Beetle

Body length: 16–26 mm. Black with a bluish or purple sheen and ridged wing-cases. **HABITAT** Grasslands in mountainous areas above 1,000 m on dung of large herbivores. **SEASON** April to October.

*Geotrupes stercorarius*

### *Trypocopris vernalis* Spring Dumble Dor

Body length: 12–20 mm. Smooth, with punctures on the thorax. Variable in colour, blue, green or pink. **HABITAT** Dry sandy soils, including grasslands mainly on dung of foxes and sheep. **SEASON** May to October (mainly spring).

*Trypocopris vernalis*

*Typhaeus momus* ♂ [MRo]

*Typhaeus typhoeus* ♂

*Anoplotrupes stercorosus*

*Geotrupes mutator*

*Geotrupes stercorarius*

*Trypocopris vernalis* [CG]

## Family Lucanidae – STAG BEETLES

Many people know that stag beetles are named after the stag-like mandibles of ♂s which vary considerably in length between individuals of the same species. Most people know what a Stag Beetle is even if they have never seen one. ♀s are usually smaller than the ♂s, with smaller mandibles. Insect collectors are keen on tropical species of these showy insects, larger specimens attracting higher prices, particularly in Japan, where they are also popularly kept as pets. The larvae feed for several years on rotting wood. There are only 14 species of stag beetles present in Europe; several well known species are discussed.

***Sinodendron cylindricum*** **[Rhinoceros Beetle]**

Body length: 10–16 mm. A smaller, black species, only the ♂ with a horn-like projection on its head. The common name is not to be confused with the mainly tropical Rhinoceros Beetles in the Scarabaeidae, or the much larger *Oryctes nasicornis*. **HABITAT** Mature woodlands including higher elevations, often bores in dead heartwood of beech *Fagus* or oak *Quercus*, also pine *Pinus* spp., occasionally seen in the daytime on rotting wood or in flight. **SEASON** May to October.

***Dorcus parallelipipedus*** **Lesser Stag Beetle**

Body length: 18–32. Much smaller than Stag Beetle and always uniformly greyish-black in colour, with small mandibles, slightly larger in the ♂. Larva pictured right. **HABITAT** Gardens, parks and woodlands. Prefers decaying, drier wood (frequently in ash *Fraxinus* spp.), above soil level. Often seen in the daytime on wood. **SEASON** May to September.

***Lucanus barbarossa***

Body length: 30–45. Black antlers in the ♂, small compared with those of *L. cervus*. **HABITAT** Woodlands, particularly mountainous areas and mid-altitude 750 m. The ♀ lays eggs in decaying tree stumps, oak *Quercus* and others, sometimes in damaged live trees. **SEASON** July to September.

***Lucanus cervus*** **Stag Beetle**

Body length: ♂ 31–85 mm, ♀ 25–49. One of Europe's most spectacular beetles (mating pair pictured left), with large stag-like antlers in the ♂, which have a reddish sheen. The wing-cases are chestnut brown. The larvae are cream, up to 8 cm long with an orange head. **HABITAT** Gardens, parks and particularly oak *Quercus* woodlands, where the ♀ lays eggs in decaying tree stumps, beech *Fagus*, oak *Quercus*, lime *Tilia* and others, the resulting larvae feeding on the dead wood in the stump and maturing in three to four years. Adults fly at dusk and are attracted to street lights and seldom feed; if they do, it is sometimes on sap oozing from trees, including those infested by Goat Moth *Cossus cossus* larvae. The antlers are used in fights for a ♀, the winner lifting and throwing the loser onto the ground, although several efforts may be made and, whilst fighting, ♂s run the risk of another ♂ walking away with the prize. The size of the antlers appears to have little influence on mating success. Whilst the antlers are harmless, if handled the ♀s can give quite a nip. Much folklore surrounds this species usually relating to bad luck or evil. Turkish good luck charms use the ♂ head and mandibles of this and other species to ward off evil. This is the only beetle listed in Appendix III of the Bern Convention (protected by law) as well as included as Red List (Near Threatened), although it is not uncommon in some countries. This large, popular insect features on several postage stamps. **SEASON** May to early August.

*Sinodendron cylindricum*

*Dorcus parallelipipedus*

*Lucanus barbarossa*

*Lucanus cervus*

*Platycerus caraboides*

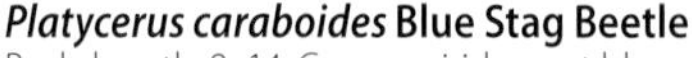

***Platycerus caraboides*** **Blue Stag Beetle**

Body length: 8–14. Green or iridescent blue. **HABITAT** Woodlands, where the larvae often develop for two to three years in rotten beech *Fagus* or oak *Quercus*, but also often in pine *Pinus* spp. **SEASON** May to July.

*Sinodendron cylindricum* ♂ (left & centre), ♀ (right)

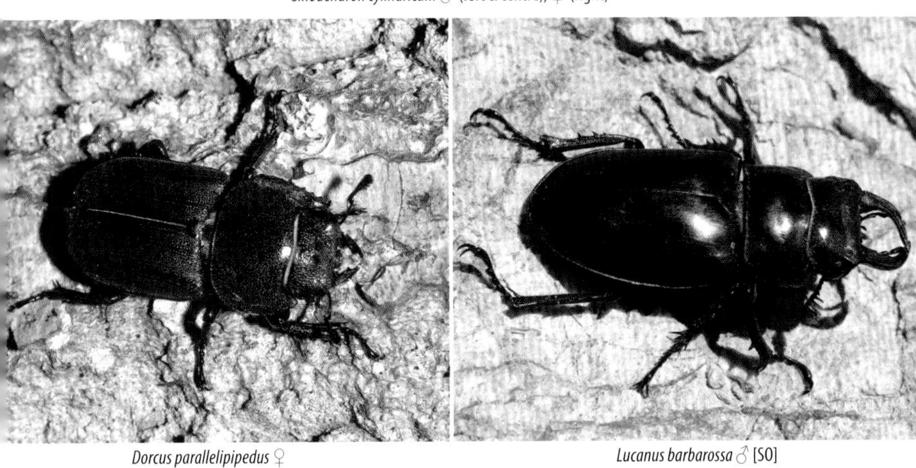

*Dorcus parallelipipedus* ♀

*Lucanus barbarossa* ♂ [SO]

*Lucanus cervus* ♂

*Platycerus caraboides* ♂ [NR]

## Family Scarabaeidae – SCARAB BEETLES

The last few segments of the antennae are expanded into flaps, which form a club or fan in the chafers. Chafers are vegetarians, with some species regarded as pests. The dung beetles are very efficient dung feeders. Some of the more colourful species of flower chafers are active by day and are regarded by some authors as belonging to a separate family, the Cetoniidae, along with some other subfamilies.
**HABITAT** Chafers are seen in a variety of habitats including grasslands and gardens, on flowers or wood. Dung beetles are very likely to be encountered in areas with livestock. Keen coleopterists (people who study beetles) carefully go through dung to locate species. The ancient Greeks and Romans considered the scarab a good luck charm, for example as protective powers in battle.

*Aphodius contaminatus*

### *Aphodius contaminatus*

Body length: 5–7 mm. Dark spots on wing-cases. Note: some regard *Nimbus* as a valid genus, rather than subgenus. **HABITAT** Grasslands, the larvae developing in dung; adults are often seen in numbers flying in to fresh dung or fungi. **SEASON** July to September.

*Aphodius fimetarius*

### *Aphodius fimetarius*

Body length: 5–8 mm. Pronotum with front angles yellow. Wing-cases red. **HABITAT** Grasslands, the larvae developing in dung. **SEASON** All year.

*Ateuchetus cicatricosus*

### *Ateuchetus cicatricosus*

Body length: 15–25 mm. Black, slightly glossy. Pronotum and wing-cases covered with large punctures (formerly in the genus *Scarabaeus*). **HABITAT** Open, often sandy sites on dung of large herbivores; this rare species is restricted to Iberia and Morocco. Also known to remove the flesh of dead animals, such as rabbits and amphibians and roll it, to provide food for offspring, as with dung. **SEASON** March to October.

*Scarabaeus pius*

### *Scarabaeus pius*

Body length: 20–28 mm. Black, slightly glossy. Characterised by absence of groove in front of basal edge of pronotum. **HABITAT** Pastures and scrublands on sheep and goat droppings. **SEASON** April to October, often seen in May.

*Sisyphus schaefferi*

### *Sisyphus schaefferi*

Body length: 8–10 mm. Black, hairs yellowish-brown or darker. Legs elongate, particularly hindlegs. **HABITAT** Pastures. **SEASON** April to September.

*Copris hispanus*

### *Copris hispanus*

Body length: 15–20 mm. Both sexes horned, the ♂ horn is particularly impressive, much longer and more curved than in *C. lunaris*. **HABITAT** Cow dung. **SEASON** April to September.

*Copris lunaris*

### *Copris lunaris* Horned Dung Beetle

Body length: 15–21 mm. Both sexes horned, the ♂ horn (pictured left) hardly curved. Pronotum shape distinct. **HABITAT** Mainly under cow dung, where the ♀ tend eggs and larvae in brood chambers. **SEASON** April to September.

*Onthophagus coenobita*

### *Onthophagus coenobita*

Body length: 6–10 mm. ♂ horned. **HABITAT** On dung, corpses and mushrooms. **SEASON** May to June.

*Aphodius contaminatus* on dung (left) [PC], on *Clathrus archeri* fungus (right)

*Aphodius fimetarius*

*Ateuchetus cicatricosus* ♂

*Scarabaeus pius* [CG]

*Sisyphus schaefferi* [CG]

*Copris hispanus* ♂

*Copris lunaris* ♀

*Onthophagus coenobita* ♂ (left), ♀ (right)

**Emilia Romagna Apennines, Italy.** Along river courses in the Appenine mountains, tiger beetles such as *Cicindela majalis* and *C. campestris* can be seen on riverine sand and gravel beaches, whilst the flanking vegetation provides a home to many other insects, including chafers and longhorn beetles. [CG]

### *Anoxia australis*
Body length: 20–25 mm. **HABITAT** Grasslands. **SEASON** May to August.

### *Melolontha melolontha* Cockchafer
Body length: 20–30 mm. Conspicuous large brown beetles, with feathery antennae; pointed extension to abdomen. **HABITAT** Gardens, agricultural sites and woodlands up to c.1,000 m where they sometimes swarm in large numbers. These noisy beetles eat leaves of various trees. The larvae take 3 to 4 years to mature and can be a pest on roots of shrubs and trees. They can be a pest in agriculture and forestry in years when there are mass flights. **SEASON** May to July.

### *Polyphylla fullo*
Body length: 32–40 mm. Large reddish brown species, with white mottling. **HABITAT** Sandy areas, such as edges of coniferous woodlands and dunes, where this uncommon species eats pine leaves. The larvae eat roots of grasses. **SEASON** May to August.

### *Amphimallon atrum*
Body length: 11–14 mm. ♂ brownish black, light brown ♀. **HABITAT** Grasslands. **SEASON** May to July.

### *Amphimallon solstitiale* Summer Chafer
Body length: 14–20 mm. Rather smaller version of the Cockchafer lacking the pointed abdomen and wing-cases are covered in long hairs. **HABITAT** Grasslands, where they eat leaves of various trees. **SEASON** June to August.

### *Omaloplia ruricola*
Body length: 5–7 mm. Black, hairy species. The wing-cases are brown with a distinctive black border. **HABITAT** Calcareous grasslands, including mountains, where they are often seen flying by day, but are also nocturnal. **SEASON** June to July.

### *Serica brunnea* Brown Chafer
Body length: 8–10 mm. Light brown. **HABITAT** Sandy lightly wooded sites, also mountains, where it flies at dusk. **SEASON** July to August.

*Anoxia australis*

*Melolontha melolontha*

*Polyphylla fullo*

*Amphimallon atrum*

*Amphimallon solstitiale*

*Omaloplia ruricola*

*Serica brunnea*

*Anoxia australis*

*Melolontha melolontha*

*Polyphylla fullo* [NR]

*Amphimallon atrum*

*Amphimallon solstitiale*

*Omaloplia ruricola*

*Serica brunnea*

### *Hoplia chlorophana*
Body length: 8–12 mm. Pale green, whitish to brown, pronotum covered in scales. **HABITAT** Grasslands, prefers areas near water, endemic in Iberia. **SEASON** May to July.

*Hoplia chlorophana*

### *Hoplia coerulea*
Body length: 8–11 mm. Stunning ♂ covered in blue scales, ♀ brownish. **HABITAT** Grasslands, including shaded damp areas. **SEASON** May to July.

*Hoplia coerulea*

### *Hoplia philanthus* [Welsh Chafer]
Body length: 8–9 mm. Ashy black non-metallic thorax with chestnut wing-cases. Some specimens with hint of bluish. **HABITAT** Open places, often on flowers. **SEASON** June to August.

*Hoplia philanthus*

### *Anomala dubia* Dune Chafer
Body length: 12–15 mm. Often green, although the wing-cases can be bluish or reddish yellow. Larva pictured right. **HABITAT** Sandy sites, including coastal dunes. **SEASON** May to July.

*Anomala dubia*

### *Anomala vitis* Vine Chafer
Body length: 14–18 mm. Emerald green, pronotum with thin yellow border. **HABITAT** Various, including agricultural areas where they can be a pest on leaves of various fruit and other trees. The larvae develop on humus and roots. **SEASON** May to July.

*Anomala vitis*

### *Phyllopertha horticola* Garden Chafer
Body length: 7–14 mm. Head and thorax metallic green, sometimes black; wing-cases light brown. **HABITAT** Grasslands. The larvae feed on grass roots. Adults are often seen on flowers or vegetation (pictured left); they feed on leaves, including fruit trees and can occur in huge numbers. Considered a pest in nurseries and at higher altitudes, swarming about late May. **SEASON** May to June.

*Phyllopertha horticola*

### *Oryctes nasicornis* Rhinoceros Beetle
Body length: 20–45 mm. Reddish or blackish brown; glossy appearance. The underside of body and legs covered in long reddish hairs. ♀ lacks the large ♂'s horn. **HABITAT** Woodlands, including lower slopes of mountains. Adults are attracted to lights. The larvae reach 100 mm and take 1–5 years to develop in wood stumps or sawdust depending on temperature and quality of the nutrition. Sometimes found in garden compost. They are parasitised by *Megascolia maculata*. **SEASON** Mainly May to July.

*Oryctes nasicornis*

### *Cetonia aurata* Rose Chafer
Body length: 14–21 mm. Metallic golden-green, with a variable number of white streaks; underside metallic reddish-copper. The apices of the wing-cases are sinuately curved. This species is replaced in Iberia (except Pyrenees) and Sardinia by ***C. carthami*** [not illustrated] (which also occurs in Corsica, together with *C. aurata*), and is distinguished from *aurata* by having much coarser puncturation on the upper surfaces and being generally smaller. **HABITAT** Gardens and woodlands, where adults are often seen obtaining pollen and nectar from various flowers. The larvae feed in rotting wood of old stumps. **SEASON** May to September.

*Cetonia aurata*

*Cetonia carthami*

*Hoplia chlorophana*

*Hoplia coerulea*

*Hoplia philanthus*

*Anomala dubia* ♀

*Anomala vitis* [NR]

*Oryctes nasicornis* ♂

*Phyllopertha horticola* mating pair

*Cetonia aurata*

### *Protaetia affinis*

Body length: 17–20 mm. Body broad, green or golden-green, but this variable species occurs in various colour forms, including a violet form in Corsica. Lower part of hind femora strongly indented. **HABITAT** Woodlands. **SEASON** May to August.

*Protaetia affinis*

### *Protaetia cuprea*

Body length: 16–23 mm. Dull coppery-green, with a variable number of white streaks (subspecies *metallica* illustrated, regarded as a valid species *P. metallica* by some specialists) and subspecies *obscura*, which is lighter green above, but purple beneath. Usually *P. cuprea* is bicoloured like that in contrast to *P. fieberi*. *P. cuprea* has a white marking on the 'knees' (the joint between the tibia and femur). Lower part of hind femora not indented. **HABITAT** Oak *Quercus* woodlands, also gardens on flowers, sap and ripe fruit. Subspecies *metallica* is an alpine insect, found only at mid to high elevation in the Alps in southern Europe, not associated with oak forests. The larvae of subspecies *metallica* only feed in rotting wood and are known to have a relationship with ants of the genus *Formica*; it is presumed that the larvae help keep the nest clean. **SEASON** May to August.

*Protaetia cuprea*

### *Protaetia fieberi*

Body length: 18–21 mm. Almost always uniform bronze, both above and below. Lacks white markings on the 'knees' present in the similar *P. cuprea*. **HABITAT** Oak *Quercus* woodlands. **SEASON** May to August.

*Protaetia fieberi*

### *Protaetia mirifica*

Body length: 23–29 mm. Stunning shiny uniform violet. **HABITAT** Oak *Quercus* woodlands. **SEASON** June to August.

*Protaetia mirifica*

### *Protaetia morio*

Body length: 13–20 mm. Black or brownish-brown, sometimes with small white spots on the thorax and wing-cases. **HABITAT** Woodlands, including in mountains and gardens; arguably the commonest *Protaetia* species, often seen on ripe fruit. **SEASON** May to August.

*Protaetia morio*

### *Protaetia oblonga*

Body length: 12–16 mm. Matt black, often with a scattering of whitish patches, particularly around margins of wing-cases (and on underside). **HABITAT** Woodlands and grasslands, up to 2,000 m in the Sierra Nevada. **SEASON** May to August.

*Protaetia oblonga*

### *Protaetia speciosissima*

Body length: 20–30 mm. Metallic greenish-gold but there are sometimes other colour forms; sparsely punctuated wing-cases. The largest cetonid (flower chafer) in Europe, formally known as *P. aeruginosa*. **HABITAT** Woodlands, where adults swarm in warm, still weather and may be found on flowers, at sap runs on trees, or on ripe fruit such as apples and pears (in the Balkans they are more likely in orchards). The larvae feed in decaying, hollowed trees. **SEASON** May to August.

*Protaetia speciosissima*

Olive groves with a diverse understorey of Mediterranean wildflowers and other vegetation, such as these near **Kalamata in the Peloponnese, Greece**, are both some of the most distinctive, and diverse Mediterranean habitats, harbouring a wide range of butterflies, including *Papilio alexanor*, and many beetles, such as *Protaetia cuprea obscura*, and other *Protaetia* species, and the dung beetles *Scarabaeus pius* and *Gymnopleurus geoffroyi*. [CG]

*Protaetia affinis* [CG]

*Protaetia fieberi* [CG]

*Protaetia cuprea* subspecies *metallica* (left), subspecies *obscura* (right) [CG]

*Protaetia mirifica* [CG]

*Protaetia morio* [PC]

*Protaetia oblonga*

*Protaetia speciosissima* [CG]

### *Tropinota hirta*
Body length: 8–14 mm. Broader thorax than *Oxythyrea funesta*, black with fewer white markings on hairy wing-cases. Scutellum punctuated laterally; a similar species *T. squalida*, has a smooth scutellum. **HABITAT** Grasslands, often in flowers. **SEASON** May to June.

*Tropinota hirta*

### *Gnorimus nobilis* Noble Chafer
Body length: 15–21 mm. Metallic coppery-green, similar to *Cetonia aurata*, but scutellum smaller and the shape is distinctive. **HABITAT** Woodlands, mostly in mountainous areas, where the larvae develop in decaying beech *Fagus*. Adults fly to flowers. **SEASON** June to August.

*Gnorimus nobilis*

### *Gnorimus variabilis* Variable Chafer
Body length: 17–22 mm. Black with white markings. **HABITAT** Mediterranean oak *Quercus* woodlands and chestnut *Castanea* groves, including mountainous areas, where adults occur on flowers or rest on tree trunks. The larvae develop in the damp wood mould of old oak *Quercus* and beech *Fagus* trees. **SEASON** June to July.

*Gnorimus variabilis*

### *Osmoderma barnabita* Hermit Beetle
Body length: 24–32 mm. Large reddish brown or black, glossy species. **HABITAT** Woodlands or habitats with suitable trees usually at lower elevations, where adults occur on flowers. The larvae develop in the damp wood mould in hollows of veteran trees, often oak *Quercus*. **SEASON** June to September.

*Osmoderma barnabita*

### *Propomacrus bimucronatus*
Body length: 30–47 mm. Spectacular large brownish black species, head and thorax with dense punctuation. Reddish yellow hair around thorax and legs. Male forelegs strongly curved inwards. **HABITAT** Woodlands and others with veteran oak *Quercus*, also cherry *Prunus* orchards, where this species breeds in tree holes; rare. **SEASON** July to August.

*Propomacrus bimucronatus*

### *Oxythyrea cinctella*
Body length: 7–13 mm. Distinguished from *O. funesta* by whitish border on pronotum. **HABITAT** Grasslands, often in flowers or on vegetation. In orchards they can damage fruit trees, by feeding on flowers. **SEASON** April to June.

*Oxythyrea cinctella*

### *Oxythyrea funesta*
Body length: 8–12 mm. Hairy. More elongate thorax than *Tropinota hirta*, with more white spots on wing-cases. **HABITAT** Grasslands, often in flowers or on vegetation. **SEASON** May to June.

*Oxythyrea funesta*

### *Trichius fasciatus* Bee Chafer
Body length: 9–12 mm. Hairy, orange and black wing-cases. Black on upper band spread across wing-case. **HABITAT** Woodlands and grasslands in mountainous areas, where adults fly by day and are often found on flowers. The larvae develop in stumps containing wood mould. **SEASON** May to August.

*Trichius fasciatus*

### *Trichius gallicus*
Body length: 9–14 mm. Upper black blotches on wing-cases similar size to other blotches. Lacks the tooth-like projection present on the mid tibiae of *T. fasciatus*. **HABITAT** Woodlands and grasslands. **SEASON** May to August.

*Trichius gallicus*

*Tropinota hirta*

*Gnorimus nobilis*

*Gnorimus variabilis* [NR]

*Osmoderma barnabita* [NR]

*Oxythyrea cinctella* [TB]

*Oxythyrea funesta*

*Propomacrus bimucronatus* [NR]

*Trichius fasciatus* [PC]

*Trichius gallicus*

## Family Buprestidae – JEWEL BEETLES

Buprestids are colourful small to large jewels with large eyes, are often metallic and usually closely associated with their host plants. In Asia the wing-cases of some species are made into popular jewellery. The larvae develop in wood or stems and can cause significant damage to trees, including oaks. A few are leafminers.
**HABITAT** Typically open parts of woodlands. These day-fliers are likely to be observed in sunny weather on flowers near host plants, or on felled logs.
**HOTSPOTS** Much of the Mediterranean is good for several species; French meadows are a good place to start looking. There are 73 species in Bulgaria and Greece, which are popular with coleopterists looking for some specialist species.

### *Acmaeodera cylindrica*

Body length: 7–11.5 mm. Black, with numerous long white hairs.
**HABITAT** Woodlands, larvae feeding on various trees. Adults often on *Convolvulus* flowers. **SEASON** May to July.

### *Acmaeodera degener*

Body length: 7.5–11.5 mm. Black, conspicuously yellow-spotted. **HABITAT** Oak *Quercus* woodlands, where the larvae develop in dead wood of old oak trees. **SEASON** May to August.

### *Acmaeodera pilosellae*

Body length: 6–10 mm. Head, pronotum and upper part of wing-cases copper; may extend to central markings. Remainder of wing-cases yellowish with brown markings. **HABITAT** Oak *Quercus* woodlands, where the larvae develop in oak branches and other trees. **SEASON** April to July.

### *Ptosima undecimmaculata*

Body length: 7–13 mm. Distinctive yellowish-red spots. **HABITAT** Includes orchards, where they are sometimes regarded as pests. **SEASON** March to July.

### *Sphenoptera rauca*

Body length: 11–17 mm. Metallic bronze. **HABITAT** Grasslands, including coastal dunes, on cardoon *Cynara cardunculus* and other related thistles, the larvae developing in the roots. **SEASON** All year.

### *Perotis lugubris*

Body length: 13–30 mm. Variable across its range. **HABITAT** Maquis, including mountainous areas. Larvae feed on the roots of live fruit trees *Malus*, *Prunus* also *Crataegus*, *Arbutus*, and *Pistacia*. **SEASON** April to August.

### *Perotis margotana*

Body length: c.19 mm. Metallic green, with reddish margin; heavily punctuated. **HABITAT** Larvae feed on the roots of live fruit trees *Prunus* and *Pistacia*. Endemic to Crete. **SEASON** April to August.

### *Capnodis cariosa*

Body length: 27–40 mm. Broad, black with variable white markings on pronotum (and distinctive black spots) and wing-cases. **HABITAT** Various, on *Pistacia*; the adults sometimes seen feeding on leaves. **SEASON** June to August.

### *Capnodis tenebrionis*

Body length: 15–30 mm. Broad, characteristic black species. **HABITAT** Various, larvae developing in the roots of fruit trees, including wild *Prunus*. Sometimes a pest in orchards, resulting in dieback of young trees. **SEASON** May to September.

### *Dicerca berolinensis*

Body length: 19–24 mm. Bronze species, with various other colours and conspicuously patterned wing-cases. **HABITAT** Woodlands, larvae developing in beech *Fagus*, birch *Betula* and others. **SEASON** May to September.

*Acmaeodera cylindrica*

*Acmaeodera degener*

*Acmaeodera pilosellae*

*Ptosima undecimmaculata*

*Sphenoptera rauca*

*Perotis lugubris*

*Perotis margotana*

*Capnodis cariosa*

*Capnodis tenebrionis*

*Dicerca berolinensis*

*Acmaeodera cylindrica* [PC]

*Acmaeodera degener*

*Acmaeodera pilosellae* [PC]

*Ptosima undecimmaculata* [PC]

*Sphenoptera rauca*

*Perotis lugubris* [TB]

*Perotis margotana* [TB]

*Dicerca berolinensis* [NR]

*Capnodis cariosa* [CG]

*Capnodis tenebrionis*

### *Poecilonota variolosa*
Body length: 13–21 mm. Black and bronze. **HABITAT** Woodlands, larvae developing in poplar *Populus*. **SEASON** May to September.

### *Ovalisia balcanica*
Body length: 10–14 mm. Stunning metallic reddish green with blue markings. The underside is violet (green in *O. festiva*). **HABITAT** The larvae develop in *Prunus*. **SEASON** May to August.

### *Ovalisia festiva* Cypress Jewel Beetle
Body length: 6–12 mm. Stunning metallic green with blue markings. **HABITAT** Considered a pest on Cupressaceae in parts of its range, following the spread of ornamental plants. The larvae develop in lower trunks. **SEASON** May to August.

### *Eurythyrea aurata*
Body length: 18–24 mm. Bronze, green, red and sometimes bluish. **HABITAT** Woodlands, where the larvae develop in poplar *Populus* and willow *Salix*. It is worth checking log piles in suitable areas. **SEASON** July to September.

### *Eurythyrea quercus*
Body length: 14–20 mm. Bronze, green and sometimes bluish. ♂ illustrated, ♀ redder. **HABITAT** Woodlands, where the larvae develop in oak *Quercus* and beech *Fagus*. **SEASON** July to September.

### *Buprestis octoguttata*
Body length: 9–18 mm. Yellow spotted species. **HABITAT** Coniferous woodlands, sometimes in boggy areas, where the larvae develop in pines. **SEASON** May to August.

### *Buprestis splendens*
Body length: 14–22 mm. Metallic green with red around margin of wing-cases. **HABITAT** Old coniferous woodlands, where the larvae develop in thick pine *Pinus* trunks. **SEASON** April to August.

### *Trachypteris picta*
Body length: 9–14 mm. Bronze with several orange spots of each wing-case. **HABITAT** Woodlands and others, where the larvae develop in poplar *Populus* and willow *Salix*. Sometimes they occur on rows of trees planted in the countryside as windbreaks and are considered pests of newly-planted *Populus*. **SEASON** April to August.

### *Anthaxia candens*
Body length: 7–11 mm. stunning characteristic colours. **HABITAT** Orchards and others, larvae developing in *Prunus* spp. **SEASON** April to August.

### *Anthaxia discicollis*
Body length: 4–5 mm. The sexes differ, the ♂ much greener than the illustrated ♀. **HABITAT** The larvae develop in *Juniperus*. **SEASON** April to August.

*Buprestis splendens* habitat in relict old growth pine *Pinus* woodlands. [NR]

*Poecilonota variolosa*

*Ovalisia balcanica*

*Ovalisia festiva*

*Eurythyrea aurata*

*Eurythyrea quercus*

*Buprestis octoguttata*

*Buprestis splendens*

*Trachypteris picta*

*Anthaxia candens*

*Anthaxia discicollis*

*Poecilonota variolosa* [NR]

*Ovalisia balcanica* [NR]

*Ovalisia festiva* [NR]

*Eurythyrea aurata* [NR]

*Eurythyrea quercus* [NR]

*Buprestis octoguttata* [NR]

*Trachypteris picta*

*Buprestis splendens* [NR]

*Anthaxia candens* [NR]

*Anthaxia discicollis* [TB]

### *Anthaxia hungarica*
Body length: 7–15 mm. Broad, rather mottled. **HABITAT** Oak *Quercus* woodlands, feeding under bark and phloem or trunk and branches, causing death of young trees. **SEASON** April to September.

*Anthaxia hungarica*

### *Anthaxia lucens*
Body length: 6–10 mm. Similar to *A. candens*. **HABITAT** Woodlands, the larvae develop in *Prunus* species. Adults visit flowers. **SEASON** April to July.

*Anthaxia lucens*

### *Anthaxia nitidula*
Body length: 5–8 mm. Conspicuous, but variable small, metallic species. The sexes differ, rare in buprestids. **HABITAT** Woodlands, the larvae developing in bark of *Prunus*, *Crataegus* and others. Adults visit flowers. **SEASON** April to August.

*Anthaxia nitidula*

### *Anthaxia podolica*
Body length: 4–7 mm. **HABITAT** Woodlands, the larvae develop in *Fraxinus* and *Cornus*. **SEASON** April to August.

*Anthaxia podolica*

### *Anthaxia salicis*
Body length: 4–8 mm. Colourful, part of a species complex distinguished by sculpturing of pronotum and extent of greenish on wing-cases. **HABITAT** Woodlands, the larvae develop in oak *Quercus*, willow *Salix* and others. Adults visit yellow and white flowers in nearby meadows, often in large numbers. **SEASON** April to July.

*Anthaxia salicis*

### *Anthaxia umbellatarum*
Body length: 5–7 mm. Broad, rather mottled. **HABITAT** Woodlands, on various trees; adults often seen on umbellifers. **SEASON** May to September.

*Anthaxia umbellatarum*

### *Chrysobothris affinis*
Body length: 11–15 mm. Bronze, with six ochre spots on the wing-cases (there are other similar species in Europe). **HABITAT** Woodlands, often observed on freshly felled oak *Quercus* and sometimes beech *Fagus* logs. **SEASON** April to August.

*Chrysobothris affinis*

### *Coraebus rubi*
Body length: 8–11 mm. Broad, rather mottled. **HABITAT** Grasslands, where larvae develop in bramble *Rubus* spp. canes. **SEASON** May to August.

*Coraebus rubi*

### *Agrilus macroderus*
Body length: c.6 mm. Bronze (note, there are a number of similar species in Europe). **HABITAT** Woodlands, where they use various host trees. **SEASON** April to July.

*Agrilus macroderus*

### *Trachys minutus*
Body length: 3–3.5 mm. Small, broad insects. **HABITAT** Various, larvae tunnelling mines in leaves. **SEASON** March to September.

*Trachys minutus*

**Gorge de Lavall** and **Forét de la Massane Reserve Naturelle, Alberes, France**: woodlands in this area are important for many jewel beetles including *Acmaeodera cylindrica*, *A. degener*, *A. pilosellae*, *Ptosima flavoguttata* and *Anthaxia* species. [PC]

*Anthaxia hungarica* ♂ (left), ♀ (right)

*Anthaxia lucens* [TB]

*Anthaxia nitidula* ♂ (left) [TB], ♀ (right) [NR]

*Anthaxia podolica* ♂ (left)[TB], ♀ (right) [TB]

*Anthaxia salicis* mating pair

*Anthaxia umbellatarum* [PC]

*Chrysobothris affinis*

*Coraebus rubi*

*Agrilus macroderus* [NR]

*Trachys minutus* [NR]

## Family Elateridae – CLICK BEETLES

Slender and often fairly drab beetles with an amazing ability to jump and right themselves if disturbed, making a clicking sound in the process; it may take more than one flip to land the correct way up. Many species are plain brown or black, or mottled, but some species have attractive orange or red patches. The larvae (wireworms) are liquid feeders, some associated with wood are predators; others feed on roots. A small selection of widespread species is included.

### *Anostirus parumcostatus*

Body length: c.10 mm. Chestnut brown, lacking black tip to abdomen in some related species. **HABITAT** Open sites. **SEASON** April to July.

### *Selatosomus aeneus*

Body length: 10–16 mm. Rather variable, metallic green, blue or bronze-blackish. **HABITAT** Grasslands. **SEASON** Late April to June.

### *Selatosomus amplicollis*

Body length: c.15 mm. Bluish sheen. **HABITAT** Grasslands, including mountainous areas. **SEASON** May to July.

### *Denticollis linearis*

Body length: 9–13 mm. Orange or brownish pronotum, wing-cases yellowish orange to black with pale margin. **HABITAT** Woodlands. **SEASON** May to July.

### *Athous bicolor*

Body length: 8–11 mm. Dark brown thorax, paler wing-cases. **HABITAT** Grasslands. **SEASON** June to August.

### *Stenagostus rhombeus*

Body length: 15–24 mm. Brown, darker crosslines on wing-cases. **HABITAT** Woodlands, beneath bark of fallen *Fagus* deadwood, where larvae are predators of longhorn beetles. **SEASON** July to August.

### *Ampedus balteatus*

Body length: 7.5–10 mm. Reddish wing-cases with broad black tip. **HABITAT** Woodlands including coniferous. **SEASON** May to July.

### *Ampedus elongantulus*

Body length: 7–8.5 mm. Small black mark at the tip of wing-cases. **HABITAT** Woodlands, mainly *Quercus*, *Fagus* and *Pinus*, developing in rotten heartwood of living trees. **SEASON** May to July.

### *Ampedus quercicola*

Body length: 9–11 mm. Brighter pinkish-red on wing-cases; one of several species with all red wing-cases often rather difficult to identify only from photographs. **HABITAT** Woodlands. **SEASON** May to July.

### *Cardiophorus signatus*

Body length: 7–8.5 mm. Reddish pronotum with black markings, sometimes all black. Wing-cases with six whitish spots or blotches. **HABITAT** Woodlands. Adults often seen on flowers or vegetation in grasslands. **SEASON** April to November.

*Anostirus parumcostatus*

*Selatosomus aeneus*

*Selatosomus amplicollis*

*Denticollis linearis*

*Athous bicolor*

*Stenagostus rhombeus*

*Ampedus balteatus*

*Ampedus elongatulus*

*Ampedus quercicola*

*Cardiophorus signatus*

*Anostirus parumcostatus*

*Denticollis linearis*

*Athous bicolor*

*Selatosomus aeneus*

*Selatosomus amplicollis* [PC]

*Stenagostus rhombeus*

*Ampedus balteatus*

*Ampedus elongatulus*

*Ampedus quercicola*

*Cardiophorus signatus* [SO]

## Family Drilidae – FALSE FIREFLY BEETLES

Adults are something like glow-worms, with large wingless ♀s and much smaller ♂s with comb-like antennae. Few European representatives.

### *Drilus flavescens*

Body length: 4–15 mm. Head and pronotum black, wing-cases brown, large wingless ♀s. **HABITAT** Grasslands including slopes, where the larvae prey on snails. ♂s usually found on flowers or vegetation. ♀s often hidden under stones or crawling. **SEASON** May to June.

*Drilus flavescens*

## Family Lycidae – NET-WINGED BEETLES

Bright, soft-bodied beetles, with long, thick, serrate antennae. The larvae inhabit well-decayed wood.

### *Platycis minutus*

Body length: 5–8 mm. Black except for red wing-cases and orange tips to antennae. **HABITAT** Woodlands with moist, decaying beech *Fagus* and birch *Betula*, Adults fly to nearby flowers, around tree trunks or logs. **SEASON** May to September.

*Platycis minutus*

## Family Lampyridae – GLOW-WORMS

Large, soft-bodied nocturnal beetles with several European representatives. The wingless or short-winged ♀, emits a yellowish-green light from the end of her abdomen (pictured left in *Lampris noctiluca*) at night. This attracts the smaller, winged ♂s. The larvae feed on snails.

### *Lampyris noctiluca* Glow-worm

Body length: 10–20 mm. Brown, ♀s wingless, about twice the size of ♂s. **HABITAT** Grasslands and verges. Attracted to lights. **SEASON** June to September.

*Lampyris noctiluca*

### *Nyctophila reichii*

Body length: 10–18 mm. Similar to *L. noctiluca*, but paler. The larvae are sometimes all dark, or with plenty of pink as illustrated. **HABITAT** Woodlands, parks and gardens. **SEASON** June to September.

*Nyctophila reichii*

## Family Cantharidae – SOLDIER BEETLES

Soldier beetles are soft-bodied, brightly coloured species which can be abundant in grasslands, roadside verges and woodland clearings and woodland rides on umbellifers and other flowers, although they can also eat other insects. The larvae are predators in soil, litter or dead wood. Example species are illustrated, which are often seen paired and in huge numbers. Identification can be a challenge, as some species are very similar in appearance and size.

### *Cantharis flavilabris*

Body length: 5–7.5 mm. Often black; pronotum variable, often plain red (scutellum black, but red in the similar *C. nigra*). Legs with red tibiae. **HABITAT** Wetlands. **SEASON** May to July.

*Cantharis flavilabris*

### *Rhagonycha fulva*

Body length: 7–10 mm. Easily recognised by the distinctive black tip to abdomen. Tarsi and also antennae (except base) black. **HABITAT** Various. **SEASON** June to August.

*Rhagonycha fulva*

### *Silis ruficollis*

Body length: 6–7 mm. Pronotum hind angle sharp; antennae black, serrate. **HABITAT** Wetlands. **SEASON** June to July.

*Silis ruficollis*

### *Malthinus flaveolus*

Body length: 4.5–5.5 mm. Pale, yellow tipped wing-cases. There are several other similar *Malthinus* species. **HABITAT** Woodlands and hedgerows. **SEASON** June to August.

*Malthinus flaveolus*

*Drilus flavescens* ♂

*Platycis minutus* mating pair

*Cantharis flavilabris* mating pair

*Lampyris noctiluca* ♂ (left), larva (right)

*Rhagonycha fulva* mating pair

*Lampyris noctiluca* ♀ emitting light (left & right)

*Silis ruficollis* mating pair

*Nyctophila reichii* ♂ (left), larva (right) [both SO]

*Malthinus flaveolus*

## Family Bostrichidae – FALSE POWDER-POST BEETLES

Rather similar to various bark beetles, the body is cylindrical but the pronotum covers the head.
**HABITAT** Woodlands, often on felled logs.

### *Bostrichus capucinus* Hooded Capuchin Beetle

Body length: 5–16 mm. Black head and thorax, red abdomen; ♀ much larger than ♂. **HABITAT** Woodlands where the larvae develop in various hardwood trees including oak *Quercus*; considered a pest in some areas. **SEASON** April to September.

*Bostrichus capucinus*

## Family Lymexylidae – SHIP-TIMBER BEETLES

Characterised by their remarkably narrow bodies and short antennae, this family are wood-borers, often in oak *Quercus* spp.

### *Hylecoetus dermestoides*

Body length: 5–18 mm. ♀s Reddish brown, much smaller ♂s dark brown. **HABITAT** Woodlands, where the larvae develop in tunnels in old oak *Quercus* and beech *Fagus*, feeding on a yeast-like fungus *Endomyces hylecoeti* in the tunnels, rather than on wood. **SEASON** April to June.

*Hylecoetus dermestoides*

### *Lymexylon navale*

Body length: 7–13 mm. Reddish brown, with dark head, much smaller ♂s with black head and thorax. **HABITAT** Ancient woodlands. **SEASON** June to July.

*Lymexylon navale*

## Family Cleridae – CHEQUERED BEETLES

Brightly coloured and hairy beetles, some clerids are associated with wood where they are predators on timber-living insects as larvae and adults. Chequer originates from the regular patterns of *Trichodes* species, which are nest robbers, often feeding on larvae and pupae of certain bees.
**HABITAT** Often in woodlands, particularly in sunny areas on logs. Many visitors to the Mediterranean will, however, encounter species easily enough away from woodlands, as the stunning *Trichodes* species are attracted to flowers.

### *Tillus elongatus*

Body length: 6–10 mm. Black; pronotum red in ♀, often black in ♂. **HABITAT** Woodlands, often on beech *Fagus* stumps, feeding on wood-boring larvae of *Ptilinus* spp. **SEASON** May to June.

*Tillus elongatus*

### *Opilo taeniatus*

Body length: 6–11 mm. Black except wing-cases red to middle, then with broad yellowish white patch. **HABITAT** Woodlands, the larvae developing in branches, including spurge *Euphorbia* spp., *Prunus* spp. and Holm Oak *Quercus ilex*. **SEASON** April to June.

*Opilo taeniatus*

### *Thanasimus formicarius* Ant Beetle

Body length: 7–12 mm. Ant-like, black with attractive red areas and two pale white cross-bands on wing-cases. **HABITAT** Mainly coniferous but also deciduous woodlands, often on tree trunks, feeding on other bark beetles and their larvae. **SEASON** April to July.

*Thanasimus formicarius*

### *Clerus mutillarius*

Body length: 8–15 mm. Ant-like, red only on upper quarter of wing-cases. Legs with long white hairs. **HABITAT** Woodlands, particularly oak *Quercus*. **SEASON** April to July.

*Clerus mutillarius*

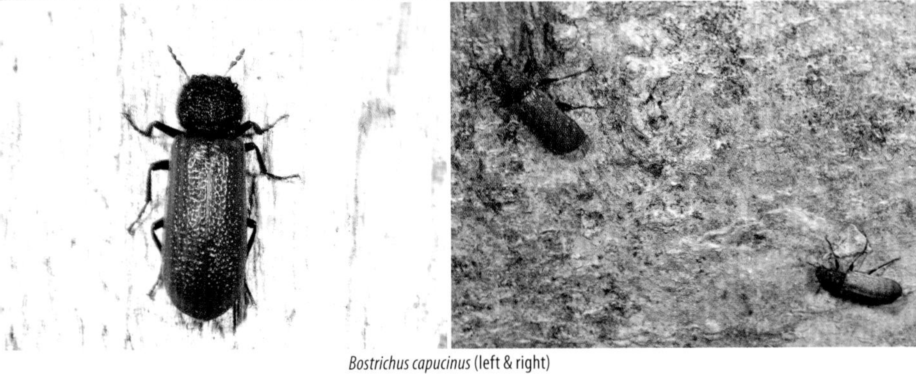

*Bostrichus capucinus* (left & right)

*Hylecoetus dermestoides* ♂ (top), ♀ (bottom)

*Lymexylon navale*, ♀ on top

*Tillus elongatus*

*Opilo taeniatus* [TB]

*Thanasimus formicarius* [PC]

*Clerus mutillarius*

### *Trichodes* spp.

These fairly hairy beetles are black and sport warning colours in the way of red and black wing-cases. A selection of species is shown but note that although the basic markings are often characteristic, they can vary in size, colour and markings within species and some species are difficult to distinguish, except for ♂s.

**HABITAT** Open areas including hillsides, where adults are attracted to flowers, mostly umbellifers. Adults feed on pollen, also small insects, particularly beetles. Eggs are laid near hives or nests of certain bees and wasps, the larvae preying on various stages of the selected host, often bees of the genera *Apis*, *Anthophora*, *Megachile* and *Osmia*.

**SEASON** Mainly May to August.

### *Trichodes alvearius* Bee-hive Beetle

Body length: 9–17 mm. Often seen with *T. apiarius*, but *alvearius* is easily recognised by a black longitudinal stripe along the edge of the wing-cases, which also have a red tip.

### *Trichodes apiarius*

Body length: 9–16 mm. Wing-cases with black tip. Hind femora very thickened.

### *Trichodes creticus*

Body length: 8–18 mm. Hind tibiae slightly curved; spur on hind tibiae nearly straight. Underside of abdomen with red marginal tip. Endemic to Crete, flies from April.

### *Trichodes favarius*

Body length: 8–18 mm. Hind tibiae straight; spur on hind tibiae anvil-like with two points.

### *Trichodes flavocinctus*

Body length: 6–13 mm. Spots yellowish. Hind tibiae curved.

### *Trichodes holtzi*

Body length: 8–11 mm. Distinctively marked wing-cases. Endemic to Turkey.

### *Trichodes leucopsideus*

Body length: 7–13 mm. Small black shoulder spot on each wing-case.

### *Trichodes octopunctatus*

Body length: 10–18 mm. Small black spots on wing-cases.

## Family Malachiidae – SOFT-WINGED FLOWER BEETLES

These soft bodied, sun-loving beetles are often seen on flowers or vegetation.

### *Malachius aeneus* Scarlet Malachite

Body length: 6–8 mm. Red and black. **HABITAT** Hay meadows, where adults obtain pollen from grasses or flowers; they also eat insects. The larvae are predators. **SEASON** May to June.

### *Clanoptilus elegans*

Body length: 5–7 mm. Green, more reddish-yellow spots on wing-cases and yellow mouthparts. **HABITAT** Grasslands. **SEASON** June to July.

*Trichodes alvearius*

*Trichodes apiarius*

*Trichodes creticus*

*Trichodes favarius*

*Trichodes flavocinctus*

*Trichodes holtzi*

*Trichodes leucopsideus*

*Trichodes octopunctatus*

*Malachius aeneus*

*Clanoptilus elegans*

*Trichodes alvearius*

*Trichodes creticus* [TB]

*Trichodes apiarius*

*Trichodes favarius* [TB]

*Trichodes flavocinctus* [SO]

*Trichodes holtzi* [TB]

*Trichodes leucopsideus*

*Trichodes octopunctatus*

*Malachius aeneus*

*Clanoptilus elegans*

## Family Coccinellidae – LADYBIRDS

Many of the species in this family look like the typical brightly coloured spotted beetles known to practically everyone, varying only in the number of spots or other conspicuous markings and colour. The remainder are small drab beetles. Most of the larger species are common and variably coloured, overwintering as adults, sometimes found in houses or outbuildings and most are straightforward to identify. The mainly aphid-eating 7-spot and 2-spot ladybirds are well-known gardeners' friends; the 'alien' Harlequin Ladybird is less popular and is building a reputation for being responsible for declines in populations of native species. Ladybirds occur in many habitats and can be seen all year, with peaks during the main season, April to September. They mainly feed on aphids, some preferring coniferous trees.

### *Exochomus nigromaculatus*

Body length: 4–5 mm. Black with broad red marks on the lateral margins of the pronotum; legs reddish-orange. **HABITAT** Grasslands and others, sometimes on vine leaves, where they feed on aphids. In Turkish apricot orchards, known to prey on *Hyalopterus pruni*, a major pest of stone fruit trees.

*Exochomus nigromaculatus*

### *Anisosticta novemdecimpunctata* Water Ladybird

Body length: 4 mm. Reddish or beige, usually with 19 black spots. **HABITAT** Wetlands, often on reeds and rushes.

*Anisosticta novemdecimpunctata*

### *Myzia oblongoguttata* Striped Ladybird

Body length: 6–8 mm. Local. Chestnut brown with 13 cream stripes and spots. **HABITAT** Coniferous woodlands.

*Myzia oblongoguttata*

### *Psyllobora vigintiduopunctata* 22-spot Ladybird

Body length: 3–4 mm. Yellow with 22 black spots. **HABITAT** Grasslands and others. Feeds on mildew.

*Psyllobora vigintiduopunctata*

### *Hippodamia variegata* Adonis Ladybird

Body length: 4–5 mm. Red with seven black spots; but some variation. **HABITAT** Grasslands and others.

*Hippodamia variegata*

### *Coccinella septempunctata* 7-spot Ladybird

Body length: 5–8 mm. Typical form red with seven black spots of varying size but there are other colour forms; number of spots varies from 0–9. **HABITAT** Various, including gardens.

*Coccinella septempunctata*

### *Adalia bipunctata* 2-spot Ladybird

Body length: 3–6 mm. Typical form red with two black spots but there are numerous colour forms. **HABITAT** Various.

*Adalia bipunctata*

### *Harmonia axyridis* Harlequin Ladybird

Body length: 5–8 mm. Typical form red with 16 black spots (range 0–21 spots). There are many other colour forms. This fast-spreading invasive species (originally introduced in Europe to control aphids) preys voraciously on soft-bodied insect larvae, ladybirds (even its own kind!). **HABITAT** Various. It is now the commonest species in many areas and is spreading in southern Europe.

*Harmonia axyridis*

### *Oenopia doublieri*

Body length: 3–4 mm. White or pinkish with c.18 black spots/markings, including larger, curved central markings. **HABITAT** Grasslands often on *Tamarix* sp..

*Oenopia doublieri*

### *Subcoccinella vigintiquattuorpunctata* 24-spot Ladybird

Body length: 3–4 mm. Russet with 24 black spots; number of spots varies from 0–24. **HABITAT** Grasslands, feeding on grasses.

*Subcoccinella vigintiquattuorpunctata*

*Exochomus nigromaculatus* [PC]

*Anisosticta novemdecimpunctata*

*Myzia oblongoguttata*

*Psyllobora vigintiduopunctata*

*Hippodamia variegata* [PC]

*Coccinella septempunctata* with aphids

*Harmonia axyridis* mating pair (left), larva (right) [PC]

*Adalia bipunctata* (top), (bottom) [PC]

*Oenopia doublieri*

*Subcoccinella vigintiquattuorpunctata*

## Family Mordellidae – TUMBLING FLOWER BEETLES

Rather clumsy, elongate beetles with a pointed tip at the end of the abdomen. Some similar species can cause identification problems. These beetles are found on a wide variety of flowers, but many are attracted to umbellifer flowers or can be found on rotting wood such as stumps. In defence, they have the ability to jump and somersault.

*Tomoxia bucephala*

### *Tomoxia bucephala*

Body length: 5–8.5 mm. Black, with plentiful greyish markings on wing-cases. Tip of abdomen broad. **HABITAT** Woodlands, where the larvae develop in decaying beech *Fagus* and others. **SEASON** May to June.

## Family Ripiphoridae – WEDGE-SHAPED BEETLES

A small family of seldom seen, peculiar-looking beetles, parasitoids of mainly bees and wasps.

*Macrosiagon ferrugineum*

### *Macrosiagon ferrugineum*

Body length: 5–8 mm. Brown. **HABITAT** A parasitoid of solitary wasps, often observed on flowers. **SEASON** July to September.

## Family Tenebrionidae – DARKLING BEETLES

Appropriately named because of the dark brown or black colour of most species, they range considerably in size and are found in a wide variety of habitats and situations. In sand dunes, large species can sometimes be seen walking along or rapidly burying in sand, such as *Erodius tibialis*). A selection of species is shown.

*Lagria hirta*

### *Lagria hirta*

Body length: 7–9 mm. Dark, hairy species with yellowish-brown wing-cases; there are several similar species. **HABITAT** Grasslands, often seen on flowers or vegetation. **SEASON** May to August.

*Akis acuminata*

### *Akis acuminata*

Body length: 18–25 mm. Black, robust species; there are several similar species, but *A. acuminata* has distinctive lateral edges on the wing-cases. **HABITAT** Sandy areas in Iberia, including dunes. **SEASON** April to October.

*Alphasida luctuosa*

### *Alphasida luctuosa*

Body length: 12–15 mm. Black with a paler border to wing-cases. **HABITAT** Grasslands, restricted to part of southern Spain. **SEASON** May to July.

*Erodius tibialis*

### *Erodius tibialis*

Body length: c.12 mm. Black. **HABITAT** Coastal, including sand dunes, restricted to Iberia. **SEASON** March to October.

*Pimelia chrysomeloides*

### *Pimelia chrysomeloides*

Body length: 15–21 mm. Black, similar punctures on wing-cases to other *Pimelia* species. **HABITAT** Coastal, including sand dunes, restricted to Iberia. **SEASON** May to September.

*Pimelia maura*

### *Pimelia maura*

Body length: 16–23 mm. Black with many dotted punctures. **HABITAT** Often coastal, restricted to Iberia. **SEASON** February to September.

*Helops caeruleus*

### *Helops caeruleus* Blue Helops Beetle

Body length: 12–20 mm. Blue or purple sheen. **HABITAT** Woodlands, in decaying oak *Quercus*. **SEASON** May to September.

*Tomoxia bucephala*

*Macrosiagon ferrugineum*

*Lagria hirta*

*Akis acuminata*

*Alphasida luctuosa* [TB]

*Pimelia chrysomeloides*

*odius tibialis* (top), burying in sand (below)

*Pimelia maura* [KM]

*Helops caeruleus*

***Nalassus laevioctostriatus***
Body length: 7–12 mm. Brownish black, one of several species of similar appearance. **HABITAT** Deciduous and coniferous woodlands, beneath bark; can be abundant. They browse on algae and lichens; the larvae develop in soil. **SEASON** May to September.

*Nalassus laevioctostriatus*

***Blaps gigas***
Body length: 32–38 mm. Large, glossy black species. **HABITAT** Barns and cellars, one of several so-called churchyard beetles, feeding on animal remains or droppings at night. In defence, they can emit an unpleasant odour. **SEASON** April to September.

*Blaps gigas*

***Scaurus punctatus***
Body length: c.14 mm. Robust, black species, heavily punctured. There are several other endemic *Scaurus* species in the Mediterranean. **HABITAT** Sandy places in Iberia, often hiding under stones by day. **SEASON** April to August.

*Scaurus punctatus*

***Cteniopus sulphureus* Sulphur Beetle**
Body length: 7–9 mm. Yellow. **HABITAT** Grasslands, on flowers. **SEASON** May to August.

*Cteniopus sulphureus*

***Heliotaurus ruficollis***
Body length: 9–11 mm. Red thorax, otherwise black, sometimes with a slightly blue sheen. **HABITAT** Grasslands including mountainous areas, on flowers, often in large numbers. **SEASON** April to June.

*Heliotaurus ruficollis*

## Family Oedemeridae – FALSE BLISTER BEETLES

These soft-bodied beetles with long antennae are known by some authors as pollen-feeding beetles. Adults of some species are plentiful on flowers in the daytime, whilst other species are nocturnal. The larvae develop in rotting wood or stems.

***Anogcodes seladonius***
Body length: 8–12 mm. Metallic green (with red thorax in ♀). Abdomen black or red. **HABITAT** Grasslands on flowers. **SEASON** April to August.

*Anogcodes seladonius*

***Oedemera femoralis***
Body length: 12–20 mm. Brown, with some darker areas. **HABITAT** Grasslands; nocturnal. **SEASON** April to September.

*Oedemera femoralis*

***Oedemera marmorata***
Body length: 12–16 mm. Brown, extensively mottled. **HABITAT** Grasslands; nocturnal species restricted to Iberia, often attracted to lights. **SEASON** May to September.

*Oedemera marmorata*

***Oedemera nobilis***
**Swollen-thighed Beetle**
Body length: 8–11 mm. Bright metallic green (♀ pictured left [PC]), ♂s with thickened hind femora. **HABITAT** Grasslands on flowers, often plentiful. The larvae live in hollow plant stems. **SEASON** April to August.

*Oedemera nobilis*

***Oedemera podagrariae***
Body length: 7–12 mm. Yellowish or brown, but with black head at least. ♂s with thickened, mainly black hind femora, otherwise legs yellowish brown. **HABITAT** Grasslands on flowers, often plentiful. **SEASON** April to August.

*Oedemera podagrariae*

*Nalassus laevioctostriatus*

*Blaps gigas* [TB]

*Scaurus punctatus*

*Cteniopus sulphureus*

*Heliotaurus ruficollis*

*Anogcodes seladonius*

*Oedemera femoralis*

*Oedemera marmorata*

*Oedemera nobilis* ♂ [PC]

*Oedemera podagrariae* ♂

## Family Meloidae – OIL BEETLES

Among our strangest and most interesting beetles are the oil beetles and blister beetles. Oil beetles are large flightless beetles with short wing-cases. These parasitic species have a complex life cycle. The plump ♀ is usually considerably larger than the ♂ and lays up to several thousand eggs in a burrow near bee colonies. The larvae, known as triungulins, climb up to reach flowers; the hook-like forelegs attach them to bees (and often, in error, to other insects). The aim is to be carried by a ground nesting ♀ solitary bee to her nest burrow, where the larva becomes more maggot-like and feeds on the bee's egg and pollen store. It pupates in the burrow and overwinters, hatching the following year into an adult beetle. In defence, adults release a pungent oily liquid. There are also blister beetles with an equally interesting life history and certain notoriety.

### *Lagorina sericea*

Body length: c.20 mm. Attractive green species, with partly red or blue tinges. **HABITAT** Grasslands, sometimes on *Ranunculus* flowers, or on vegetation. Restricted to parts of southern Spain. **SEASON** March to May.

### *Cerocoma schaefferi*

Body length: 7–10 mm. Green with yellowish legs. The ♂s have cumbersome-looking antennae. **HABITAT** Grasslands, where adults feed on pollen and nectar. Larvae are known to feed on paralysed mantids collected by wasps. **SEASON** March to May.

### *Lytta vesicatoria* Spanish Fly

Body length: 9–21 mm. Bright emerald green. **HABITAT** Grasslands with some trees and also rich with the hosts, various solitary bees. Adults feed on leaves of ash *Fraxinus* and some other trees. The larvae are parasitic in underground nests of solitary bees, hence adults may be found near concentrations of bees, or on vegetation. **SEASON** April to July. These beetles are the source of the aphrodisiac cantharidin (Spanish Fly). If swallowed, cantharidin can result in poisoning to humans and animals; powder derived from ♂ beetles has been used by various poisoners. It has been used in 'love potions' since the Middle Ages. Diluted solutions are still used as a topical skin irritant to remove warts.

### *Oenas fuscicornis*

Body length: c.12 mm. Black, with orange-yellow pronotum. **HABITAT** Grasslands, restricted to Spain. **SEASON** Late May to August.

### *Mylabris flexuosa*

Body length: 10–12 mm. Wing-cases with six spots, generally joined in bands. **HABITAT** Mountains. **SEASON** July to August.

### *Mylabris heiracii*

Body length: 10–22 mm. Wing-cases with elliptical design of six spots. **HABITAT** Grasslands. **SEASON** July to August.

### *Mylabris nevadensis*

Body length: 6–8 mm. Wing-cases yellowish with black bands and markings. **HABITAT** Mountain grasslands in Sierra Nevada 2,000 to 3,100 m. **SEASON** July to early August.

### *Mylabris quadripunctata*

Body length: 13–16 mm. Wing-cases red with four black spots. **HABITAT** Mountain grasslands to 4,000 m. **SEASON** April to September.

### *Mylabris variabilis*

Body length: 7–16 mm. Wing-cases yellowish orange with wavy black bands; rather variable. **HABITAT** Grasslands, including mountains up to 3,200 m, often on flowers. **SEASON** April to October.

*Lagorina sericea*

*Cerocoma schaefferi*

*Lytta vesicatoria*

*Oenas fuscicornis*

*Mylabris flexuosa*

*Mylabris hieracii*

*Mylabris nevadensis*

*Mylabris quadripunctata*

*Mylabris variabilis*

Lagorina sericea

*Cerocoma schaefferi* ♀ (left) [PC], mating group ♂s on top (right) [FR]

*Oenas fuscicornis* [TB]

*Lytta vesicatoria* mating pair, ♂ on left

*Mylabris flexuosa* [PC]

*Mylabris hieracii* [PC]

*Mylabris nevadensis*

*Mylabris quadripunctata*

*Mylabris variabilis* [PC]

### *Berberomeloe insignis*
Body length: 12–49 mm. Black except small part of back of head red. **HABITAT** Grasslands, including mountainous areas in a restricted range. **SEASON** March to May.

*Berberomeloe insignis*

### *Berberomeloe majalis*
Body length: 15–75 mm. Striking and usually large, black and red species, although variable in size, hence occasional small ♂s. A rarer black form, var. *laevigatus* (pictured below in Sierra Nevada, Spain, ♀ on right), occurs in some areas. **HABITAT** Grasslands and woodland glades, up to 3,000 m, where adults eat leaves of various Asteraceae. **SEASON** April to July.

*Berberomeloe majalis*

*Meloe cicatricosus*

*Meloe proscarabaeus*

**Sierra de las Nieves, a mountain range in Andalusía.** A number of *Berberomeloe majalis* were observed crawling on short vegetation close to a dried up river bed.

### *Meloe cicatricosus*
Body length: 16–45 mm. Black, apart from size, pronotum with angulate front corners (usually rounded in other species). **HABITAT** Grasslands. **SEASON** March to April.

### *Meloe proscarabaeus* Black Oil Beetle
Body length: 13–32 mm. Square-shaped thorax. Shiny bluish-black or black, antennae with kink; thorax with coarse punctures, straight base to thorax, with slight rounded tooth, otherwise very similar to *M. violaceus*. **HABITAT** Grasslands, often seen on tracks in the day. **SEASON** March to June.

*Berberomeloe insignis* ♀ [SO]

*Meloe cicatricosus* [NR]

*Berberomeloe majalis* ♀

*Meloe proscarabaeus* pair with ♀ on left (left), triungulin attached to the femur of a longhorn beetle *Cerambyx scopolii* (right)

### *Meloe scabriusculus*
Body length: 6–25 mm. Smaller, more dumpy black species. **HABITAT** Open grasslands, including mountainous areas. Hosts include *Andrena vaga*. **SEASON** April to May.

*Meloe scabriusculus*

### *Meloe variegatus*
Body length: 11–38 mm. Easily recognised by the stunning coloured abdominal segments. **HABITAT** Grasslands. **SEASON** April to July.

*Meloe variegatus*

### *Meloe violaceus* Violet Oil Beetle
Body length: 10–32 mm. Square-shaped thorax. Shiny bluish-black or black, antennae with kink; thorax with fine punctures, indented base to thorax, with distinct tooth, otherwise very similar to *M. proscarabaeus*. **HABITAT** Grasslands and woodlands. **SEASON** March to June.

*Meloe violaceus*

### *Sitaris rufipennis*
Body length: 7–13 mm. Reddish brown wing-cases. **HABITAT** Where Hymenoptera prey occurs, restricted to parts of south-east Spain with very few records. **SEASON** August.

*Sitaris rufipennis*

## Family Pyrochroidae – CARDINAL BEETLES
Brightly coloured beetles with comb-like antennae and a distinctive satin-like sheen to the dorsal surface of the wing-cases.

### *Pyrochroa coccinea* Black-headed Cardinal
Body length: 12–18 mm. Red with a black head, legs and antennae (larva pictured left). **HABITAT** Woodlands. **SEASON** May to July.

*Pyrochroa coccinea*

### *Pyrochroa serraticornis* Red-headed Cardinal
Body length: 10–18 mm. Red, with black legs and antennae. **HABITAT** Woodlands, where the larvae feed on other insects beneath the bark of freshly dead broadleaved trees. **SEASON** May to July.

*Pyrochroa serraticornis*

## Family Anthicidae – ANT-LIKE FLOWER BEETLES
Small, fast-moving beetles (to 5 mm), somewhat ant-like in appearance i.e. a narrow-waisted thorax. Some are brightly coloured and larvae develop in heaps of decaying organic matter in various situations including saltmarsh habitat.

### *Anthicus antherinus*
Body length: c.3 mm. Black, variably red marked on wing-cases. **HABITAT** Open areas, grasslands including the sea shore. **SEASON** March to November.

*Anthicus antherinus*

### *Notoxus monoceros* Monoceros Beetle
Body length: 4–5 mm. Yellowish brown with variable black marks on wing-cases (all black form uncommon). Pronotum with horn on front margin. **HABITAT** Open, often sandy areas such as grasslands, including the sea shore. This species has been recorded feeding on secretions of oil beetles (Meloidae) and Oedemeridae in order to obtain and secrete cantharidin. **SEASON** April to October.

*Notoxus monoceros*

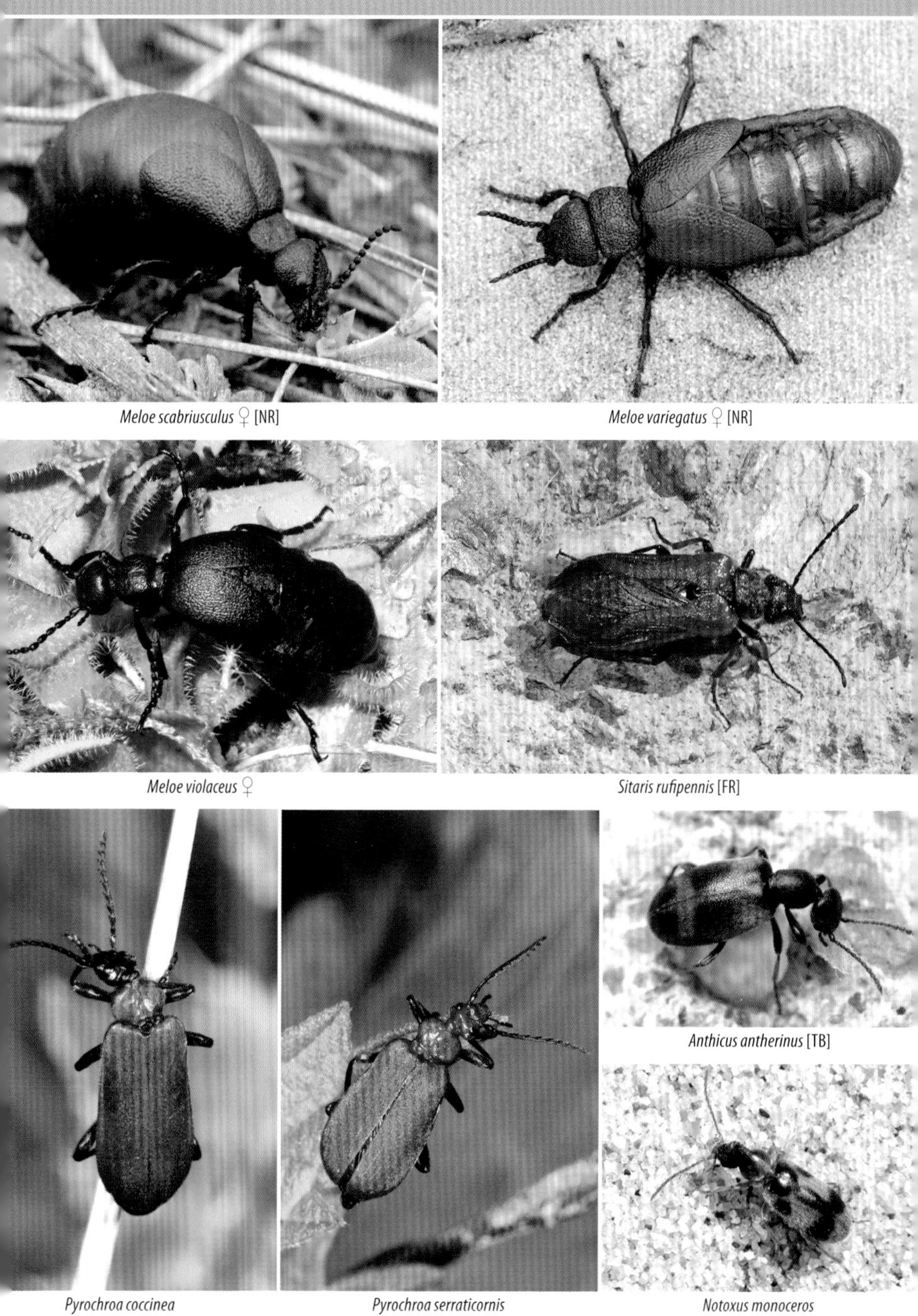

*Meloe scabriusculus* ♀ [NR]

*Meloe variegatus* ♀ [NR]

*Meloe violaceus* ♀

*Sitaris rufipennis* [FR]

*Anthicus antherinus* [TB]

*Pyrochroa coccinea*

*Pyrochroa serraticornis*

*Notoxus monoceros*

## Family Cerambycidae – LONGHORN BEETLES

Easily recognised by their long antennae, longhorns have slender bodies and long legs, and are amongst our most attractive insects. If handled, some longhorns stridulate loudly and the larger species have a strong grip. The larvae mostly feed in dead wood and may take several years to mature; a few species are forestry pests and also known in other continents. However, the larvae of some species feed on living plant tissue. There are c.600 species in southern Europe and the Mediterranean. Adults are short-lived and vary in size and sometimes in colour or markings, within species.

**HABITAT** Often in woodlands, particularly along sunny rides on dead and dying trees, although such trees may occur in other habitats. At night nocturnal species may be searched for by torchlight and some species are attracted to lights. However, many species are easily seen by walkers during the day in grasslands or woodland edges, attracted to flowers, or on wood piles.

**HOTSPOTS** Many, but particularly species rich in the far south excluding the Iberian Peninsula; see www.cerambyx.uochb.cz/ for details of expeditions, such as to Turkey.

*Prionus coriarius*

*Aegosoma scabricorne*

*Rhagium inquisitor*

*Rhagium mordax*

*Dinoptera collaris*

*Grammoptera ustulata*

*Pseudovadonia livida*

*Anoplodera sexguttata*

*Lepturobosca virens*

### *Prionus coriarius* Tanner Beetle

Body length: 18–45 mm. A large robust dark reddish brown to black beetle. **HABITAT** Woodlands, the larvae develop in the roots of dead trees for 3–4 years, mainly oak *Quercus* and deciduous trees, but sometimes conifers. Adults likely at dusk and may be attracted to lights. **SEASON** July to September.

### *Aegosoma scabricorne*

Body length: 28–50 mm. Large, robust yellowish brown or reddish beetle with 3 or 4 distinct ridges on the wing-cases. **HABITAT** Woodlands, the larvae developing in moist decaying wood of many trees for at least 3 years, particularly poplar *Populus* and willow *Salix*; nocturnal. **SEASON** July to August.

### *Rhagium inquisitor* Ribbed Pine Borer

Body length: 9–22 mm. Black, mottled with light brown; antennae rather short. Wing-cases with several black marks, along with its darker appearance, distinguishing it from the similar ***R. mordax*** **Black-spotted Longhorn Beetle** [not illustrated]. **HABITAT** Mainly coniferous woodlands. **SEASON** April to July.

### *Dinoptera collaris* Red-collared Longhorn Beetle

Body length: 6–9 mm. Black species, with slight bluish tinge. Immediately recognised by the red pronotum. **HABITAT** Woodlands. **SEASON** May to August.

### *Grammoptera ustulata* Burnt-tip Grammoptera

Body length: 5–9 mm. Small, covered in a fine, golden pubescence, except for a black wing-case tip. **HABITAT** Usually oak *Quercus* woodlands. **SEASON** Late April to July.

### *Pseudovadonia livida* Fairy-ring Longhorn Beetle

Body length: 5–9 mm. A small, broad black species with yellowish brown wing-cases. **HABITAT** Grasslands, where the larvae develop in soil infested by the Fairy Ring Champignon fungus *Marasmius oreades*. **SEASON** April to September.

### *Anoplodera sexguttata* Six-spotted Longhorn Beetle

Body length: 7–12 mm. Black with three yellow spots on each wing-case, the spots sometimes fused. **HABITAT** Woodlands. **SEASON** May to July.

### *Lepturobosca virens*

Body length: 14–22 mm. Brown with golden pubescence. Antennae banded. **HABITAT** Deciduous and coniferous woodlands in mountainous areas. **SEASON** June to August.

*Prionus coriarius*

*Aegosoma scabricorne* [NR]

*Rhagium inquisitor* [GJ]

*Dinoptera collaris*

*Lepturobosca virens* [PC]

*Grammoptera ustulata*

*Pseudovadonia livida*

*Anoplodera sexguttata* mating pair

***Stictoleptura cordigera***
Body length: 14–20 mm. Black, except wing-cases red with black central blotch, narrowing sharply to black tip (but sometimes all red or black). **HABITAT** Woodlands, where the larvae develop in oak *Quercus*, *Pistacia* and others. **SEASON** June to August.

*Stictoleptura cordigera*

***Stictoleptura fontenayi***
Body length: 10–20 mm. Black head and legs, thorax black in ♂, red in ♀; wing-cases red. **HABITAT** Deciduous and coniferous woodlands. **SEASON** May to July.

*Stictoleptura fontenayi*

***Stictoleptura fulva* Tawny Longhorn Beetle**
Body length: 9–14 mm. Black except for black-tipped yellowish brown wing-cases; rather broader than a ♂ *Anastrangalia sanguinolenta*. **HABITAT** Woodlands, where the larvae develop in decaying wood. Adults often visit flowers. **SEASON** June to August.

*Stictoleptura fulva*

***Stictoleptura rubra* Red Longhorn Beetle**
Body length: 10–20 mm. The lateral swelling on the pronotum distinguishes this species from *Anastrangalia sanguinolenta*, in addition to yellow tibiae and, in the ♀, red pronotum. **HABITAT** Coniferous woodlands. **SEASON** May to September.

*Stictoleptura rubra*

***Stictoleptura scutellata* Large Black Longhorn Beetle**
Body length: 12–20 mm. Black, with a yellow mark between the wing-cases (this is the scutellum, covered in golden hairs). **HABITAT** Woodlands. **SEASON** June to September.

*Stictoleptura scutellata*

***Anastrangalia dubia***
Body length: 8–16 mm. ♂ yellowish wing-cases with black tip and sides. ♀ variable, often wing-cases red with black tip, may be all black or have black central blotch on wing-cases. **HABITAT** Coniferous woodlands. **SEASON** May to August.

*Anastrangalia dubia*

***Anastrangalia sanguinolenta* Blood-red Longhorn Beetle**
Body length: 8–13 mm. Black apart from wing-cases, which are yellowish in the ♂ (black-tipped), red in the ♀. **HABITAT** Coniferous woodlands. **SEASON** May to August.

*Anastrangalia sanguinolenta*

***Pachytodes cerambyciformis* Speckled Longhorn Beetle**
Body length: 7–12 mm. Black except for pale yellow wing-cases, often broken by black bands and spots. **HABITAT** Deciduous and coniferous woodlands. **SEASON** May to August.

*Pachytodes cerambyciformis*

***Pachytodes erraticus***
Body length: 7–12 mm. More elongate than *P. cerambyciformis*, with larger black spots, which are often joined. **HABITAT** Woodland clearings. **SEASON** May to August.

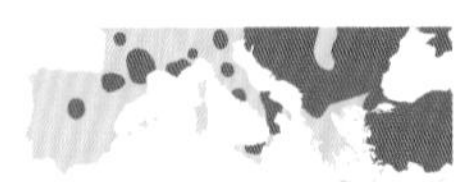
*Pachytodes erraticus*

***Leptura aurulenta* Golden-haired Longhorn Beetle**
Body length: 12–25 mm. Black, with four wavy yellow (sometimes reddish) bands on the wing-cases, similar to ***L. quadrifasciata* Four-banded Longhorn Beetle** [not illustrated or mapped], but there are golden yellow hairs on the front and back of the pronotum; legs reddish black. **HABITAT** Woodlands. Adults are most likely on dead wood or flying nearby. **SEASON** June to August.

*Leptura aurulenta*

*Stictoleptura cordigera* [PC]

*Stictoleptura fontenayi* ♂ (left), ♀ (right) [RP]

*Stictoleptura fulva* [PC]

*Stictoleptura rubra* ♂ (left), ♀ (right) [JE]

*Stictoleptura scutellata*

*Anastrangalia dubia*

*Anastrangalia sanguinolenta*, ♂ on top [PC]

*Pachytodes cerambyciformis*

*Pachytodes erraticus*

*Leptura aurulenta*

***Rutpela maculata*** **Black-and-yellow Longhorn Beetle**
Body length: 13–20 mm. Large and elongate, variable species; the bright yellow wing-cases usually with two to three black bands and variable black spotting towards the front of the wing-cases. **HABITAT** Woodlands. **SEASON** May to September.

*Rutpela maculata*

***Stenurella bifasciata***
Body length: 6–10 mm. Black with reddish-brown, black-tipped wing-cases and ♀ with black blotches on the wing-cases. **HABITAT** Woodlands. **SEASON** May to September.

*Stenurella bifasciata*

***Stenurella melanura*** **Black-striped Longhorn Beetle**
Body length: 6–10 mm. Small and slender, black with reddish-yellow, black-tipped wing-cases and a dark elongate streak of variable width running longitudinally between the wing-cases. **HABITAT** Woodlands. **SEASON** May to September.

*Stenurella melanura*

***Stenurella nigra*** **Small Black Longhorn Beetle**
Body length: 6–9 mm. All black upperside, abdomen mostly orange. **HABITAT** Woodlands. **SEASON** May to August.

*Stenurella nigra*

***Stenurella septempunctata***
Body length: 7–12 mm. Yellow with some black markings, including seven marks on the wing-cases. **HABITAT** Woodlands. **SEASON** May to August.

*Stenurella septempunctata*

***Pedostrangalia emmipoda***
Body length: 11–16 mm. Black with reddish areas on wing-cases and femora. **HABITAT** Woodlands. **SEASON** May to June.

*Pedostrangalia emmipoda*

***Arhopalus ferus***
**Burnt-pine Longhorn Beetle**
Body length: 10–27 mm. Large, brown species, similar to ***A. rusticus*** **Dusky Longhorn Beetle** [pictured left, not mapped] but with hairless eyes. **HABITAT** Coniferous woodlands. Adults are nocturnal and attracted to lights. **SEASON** June to September.

*Arhopalus ferus*

***Molorchus minor*** **Spuce Shortwing Beetle**
Body length: 6–16 mm. Black, with reddish-brown wing-cases, antennae and legs; the femora are partly swollen. Oblique yellow markings on the wing-cases. **HABITAT** Coniferous woodlands. **SEASON** May to August.

*Molorchus minor*

***Stenopterus mauritanicus***
Body length: 7–16 mm. Black, with head, antennae, legs and wing-cases red or tawny. Upper and lower margin of pronotum yellowish. **HABITAT** Woodlands. **SEASON** May to July.

*Stenopterus mauritanicus*

***Stenopterus rufus***
Body length: 7–16 mm. Similar to *S. mauritanicus* but with apex of femora black-banded; yellowish blotches on pronotum. **HABITAT** Woodlands. **SEASON** May to August.

*Stenopterus rufus*

*Rutpela maculata*

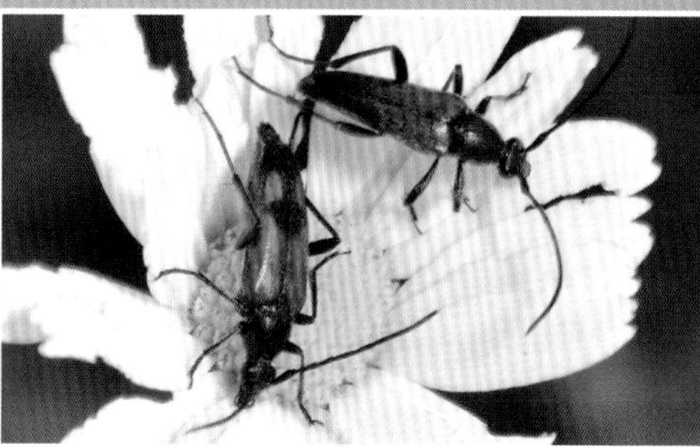

*Stenurella bifasciata* pair (♂ above)

*Stenurella melanura*

*Stenurella nigra*

*Stenurella septempunctata* [TB]

*Pedostrangalia emmipoda* [TB]

*Arhopalus ferus* mating pair

*Molorchus minor*

*Stenopterus mauritanicus*

*Stenopterus rufus*

***Cerambyx scopolii***
Body length: 17–30 mm. Black with rugged wing-cases. Typical long antennae of this genus, commonly known as Capricorn beetles (***C. cerdo*** **Great Capricorn Beetle** [not illustrated] is one of the longest beetles in Europe, rather similar in appearance but broader; body length 24–60 mm). **HABITAT** Woodlands, where the larvae feed beneath the bark initially, then excavate a gallery 8–10 cm long into the heartwood. **SEASON** April to August.

***Cerambyx welensii***
Body length: 25–65 mm. Black; one of the longest beetles in Europe. The wing-cases have a fine pubescence and are smoother and more brownish than the commoner *C. cerdo*. **HABITAT** Oak *Quercus* woodlands. **SEASON** May to August.

***Purpuricenus budensis***
Body length: 10–20 mm. Black except for reddish wing-cases surrounding black central patch and tip. **HABITAT** Woodlands. **SEASON** May to August.

***Purpuricenus dalmatinus***
Body length: 14–20 mm. Red face-like markings on thorax, also bold red central mark on wing-cases, as well as tip. **HABITAT** Oak *Quercus* woodlands. **SEASON** May to July.

***Purpuricenus desfontainei***
Body length: 10–20 mm. Red thorax with variable black spots and marks; wing-cases red, except for broad black basal patch. **HABITAT** Woodlands. **SEASON** May to July.

***Purpuricenus kaehleri***
Body length: 10–24 mm. Black except for variable amount of red on side of thorax and red wing-cases surrounded very broad band central patch. **HABITAT** Woodlands, the larvae mainly developing in branches of oak *Quercus* and chestnut *Castanea*, particularly those damaged by a jewel beetle *Coraebus florentinus*. **SEASON** May to July.

***Aromia moschata* Musk Beetle**
Body length: 13–35 mm. Large, stunning metallic green species, sometimes bluish in some ♀s, or mauve in ♂s (pictured below); the metallic appearance relates to reflected light (a subspecies has a reddish thorax). **HABITAT** Adults are found in wetlands visiting flowers. Larvae live in young, healthy wood of willow *Salix*. Sometimes large numbers of adults are found on one tree, giving it a characteristic musky smell. **SEASON** May to September.

*Cerambyx scopolii*

*Cerambyx cerdo*

*Cerambyx welensii*

*Purpuricenus budensis*

*Purpuricenus dalmatinus*

*Purpuricenus desfontainei*

*Purpuricenus kaehleri*

*Aromia moschata*

*Cerambyx scopolii*

*Cerambyx welensii* [NR]

*Purpuricenus budensis* [MS]

*Purpuricenus dalmatinus* [TB]

*Purpuricenus desfontainei* [TB]

*Purpuricenus kaehleri* [PC]

*Aromia moschata*

The stunning *Rosalia alpina* can be found in extensive Beech *Fagus sylvatica* forests. [NR]

*Rosalia alpina*

### *Rosalia alpina* Alpine Longhorn Beetle
Body length: 15–38 mm. Unmistakeable greyish-blue with large black spots (with black tufts of hair on central antennal segments). **HABITAT** Woodlands, most often at mid elevations in montane areas where the larvae develop on beech *Fagus* and several other trees. **SEASON** June (but usually from mid July in mountains) to August. Note: Protected by law in several European countries where populations have significantly declined, but only regarded as of 'Least Concern' when assessed at Red List level in 2010 as it is widespread in some parts of Western Europe. One of Europe's most striking insects, sometimes featured on postage stamps.

*Ropalopus macropus*

### *Ropalopus macropus*
Body length: 7–14 mm. All black, robust species with thickened femora. **HABITAT** Woodlands, including oak *Quercus*. **SEASON** April to July.

*Pyrrhidium sanguineum*

### *Pyrrhidium sanguineum* Welsh Oak Longhorn Beetle
Body length: 6–15 mm. A broad, rather flat red species, except for the black head and legs. **HABITAT** Deciduous woodlands, mainly oak *Quercus*. **SEASON** April to June.

*Poecilium alni*

### *Poecilium alni* White-banded Longhorn Beetle
Body length: 3–7 mm. Small, well-marked species, wing-cases black and reddish with white marks. **HABITAT** Woodlands, often oak *Quercus*. **SEASON** April to June.

*Poecilium pusillum*

### *Poecilium pusillum*
Body length: 5–10 mm. Dark brown to blackish, pubescent. **HABITAT** Oak *Quercus* woodlands. **SEASON** April to June.

*Anaglyptus mysticus*

### *Anaglyptus mysticus* Rufous-shouldered Longhorn Beetle
Body length: 8–15 mm. Mostly black with various markings on the wing-cases, the upper half often reddish; the tip has a grey pubescence. **HABITAT** Woodlands. **SEASON** April to July.

*Xylotrechus arvicola*

### *Xylotrechus arvicola*
Body length: 8–20 mm. Black with distinctive yellows marks and reddish legs. **HABITAT** Woodlands. **SEASON** May to August.

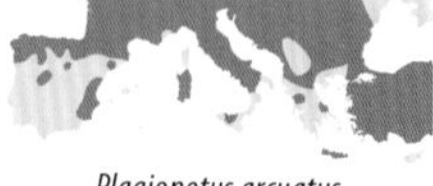

*Plagionotus arcuatus*

### *Plagionotus arcuatus*
Body length: 8–20 mm. Again black with distinctive bright yellow marks and reddish legs. **HABITAT** Woodlands, mainly on oak *Quercus*, damaging dead standing trees or fallen trunks. The larvae form galleries under the bark and later, in the wood. **SEASON** May to July.

*Rosalia alpina* [NR]

*Ropalopus macropus* [TB]

*Pyrrhidium sanguineum* [PC]

*Poecilium alni* [TP]

*Poecilium pusillum* [NR]

*Anaglyptus mysticus*

*Xylotrechus arvicola*

*Plagionotus arcuatus* ♀

### *Chlorophorus figuratus*
Body length: 8–13 mm. Black with distinctive grey bands and markings. **HABITAT** Woodlands. **SEASON** May to August.

### *Chlorophorus glabromaculatus*
Body length: 8–18 mm. Yellowish olive. Each wing-case with three black spots and an elongated spot on the shoulder. **HABITAT** Woodlands. **SEASON** June to August.

### *Chlorophorus trifasciatus*
Body length: 6–11 mm. Abdomen black with distinctive cream bands and reddish thorax. **HABITAT** Woodlands. **SEASON** May to July.

### *Chlorophorus varius*
Body length: 8–14 mm. Yellowish with black bands, sometimes grey with black bands (pictured left [PC]). **HABITAT** Woodlands. **SEASON** May to September.

### *Clytus arietis* Wasp Beetle
Body length: 6–15 mm. An attractive black and yellow patterned species with reddish legs which has a superficial resemblance to a wasp. **HABITAT** Woodlands to 2,000 m, various trees including oak *Quercus* and beech *Fagus*. **SEASON** May to July.

### *Clytus rhamni*
Body length: 6–12 mm. Small yellowish marks on upper part of wing-cases. **HABITAT** Woodlands. **SEASON** May to August.

### *Mesosa nebulosa* White-clouded Longhorn Beetle
Body length: 9–16 mm. Robust and stocky, attractively marked with yellowish brown, black and white markings. **HABITAT** Woodlands. The adults are nocturnal. **SEASON** April to August.

### *Monochamus sutor*
Body length: 15–24 mm. Black species with variable yellowish mottling. **HABITAT** Coniferous woodlands. **SEASON** July to September. **SIMILAR SPECIES** ***M. galloprovincialis*** (picured below [NR]), similar in size with black with variable whitish or brownish mottling, is also found in coniferous woodlands.

### *Morimus asper*
Body length: 15–40 mm. Stout black species, there is some discussion as to whether the spotted *funereus* [illustrated] is a subspecies, synonym or different species. **HABITAT** Deciduous and coniferous woodlands. Nocturnal but may be found on stumps by day. **SEASON** March to October.

*Chlorophorus figuratus*

*Chlorophorus glabromaculatus*

*Chlorophorus trifasciatus*

*Chlorophorus varius*

*Clytus arietis*

*Clytus rhamni*

*Mesosa nebulosa*

*Monochamus sutor*

*Monochamus galloprovincialis*

*Morimus asper*

*Chlorophorus figuratus*

*Chlorophorus glabromaculatus*

*Chlorophorus trifasciatus*

*Chlorophorus varius* [PC]

*Clytus arietis*

*Clytus rhamni* [TB]

*Mesosa nebulosa*

*Morimus asper* [KB]

*Monochamus sutor*

### *Neodorcadion bilineatum*
Body length: 10–14 mm. Robust, black or dark brown, two longitudinal stripes on wing-cases. **HABITAT** Grasslands, where the larvae feed on roots of herbaceous plants and grasses. **SEASON** March to June.

*Neodorcadion bilineatum*

### *Iberodorcadion fuliginator*
Body length: 10–14 mm. Black, often with greyish longitudinal stripes on wing-cases. This and related species are flightless. **HABITAT** Grasslands. **SEASON** April to June.

*Iberodorcadion fuliginator*

### *Iberodorcadion lorquinii*
Body length: 10–20 mm. Robust, black, glossy species. **HABITAT** Mountain grasslands, where the larvae feed on roots of grasses. Only in the Sierra Nevada, Spain and surrounds, typically 2,000–3,000 m. **SEASON** July to September.

*Iberodorcadion lorquinii*

### *Iberodorcadion pyrenaeum*
Body length: 10–14 mm. Robust, black species, with five whitish longitudinal stripes on wing-cases. **HABITAT** Mountain grasslands, where the larvae feed on roots of herbaceous plants and grasses. **SEASON** April to July.

*Iberodorcadion pyrenaeum*

**Puigmal, eastern Pyrenees, France.** Mountain grassland and scree at over 2,000 m, habitat for the endemic flightless *Iberodorcadion pyrenaeum* and other rare montane insects including *Erebia lefebvrei* Lefebvre's Ringlet and *Cophopodisma pyrenaica* Pyrenean Mountain Grasshopper. [PC]

### *Dorcadion fulvum*
Body length: 14–18 mm. Elongate, black, heavily punctured. Wing-cases, 1st antennal segment and legs except tarsi are brown, sometimes black [as shown]. **HABITAT** Grasslands. **SEASON** April to June.

*Dorcadion fulvum*

### *Niphona picticornis*
Body length: 10–19 mm. Brown species with variable whitish mottling on body and legs. **HABITAT** Woodlands. **SEASON** April to October.

*Niphona picticornis*

### *Pogonocherus hispidulus* Greater Thorn-tipped Longhorn Beetle
Body length: 5–8 mm. Small, broad species rather like a bird dropping with brown and white wing-cases and a white scutellum. Sharp spine at end of wing-case. **HABITAT** Woodlands, where the larvae develop in dead twigs. Seldom seen in the daytime. **SEASON** April to October.

*Pogonocherus hispidulus*

### *Pogonocherus ovatus*
Body length: 3–6 mm. Broad 'v' shaped whitish band on wing-cases, otherwise brown and rather mottled. **HABITAT** Deciduous and coniferous woodlands. **SEASON** All year.

*Pogonocherus ovatus*

### *Anaesthetis testacea*
Body length: 6–10 mm. Brown with black legs and antennae. **HABITAT** Woodlands. **SEASON** May to August.

*Anaesthetis testacea*

### *Acanthocinus aedilis* Timberman
Body length: 12–20 mm. Grey with brownish markings and remarkably long antennae. **HABITAT** Coniferous woodlands, mainly on Scots Pine *Pinus silvestris*. **SEASON** March to September.

*Acanthocinus aedilis*

*Neodorcadion bilineatum* [TB]

*Iberodorcadion fuliginator*

*Iberodorcadion lorquinii*

*Iberodorcadion pyrenaeum* [PC]

*Dorcadion fulvum* [NR]

*Niphona picticornis* [TB]

*Pogonocherus hispidulus*

*Pogonocherus ovatus* [TB]

*Anaesthetis testacea* [TB]

*Acanthocinus aedilis*

### *Aegomorphus clavipes*
Body length: 7–17 mm. Brown and greyish mottled, with brown and grey banded antennae and legs. **HABITAT** Woodlands. **SEASON** May to August.

*Aegomorphus clavipes*

### *Saperda populnea* Small Poplar Beetle
Body length: 9–15 mm. Mottled wing-cases with several yellow spots. **HABITAT** Woodlands, where the larvae develop in poplar *Populus* trees. Adults eat leaves. **SEASON** May to July.

*Saperda populnea*

### *Saperda scalaris* Ladder-marked Longhorn Beetle
Body length: 11–19 mm. Yellow ladder-like markings on black wing-cases. **HABITAT** Woodlands, where the larvae develop for 1–2 years under bark and outer sapwood of deciduous trees. **SEASON** May to July.

*Saperda scalaris*

### *Stenostola dubia* Lime Longhorn Beetle
Body length: 8–14 mm. Elongate black species, with a bluish sheen. **HABITAT** Woodlands, where the larvae develop in dead branches of mainly lime *Tilia*; adults eat lime leaves. **SEASON** May to July.

*Stenostola dubia*

*Stenostola dubia* is a specialist on lime *Tilia*, but when in flower such as this one near **Lalinde, in the Dordogne, south-western France**, hundreds of longhorn beetles are attracted. *Grammoptera* species and *Stenurella nigra* are particularly common.

### *Oberea linearis*
Body length: 11–15 mm. Elongate black species, with pale orange legs. The wing-cases pitted. **HABITAT** Woodlands and roadsides. **SEASON** May to July.

*Oberea linearis*

### *Phytoecia affinis*
Body length: 9–16 mm. Black species, with bright orange on legs (except tarsi) and much of thorax. **HABITAT** Grasslands, the larvae developing in umbellifers. **SEASON** May to July.

*Phytoecia affinis*

### *Phytoecia humeralis*
Body length: 5–12 mm. Mainly black species, with some reddish areas as illustrated. **HABITAT** Grasslands, the larvae associated with *Centaurea*. **SEASON** April to June.

*Phytoecia humeralis*

### *Phytoecia pustulata*
Body length: 5–9 mm. Black with part reddish femora. Thorax with a central red longitudinal mark. **HABITAT** Grasslands, the larvae developing in members of the daisy family. **SEASON** April to July.

*Phytoecia pustulata*

### *Opsilia coerulescens*
Body length: 6–14 mm. Uniform greyish green. **HABITAT** Grasslands, the larvae developing in the roots of herbaceous plants. **SEASON** April to July.

*Opsilia coerulescens*

### *Calamobius filum*
Body length: 5–11 mm. Slender blackish species with yellow central line on thorax. **HABITAT** Grasslands, the larvae gnaw grass stems of various species, causing the ears to fall. **SEASON** April to July.

*Calamobius filum*

*Aegomorphus clavipes*

*Saperda populnea*

*Saperda scalaris* [TB]

*Stenostola dubia*

*Oberea linearis*

*Phytoecia affinis*

*Phytoecia humeralis* [TB]

*Phytoecia pustulata* pair

*Opsilia coerulescens*

*Calamobius filum*

***Agapanthia annularis***
Body length: 7–15 mm. Mainly brown (including wing-cases) with yellow markings on scutellum and sides of thorax; antennae black and yellow banded. **HABITAT** Grasslands, the larvae developing in the roots of herbaceous plants. **SEASON** April to June.

***Agapanthia asphodeli***
Body length: 15–20 mm. Dark grey with dense yellow pubescence, also stripes on the head and pronotum. Similar to some other *Agapanthia* species, but the antennae have noticeably reddish segments. **HABITAT** Grasslands. **SEASON** April to June.

***Agapanthia cardui***
Body length: 6–14 mm. Black with grey wing-case margin; antennae black and grey banded. **HABITAT** Grasslands, the larvae developing in the roots of herbaceous plants. **SEASON** March to July.

***Agapanthia cretica***
Body length: 13–16 mm. Similar to *A. cynarae*. Wing-cases with irregular yellow pubescence; edges with long black hairs. **HABITAT** Grasslands, the larvae developing in the stems of *Asphodelina lutea*. Endemic to Crete. **SEASON** March to July.

***Agapanthia cynarae***
Body length: 14–23 mm. Similar to *A. asphodeli*, but antennae black and grey banded, not reddish; base of 3rd antennal segment with small white ring, otherwise black. **HABITAT** Grasslands, the larvae developing in the roots of herbaceous plants. **SEASON** May to June.

***Agapanthia intermedia***
Body length: 7–13 mm. Looks blackish in the field, but with a bluish sheen. **HABITAT** Grasslands, the larvae developing in the roots of Field Scabious *Knautia arvensis*. **SEASON** May to August.

***Agapanthia irrorata***
Body length: 13–23 mm. Easily recognisable by the spotted wing-cases. Pronotun covered with many wrinkles. **HABITAT** Grasslands, the larvae developing in the roots of herbaceous plants. **SEASON** April to June.

***Agapanthia suturalis***
Body length: 6–13 mm. Distinctly slenderer tip to abdomen compared with the similar *A. cardui*; very yellowish pubescence. **HABITAT** Grasslands, the larvae developing in the roots of herbaceous plants. **SEASON** March to July.

***Agapanthia villosoviridescens* Golden-bloomed Grey Longhorn Beetle**
Body length: 10–22 mm. Elongate, dark grey with dense yellow or golden pubescence, also stripes on the head and pronotum. The antennae have black tips to segments. **HABITAT** Grasslands including chalky soils, where the larvae develop in stalks of various herbaceous plants, including thistle *Carduus*, *Angelica*, *Salvia* and nettle *Urtica*. **SEASON** May to September.

*Agapanthia annularis*

*Agapanthia asphodeli*

*Agapanthia cardui*

*Agapanthia cretica*

*Agapanthia cynarae*

*Agapanthia intermedia*

*Agapanthia irrorata*

*Agapanthia suturalis*

*Agapanthia villosoviridescens*

*Agapanthia annularis* mating pair

*Agapanthia asphodeli*

*Agapanthia cardui* mating pair

*Agapanthia cretica* [TB]

*Agapanthia cynarae* [TB]

*Agapanthia intermedia* [TB]

*Agapanthia irrorata*

*Agapanthia suturalis*

*Agapanthia villosoviridescens*

## Family Chrysomelidae – LEAF BEETLES

A large family which includes larger, often attractive leaf beetles, strikingly metallic or glossy in appearance. Flea beetles are generally small with enlarged hind femora, allowing them to leap away from predators, and the tortoise beetles, are a small group of species characterised by modified wing-cases and thorax which are flattened at their margins, hiding the head and most of the legs. The vast majority of leaf beetles feed on vegetation in various habitats. Some are regarded as pests where they are found on agricultural crops or garden herbs. *Donacia*, *Plateumaris* and few other species are the only aquatic leaf beetles. A selection of leaf beetle species is shown.

### *Donacia bicolora*

Body length: 8.5–11 mm. Greenish-gold, sometimes bluish in late season. **SEASON** May to September.

### *Donacia crassipes* Water-lily Reed Beetle

Body length: 9–11 mm. Purplish or copper, sometimes greenish; hind legs long and curved. **SEASON** May to early August.

### *Plateumaris sericea*

Body length: 7–10 mm. One of several metallic colours. Pronotum with fine, even punctures in mid-line. **HABITAT** Non-acidic aquatic sites, mainly on sedges *Carex*. **SEASON** March to December.

### *Oulema melanopus* Cereal Leaf Beetle

Body length: 4–5 mm. Thorax and legs reddish; head, antennae and wing-cases dark blue. **HABITAT** Agricultural sites and grasslands, where they damage cereal crops. **SEASON** All year.

### *Crioceris asparagi* Asparagus Beetle

Body length: 5–6 mm. Distinctive colours. **HABITAT** Wherever Asparagus grows; regarded as a pest in gardens and where grown commercially. Adults and larvae strip the outer bark from the stem and resulting areas become yellowish-brown. **SEASON** All year.

### *Lilioceris lilii* Lily beetle

Body length: 6–8 mm. Vivid red with black head and antennae. **HABITAT** Gardens where they may be regarded as a pest on lilies *Lilium*. **SEASON** All year.

### *Lachnaia paradoxa*

Body length: 6–12 mm. Black, red wing-cases with six bold black spots. **HABITAT** Woodlands. **SEASON** April to June.

### *Lachnaia variolosa*

Body length: 6–11 mm. Black, red wing-cases punctuated with large black spots. **HABITAT** Various areas with Mastic Tree *Pistacia lentiscus* bushes. **SEASON** April to June.

### *Tituboea sexmaculata*

Body length: 8–13 mm. Reddish-orange except for black at upper part of head and six black spots in all, often large. **HABITAT** Various. **SEASON** May to July.

*Donacia bicolora*

*Donacia crassipes*

*Plateumaris sericea*

*Oulema melanopus*

*Crioceris asparagi*

*Lilioceris lilii*

*Lachnaia paradoxa*

*Lachnaia variolosa*

*Tituboea sexmaculata*

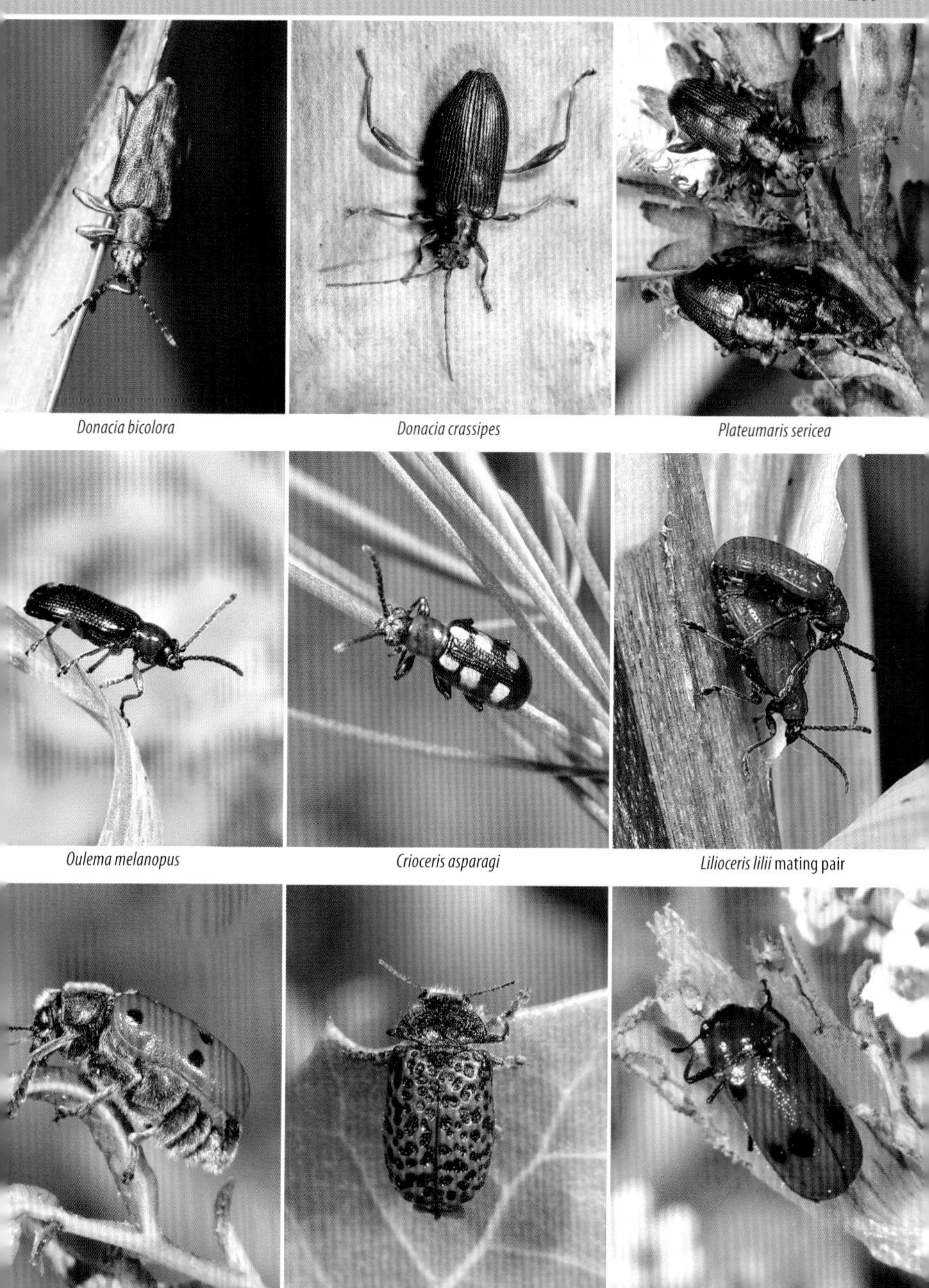

*Donacia bicolora*

*Donacia crassipes*

*Plateumaris sericea*

*Oulema melanopus*

*Crioceris asparagi*

*Lilioceris lilii* mating pair

*Lachnaia paradoxa*

*Lachnaia variolosa*

*Tituboea sexmaculata* [PC]

***Clytra anthraphaxidis***
Body length: 6–11 mm. Reddish-orange with bold black spots and blotches, including on pronotum. **HABITAT** Woodlands and others around willow *Salix*. **SEASON** June to July.

***Clytra quadripunctata***
Body length: 7–11 mm. Black; wing-cases yellowish red, each with two black spots. **HABITAT** Woodlands, near *Formica* ant nests, the larvae possibly feeding on debris in the nests. Adults feed on various leaves and flowers. **SEASON** April to December.

***Coptocephala scopolina***
Body length: 5–7 mm. Black head. Reddish-orange with bold black blotches on wing-cases. Legs black. **HABITAT** Various, on umbellifers. **SEASON** April to October.

***Cryptocephalus aureolus***
Body length: 6–8 mm. Metallic green, golden or bluish with coarse punctures on the pronotum. **HABITAT** Grasslands, often on yellow flowers. **SEASON** April to early September.

***Cryptocephalus bilineatus***
Body length: 2–3 mm. Pronotum black with yellow margins and often two yellow spots; wing-cases yellow with black longitudinal bands. **HABITAT** Calcareous grasslands, often on Oxeye Daisy *Leucanthemum vulgare*. **SEASON** May to September.

***Crypocephalus bipunctatus***
Body length: 4–6 mm. Wing-cases reddish with bold black spots, or in form *sanguinolentus* with black stripes. **HABITAT** Grasslands and woodlands where they may be found on various trees or on flowers. **SEASON** April to August.

***Cryptocephalus hypochaeridis***
Body length: 4–5.5 mm. As *C. aureolus* but noticeably smaller and with fine punctures on the pronotum. **HABITAT** Calcareous grasslands, often on yellow flowers. **SEASON** May to August.

***Cryptocephalus loreyi***
Body length: 7–9 mm. Largest European *Cryptocephalus* species. Black except for reddish wing-cases, which are black-blotched or spotted. **HABITAT** Grasslands. **SEASON** April to June.

***Cryptocephalus octoguttatus***
Body length: 3.5–5 mm. Black except for up to eight yellowish or orange spots (or blotches) on wing-cases, often also present laterally in centre of wing-cases, absent in the example illustrated. **HABITAT** Grasslands. **SEASON** May to July.

***Cryptocephalus octopunctatus***
Body length: 5–6 mm. Cream and black pronotum, Wing-cases reddish with up to eight large black spots, sometimes merged together. **HABITAT** Various including woodland edges on willow *Salix* and others. **SEASON** May to July.

*Clytra anthraphaxidis*

*Clytra quadripunctata*

*Coptocephala scopolina*

*Cryptocephalus aureolus*

*Cryptocephalus bilineatus*

*Cryptocephalus bipunctatus*

*Cryptocephalus hypochaeridis*

*Cryptocephalus loreyi*

*Cryptocephalus octoguttatus*

*Cryptocephalus octopunctatus*

*Clytra anthraphaxidis* [PC]

*Clytra quadripunctata*

*Coptocephala scopolina* mating pair [PC]

*Cryptocephalus aureolus*

*Cryptocephalus hypochaeridis*

*Cryptocephalus bilineatus* [TB]

*Cryptocephalus bipunctatus* (left), mating pair of form *sanguinolentus* (right)

*Cryptocephalus loreyi*

*Cryptocephalus octoguttatus* [PC]

*Cryptocephalus octopunctatus*

***Cryptocephalus rugicollis***
Body length: 4–5 mm. Black. Wing-cases yellowish with up to six large black spots or streaks, possibly merged. **HABITAT** Grasslands, often on yellow flowers. **SEASON** March to July.

***Cryptocephalus sericeus***
Body length: 5.5–7.5 mm. Metallic green, blue or golden, except black head and antennae. Similar to *C. aureolus* but pronotum longer and more convex with the punctuation finer and shallower. Coleopterists will usually dissect this and similar species to be certain. **HABITAT** Grasslands, often on yellow flowers. **SEASON** May to August.

***Cryptocephalus violaceus***
Body length: 4–7 mm. Metallic mauve or blue. **HABITAT** Grasslands. **SEASON** June to August.

***Cryptocephalus vittatus***
Body length: 4–4.5 mm. Black with characteristic yellowish bands on the wing-cases. **HABITAT** Grasslands, on Asteraceae. **SEASON** May to August.

***Timarcha asturiensis***
Body length: c.10 mm. Femora red except for black knees. **HABITAT** Open sites, restricted to northern and eastern Spain. **SEASON** May to July.

***Timarcha goettingensis* Small Bloody-nosed Beetle**
Body length: 8–11 mm. Rather smaller than the Bloody-nosed Beetle, more shiny and with dense, moderately-sized punctures. **HABITAT** Open sites on bedstraws and others. **SEASON** Late February to December.

***Timarcha gravis***
Body length: c.10 mm. Fairly smooth. **HABITAT** Open sites, restricted to parts of Andalusia, Spain. **SEASON** May to November.

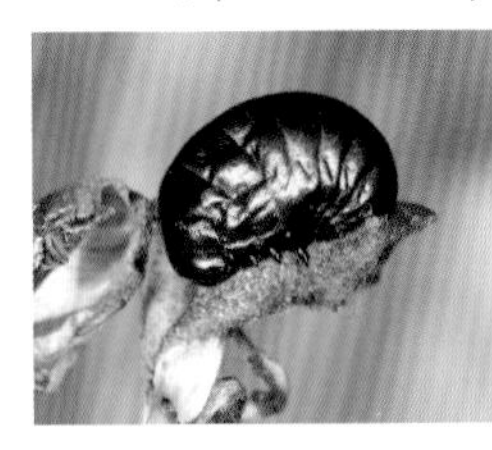

***Timarcha tenebricosa* Bloody-nosed Beetle**
Body length: 10–20 mm. Tiny punctures. Defends itself when disturbed by exuding a red fluid from its mouth, hence the vernacular name (the robust-looking larva is illustrated [left]). **HABITAT** Open sites feeding on leaves and stems of bedstraws *Galium* and others. **SEASON** All year.

***Chrysolina americana* Rosemary Beetle**
Body length: 6–8 mm. Metallic dark green with red stripes and markings on pronotum and wing-cases. **HABITAT** Parks, gardens and nurseries, feeding on *Rosemarinus*, *Lavendula* and *Thymus*. **SEASON** All year.

***Chrysolina banksii***
Body length: 6–12 mm. Metallic bronze. **HABITAT** Open sites feeding on Lamiaceae, mainly *Marrubium vulgare*. **SEASON** All year.

*Cryptocephalus rugicollis*

*Cryptocephalus sericeus*

*Cryptocephalus violaceus*

*Cryptocephalus vittatus*

*Timarcha asturiensis*

*Timarcha goettingensis*

*Timarcha gravis*

*Timarcha tenebricosa*

*Chrysolina americana*

*Chrysolina banksii*

*Cryptocephalus rugicollis*

*Cryptocephalus sericeus*

*Cryptocephalus violaceus* [PC]

*Cryptocephalus vittatus*

*Timarcha asturiensis*

*Timarcha goettingensis*

*Timarcha gravis* [TB]

*Chrysolina americana*

*Timarcha tenebricosa*

*Chrysolina banksii*

***Chrysolina cerealis*** **Rainbow Leaf Beetle**
Body length: 6–10 mm. Bands of metallic green, blue and red or gold. **HABITAT** Mountain grasslands mainly feeding on *Thymus serpyllum*. **SEASON** April to October.

*Chrysolina cerealis*

***Chrysolina fastuosa*** **Dead-nettle Leaf Beetle**
Body length: 5–6 mm. Metallic green or bronze, with bluish. **HABITAT** Mainly wetlands on Common Hemp-nettle *Galeopsis tetrahit* and dead-nettles *Lamium*. **SEASON** March to December.

*Chrysolina fastuosa*

***Chrysolina herbacea*** **Mint Leaf Beetle**
Body length: 7–11 mm. Metallic green, often with golden reflection. **HABITAT** Wetlands mainly on mint *Mentha*. **SEASON** March to October.

*Chrysolina herbacea*

***Chrysolina hyperici***
Body length: 5–7 mm. Dark metallic bronze or green. **HABITAT** Grasslands on St John's-wort *Hypericum*. **SEASON** All year.

*Chrysolina hyperici*

*Chrysolina hyperici* larva feeding on St John's-wort *Hypericum* leaves

***Chrysolina sanguinolenta*** **Toadflax Leaf Beetle**
Body length: 6–9 mm. Very local. Dark blue with yellowish-red margin. **HABITAT** Woodland clearings and edges on Common Toadflax *Linaria vulgaris*. **SEASON** March to October.

*Chrysolina sanguinolenta*

***Oreina alpestris***
Body length: 7–11 mm. Variable, metallic golden-green or bluish-green with margins and central part of wing-cases with a blue or purple band. Some specimens, as illustrated, with bold reddish bands in between. **HABITAT** Mountain grasslands 900 to 2,000 m on Apiaceae. **SEASON** June to July.

*Oreina alpestris*

***Oreina cacaliae***
Body length: 8–11 mm. Metallic blue, green or bluish-green. **HABITAT** Mountain grasslands 1,000 to 2,400 m on Asteraceae. **SEASON** May to August.

*Oreina cacaliae*

***Oreina speciosa***
Body length: 9–13 mm. Metallic golden-green or bluish-green, with the wing-case sutures and a band near the margins dark blue or violet. Head and pronotum often blue or black. Rather variable, sometimes with two golden or red bands (form *superba* and *excellens*). **HABITAT** Mountain grasslands on Apiaceae, including *Angelica sylvestris*. **SEASON** June to August.

*Oreina speciosa*

***Oreina speciosissima***
Body length: 6–9 mm. Metallic golden-green or bluish-green (sometimes very reddish), with the wing-case sutures and a band near the margins dark blue or violet. **HABITAT** Mountain grasslands 1,600 to 2,400 m on Asteraceae, particularly *Doronicum* species. **SEASON** July to August.

*Oreina speciosissima*

***Gastrophysa viridula*** **Green Dock Beetle**
Body length: 4–8 mm. Metallic golden-green, green, brassy or bronze, rarely blue. **HABITAT** Various on dock *Rumex*. The huge swollen abdomen is visible in impregnated ♀s. **SEASON** All year.

*Gastrophysa viridula*

*Chrysolina herbacea* mating pair

*Chrysolina cerealis*

*Chrysolina fastuosa* [PC]

*Chrysolina hyperici*

*Chrysolina sanguinolenta* [PC]

*Oreina alpestris*

*Oreina cacaliae* [PC]

*Oreina speciosa* [CG]

*Oreina speciosissima*

*Gastrophysa viridula*

Larvae of *Chrysomela populi* feeding on poplar *Populus* leaf

*Chrysomela populi*

*Gonioctena decemnotata*

*Galeruca tanaceti*

*Xanthogaleruca luteola*

*Exosoma lusitanicum*

*Agelastica alni*

*Crepidodera aurata*

*Cassida azurea*

*Cassida flaveola*

*Cassida viridis*

**_Chrysomela populi_ Red Poplar Leaf Beetle**
Body length: 10–12 mm. Metallic blue, greenish or black head and thorax, with red or reddish brown wing-cases with a dark spot at the tip. **HABITAT** Various, feeding on willow *Salix* and poplar *Populus*. **SEASON** April to September.

***Gonioctena decemnotata***
Body length: 5–7 mm. Mostly black head; wing-cases reddish brown or yellow with c.10 black spots; legs pale. **HABITAT** Open parts of woodlands and commons on Aspen *Populus tremula*, sometimes others. **SEASON** April to August.

***Galeruca tanaceti***
Body length: 6–11 mm. Black. **HABITAT** Grasslands on various plants. **SEASON** June to October. **SIMILAR SPECIES** ***G. monticola*** (6–12 mm) [not mapped], an uncommon mountain species in France and Spain, ♀ with yellow, instead of black tergites.

***Xanthogaleruca luteola***
Body length: 5.5–7 mm. Yellowish, head, pronotum and wing-cases with dark streaks. **HABITAT** Various, often in numbers on young elm *Ulmus minor* trees. **SEASON** April to September.

***Exosoma lusitanicum***
Body length: 6.5–10 mm. Head, legs and antennae black, otherwise yellowish or reddish-brown, with some brownish markings. **HABITAT** Grasslands on various flowers. **SEASON** May to August.

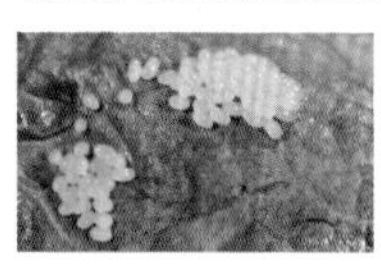

**_Agelastica alni_ Alder Leaf Beetle**
Body length: 6–7 mm. Deep bluish-violet, rarely black or copper. **HABITAT** Woodlands and others, the adults and larvae mainly feeding on alder *Alnus* (eggs pictured left). **SEASON** April to September.

***Crepidodera aurata***
Body length: 2–4 mm. Pronotum reddish, wing-cases bright metallic green. One of the so-called flea beetles, able to jump. **HABITAT** Various on willow *Salix*, poplar *Populus* and others. **SEASON** All year.

***Cassida azurea***
Body length: 4–7 mm. Often reddish inner part of wing-cases, but variable. **HABITAT** Grasslands, on Bladder Campion *Silene vulgaris*. **SEASON** May to August.

***Cassida flaveola***
Body length: 4–6 mm. Dull brownish-yellow or pale yellow; wing-cases often with dark spots. **HABITAT** Various on the pink family (Caryophyllaceae). **SEASON** All year.

**_Cassida viridis_ Green Tortoise Beetle**
Body length: 7–10 mm. Green. **HABITAT** Various on mints *Mentha*, dead-nettles *Lamium* and others. **SEASON** Mainly April to October.

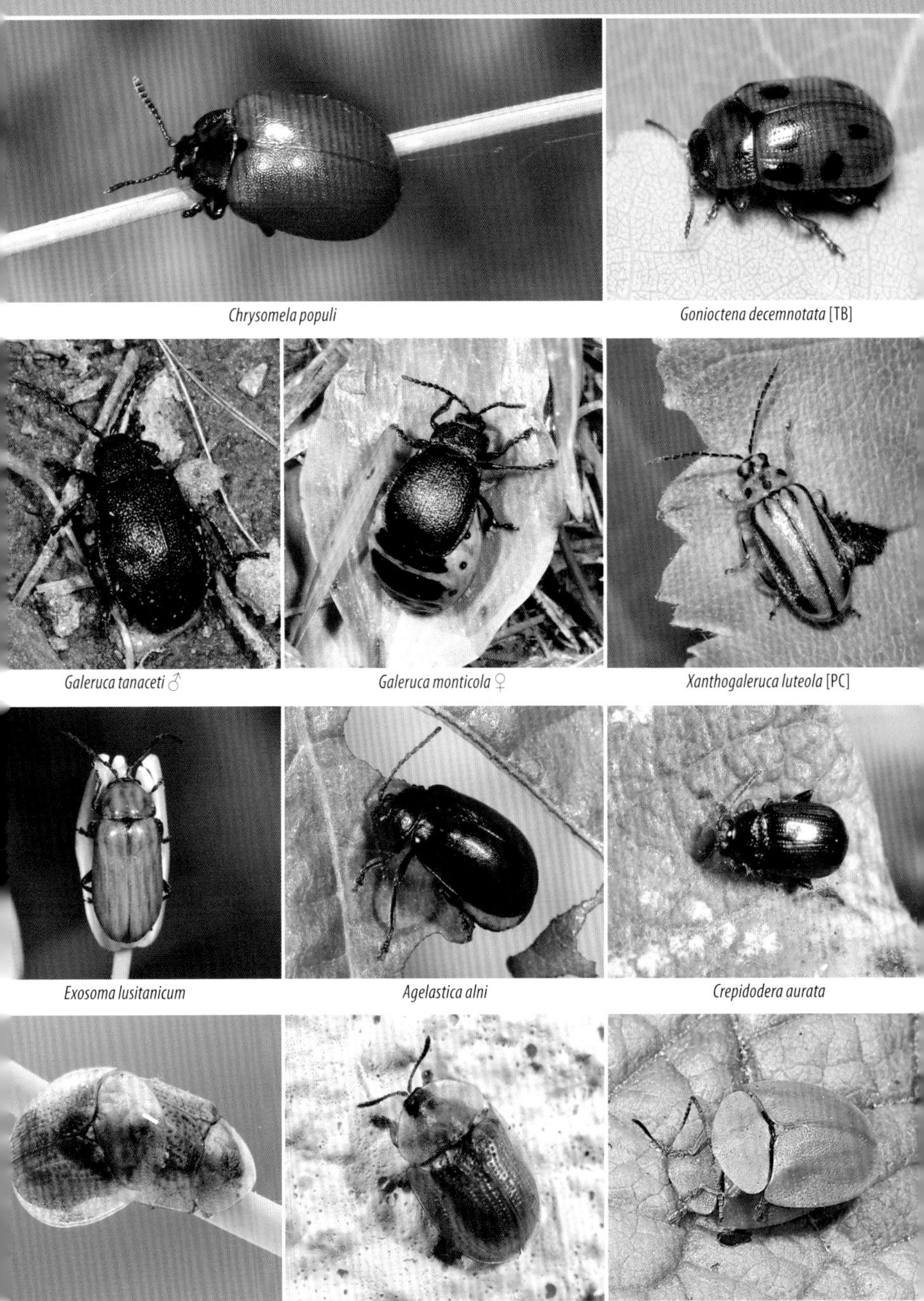

*Chrysomela populi*

*Gonioctena decemnotata* [TB]

*Galeruca tanaceti* ♂

*Galeruca monticola* ♀

*Xanthogaleruca luteola* [PC]

*Exosoma lusitanicum*

*Agelastica alni*

*Crepidodera aurata*

*Cassida azurea* [NR]

*Cassida flaveola*

*Cassida viridis* mating pair

**WEEVILS** – The beetles section concludes with several families of weevils, characterised by an elongate rostrum (snout) on the head, which has mouthparts, the latter used for cutting into plant tissues for egglaying. Most weevils feed on plants, although a few specialise on decaying wood and fungi, or are predators. Some are considered to be pests of trees and crops.

## Family Anthribidae – FUNGUS WEEVILS

This small family includes some stunning larger more primitive weevils, most species feeding on fungi or fungoid wood.

***Platyrhinus resinosus* Cramp-ball Fungus Weevil**
Body length: 7–15 mm. Black and brownish or grey, with same paler areas on head and tip of wing-cases. **HABITAT** Woodlands, including mountainous areas, where the larvae often remain on fallen beech *Fagus* and other stumps and logs, feeding on fungus, often *Daldinia concentrica*. **SEASON** May to September.

***Platystomos albinus***
Body length: 7–10 mm. Blackish brown, much more whitish areas than *Platyrhinus*, notably tip of wing-cases and bands on tibiae. **HABITAT** Woodlands, on various dead and decaying trees, often beech *Fagus*. **SEASON** May to September.

## Family Rhynchitidae – TOOTH-NOSED SNOUT WEEVILS

A small family of mainly metallic-coloured weevils in which the ♀ often rolls a leaf to provide shelter and food for the developing larvae.

***Byctiscus betulae***
Body length: 4-5.5 mm. Metallic golden-green, sometimes crimson or dark bronze. Rostrum oblong, tooth-nosed. **HABITAT** On poplar, where the ♀ rolls the decaying part of a leaf, laying several eggs inside. **SEASON** Mid May to June.

## Family Attelabidae – LEAF-ROLLING WEEVILS

The antennae are located near the base of the rostrum. The ♀ lays eggs through a slit cut into leaves and rolls the part of the leaf in which the larvae feed.

***Apoderus coryli* Hazel Leaf-roller Weevil**
Body length: 6–8 mm. Easily recognised by its black head and narrow neck. Wing-cases red. **HABITAT** Woodlands, on hazel *Corylus*. **SEASON** April to September. **SIMILAR SPECIES** ***Attelabus nitens* Oak Leaf-roller Weevil** (4–6 mm), found in woodlands on oak *Quercus*, lacks such a distinctive neck. Pronotum and wing-cases red; rarely black.

## Family Apionidae – APIONID WEEVILS

A large family of small, plant-feeding, fairly elongate weevils which are mostly uniformly black, grey or blue in colour. However, there are several red species.

***Apion frumentarium***
Body length: 3–4 mm. Red. **HABITAT** Grasslands, including mountains, on *Rumex*, the larvae developing in galls. **SEASON** May to October.

*Platyrhinus resinosus*

*Platystomos albinus*

*Byctiscus betulae*

*Apoderus coryli*

*Attelabus nitens*

*Apion frumentarium*

*Perapion violaceum*

*Rhynchophorus ferrugineus*

***Perapion violaceum***
Body length: 3–4 mm. Wing-cases bluish or black. **HABITAT** Grasslands including mountains, on *Rumex*. **SEASON** April to October.

## Family Dryophthoridae – DRYOPHTHORID WEEVILS

A small family of small to large species, notably including a well-known pest species, discussed below.

***Rhynchophorus ferrugineus* Red Palm Weevil**
Body length: c. 30 mm. Typical form reddish with some black marks on the pronotum. **HABITAT** Coastal and other areas wherever palm trees are grown. Since reaching the Mediterranean in the 1980s, this species has expanded and is considered a major pest. Larvae burrow into the palms; infected palms wilt and some die, decimating some historic parks and beach resorts. **SEASON** April to October.

*Platyrhinus resinosus*

*Platystomos albinus*

*Byctiscus betulae* [PC]

*Apoderus coryli*

*Attelabus nitens* [TP]

*Apion frumentarium*

*Perapion violaceum*

*Rhynchophorus ferrugineus* [MR] (left), palm weevil damage (right)

## Family Curculionidae – TRUE WEEVILS

The largest family after rove beetles. The snout or rostrum length taken to an extreme in some species. A small selection of species is shown. Many of the species in this family present a challenge to the entomologist.

### *Curculio glandium* Acorn Weevil

Body length: 4–7.5 mm. Elongated snout. **HABITAT** Woodlands, often on oak *Quercus*, where the larvae develop in acorns. **SEASON** April to December.

*Curculio glandium*

### *Curculio nucum* Nut Weevil

Body length: 6–8 mm. Broader segments at the tip of the antenna and the segments are covered in bristles. **HABITAT** Woodlands, on hazel *Corylus*. **SEASON** April to November.

*Curculio nucum*

### *Orchestes pilosus*

Body length: 3–4 mm. Wing-cases black with variable markings, often brown and whitish. **HABITAT** Woodlands on oak *Quercus*. **SEASON** March to October.

*Orchestes pilosus*

### *Mogulones geographicus*

Body length: c.3 mm. White scales forming map-like pattern. **HABITAT** Grasslands on *Echium*. **SEASON** April to October.

*Mogulones geographicus*

### *Cionus hortulanus*

Body length: c.4 mm. Black, with paler markings. Wing-cases with near central large black spot and another near the tip. Legs dark brown except femora blackish. **HABITAT** Gardens and others, often abundant on figwort *Scrophularia* (larva pictured left) and mullein *Verbascum*. **SEASON** May to November.

*Cionus hortulanus*

### *Cionus scrophulariae* Figwort Weevil

Body length: 3.5–5 mm. Similar to C. hortulanus, but thorax covered with whitish or yellowish hairs. **HABITAT** Gardens and others, often abundant on figwort *Scrophularia*. **SEASON** April to November.

*Cionus scrophulariae*

### *Otiorhynchus armadillo* Armadillo Weevil

Body length: 7–12 mm. Black with brownish markings, similar to *O. sulcatus*, but less robust. **HABITAT** Gardens, parks and others, on various shrubs, including alder *Alnus*. **SEASON** Late April to early July.

*Otiorhynchus armadillo*

### *Otiorhynchus morio*

Body length: 9–15 mm. Black, punctures on wing-cases. **HABITAT** Grasslands and others, mainly in mountains to subalpine or alpine zones, on roots of various plants. Also in wetlands. **SEASON** May to September.

*Otiorhynchus morio*

### *Otiorhynchus singularis* Clay-coloured Weevil

Body length: 6-8 mm. Black with brown and yellowish scales. Pronotum and wing-cases with numerous tubercles. **HABITAT** Mixed woodlands. Although parthenogenetic in some areas i.e. no ♂s, both sexes are known in southern France. **SEASON** All year.

*Otiorhynchus singularis*

### *Otiorhynchus sulcatus* Vine Weevil

Body length: 7–10 mm. Pronotum with many tubercles. Antennae and tarsi brownish. **HABITAT** Various, including gardens where it is known as a pest to gardeners, the larvae feeding beneath the soil in the roots of many plants, including ornamental plants and fruits. Reproduces parthenogenetically (♀s only). **SEASON** May to August.

*Otiorhynchus sulcatus*

*Curculio glandium*

*Curculio nucum*

*Orchestes pilosus*

*Cionus scrophulariae* mating pair [PC]

*Mogulones geographicus*

*Cionus hortulanus*

*Otiorhynchus armadillo* mating pair

*Otiorhynchus morio* [PC]

*Otiorhynchus singularis*

*Otiorhynchus sulcatus*

***Otiorhynchus tenebricosus* Red-legged Weevil**
Body length: 9–15 mm. Black with reddish legs, although there are various forms. **HABITAT** Grasslands, often calcareous. **SEASON** March to October.

*Otiorhynchus tenebricosus*

***Phyllobius pomaceus* Green Nettle Weevil**
Body length: 7–9 mm. As with all the green species in the genus *Phyllobius*, the colour comes from dense scales which may rub off over time, leaving a dark body colour, thus making identification more difficult. **HABITAT** Various, on nettle *Urtica* and *Filipendula*. **SEASON** April to July.

*Phyllobius pomaceus*

***Polydrusus pterygomalis***
Body length: 4–5.5 mm. Black, with dense golden-green scales. Legs orange. **HABITAT** Woodlands. **SEASON** May to September.

*Polydrusus pterygomalis*

***Liophloeus tessulatus***
Body length: 7–13 mm. Robust brown, spotted, short-winged (flightless). **HABITAT** Woodlands and others, including mountainous areas around roots of ivy *Hedera*, hogweed *Heracleum* and many others, sometimes reproducing parthenogenetically. **SEASON** Late March to August.

*Liophloeus tessulatus*

***Leucomigus tesselatus***
Body length: 9–15 mm. Brown, with numerous whitish spots and markings. **HABITAT** Mountainous areas including Sierra Nevada. **SEASON** Mid July to mid September.

*Leucomigus tesselatus*

***Larinus carlinae***
Body length: 5–9 mm. Black, grey pubescence on wing-cases. **HABITAT** Grasslands, including coastal, often on thistles *Cirsium* and *Carduus*, where larvae develop in the flowerheads. **SEASON** April to September.

*Larinus carlinae*

***Rhinocyllus conicus***
Body length: 4–7 mm. Black, pale pubescence forms mottled pattern on wing-cases; snout shorter than in *Larinus carlinae*. **HABITAT** Grasslands, often on thistles *Cirsium* and *Carduus*, where larvae develop in the flowerheads. **SEASON** May to October.

*Rhinocyllus conicus*

***Lixus scabricollis***
Body length: 4–6 mm. Local. Black, pale pubescence forms mottled pattern on wing-cases; snout shorter than in *Larinus planus* and some other *Lixus* species, but identification of *Lixus* species can be problematical. **HABITAT** Where coastal, often feeding on Sea Beet *Beta maritima* and Beet *B. vulgaris*. **SEASON** March to November.

*Lixus scabricollis*

***Liparus glabrirostris***
Body length: 17–21 mm. Black, with a variable number of orange spots. Europe's largest species of weevil. **HABITAT** Mountainous areas from the Pyrenees to the Carpathians, to 2,000 m.; often feeding on vegetation such as Butturbur *Petasites hybridus* close to streams and rivers. **SEASON** June to August.

*Liparus glabrirostris*

***Hylobius abietis* Pine Weevil**
Body length: 8–13 mm. Dark, with brownish-orange markings. **HABITAT** Coniferous woodlands, where the larvae live in dead stumps of pine *Pinus* and spruce *Picea*. Adults may be seen on log piles. Considered a major pest of young conifer stands. **SEASON** All year.

*Hylobius abietis*

*Otiorhynchus tenebricosus*

*Phyllobius pomaceus* [PC]

*Polydrusus pterygomalis* [PC]

*Liophloeus tessulatus*

*Leucomigus tesselatus*

*Larinus carlinae* [TB]

*Rhinocyllus conicus*

*Lixus scabricollis*

*Liparus glabrirostris* [PC]

*Hylobius abietis*

# Order STREPSIPTERA – TWISTED-WING PARASITES

**Southern Europe & Mediterranean: many of Europe's 32 species**

Twisted-wing parasites (also known as strepsipterans or stylops) are a group of small, internal parasitoids of aculeate Hymenoptera (mainly bees and wasps) or Homoptera (planthoppers), which are rarely encountered. Adult ♂s have large bulging compound eyes and do not live long, but may be encountered in flight; they have conspicuous large hindwings, but tiny drum-stick forewings. In contrast, the larger ♀s are grub-like, remaining in the host, even when mating. The life cycle is egg, larva, pupa and adult. Pupation occurs within the host. Newly-hatched larvae (triungulins) rest on flowers visited by the host, hoping to attach themselves to a suitable host.

## Family Stylopidae

### *Stylops melittae*

Body length: 1–6 mm. Wingless ♀s brown, ♂s black with transparent wings.
**HABITAT** Grasslands, gardens and places where host bees occur.
**SEASON** March to May.

*Stylops melittae*

# Order DIPTERA – FLIES

**Southern Europe & Mediterranean: many of Europe's c.19,400 species**

Flies are a large order, with probably in the region of 160,000 species worldwide. In Europe there are tiny midges less than 1 mm long to a cranefly with a 60 mm wingspan. Whilst flies may have a bad reputation, being associated with rotting flesh and disease, as well as being a nuisance for 'biting' people, some have amazing colours and are an attractive part of our insect fauna, with many beneficial as pollinators, or by eating aphids. Diptera means 'two-winged' which applies to most species, although they do have a pair of tiny pin-shaped hindwings, known as halteres. A small number of flies completely lack wings. In all cases the life history is one of complete metamorphosis, so adults lay eggs which hatch into larvae, legless maggots, some with biting jaws, others without, as they may just suck up liquids. The larva forms a pupa, before the adult emerges. Some larvae are beneficial, including maggots which are still used in some hospitals to clean wounds, eating the dead tissue. More typically, the maggots of many species break down organic material, for example feeding in rotting wood, fungi, decaying flesh, flowers, seedheads and dung. Some live in the soil or water; others are leaf miners, or are parasites of larvae or predators. Adults lack jaws; mouthparts are designed to suck moisture or nectar, although this is adapted in some species for piercing surfaces to suck blood. The relatively few dipterists (specialists studying flies) means that most families are not well researched in Europe, except for popular groups such as hoverflies, so many species are as yet undescribed. Flies are particularly conspicuous to the public when visiting flowers. The coverage in this book is a small selection of the ordinary, spectacular and rare species; hence few families are included. Whilst many of the species included are distinctive, numerous flies are small and difficult or impossible to identify with certainty in the field.
**HOTSPOTS** For a wide range of species, try river valleys or by streams, where there are plentiful flowers. There are c.6,000 recorded species of flies in Spain.

**Spain: Serranía de Ronda.** Rivers, mainly the Genal, the Guadiaro and their tributaries, form a rich ecosystem attractive to many flies. Representatives of the families Conopidae, Syrphidae, Tachinidae and many others occur on riverside flowers in abundance, in addition to other insect orders.

*Stylops melittae* ♂ [JS]

*Stylops melittae* mating pair on *Andrena vaga* [JS]

*Stylops* ♀ parasite on *Andrena carantonica*

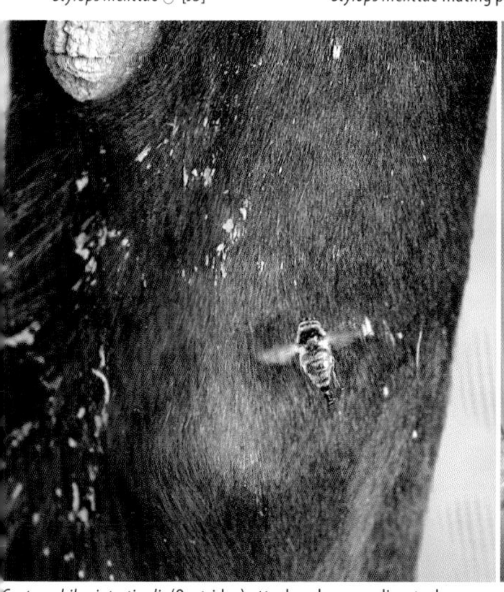

*Gasterophilus intestinalis* (Oestridae) attack and eggs on livestock

*Trichopida pennipes* mating pair (Tachinidae) [PC]

A *Lomatia* sp. (Bombyliidae) egglaying [PC]

*Eristalis tenax* larva (Syrphidae)

# Suborder Nematocera

**CRANEFLIES** – small to large, slim-bodied craneflies known as 'Daddy Long Legs', with long legs. In size species range from only having a wingspan of a few millimetres to the Giant Cranefly *Tipula maxima* with a wingspan of c.60 mm. Adults have reduced mouthparts but some feed on flowers; larvae of the large craneflies are sometimes known as 'leather jackets' and live in soil; a few attack roots but most feed on decaying leaf-litter or sometimes in moss or decaying wood and many are aquatic. Several families of flies count as craneflies. The larger species mostly belong to the families shown below and are often recognised by their distinct wing pattern. Habitats include grasslands, gardens, wetlands and woodlands, often in damper places. Craneflies fly by day or at night and are sometimes attracted to lights.

## Family Tipulidae – LONG-PALPED CRANEFLIES

### *Ctenophora pectinicornis*

Wing length: 15–19 mm. Attractive large black and yellow wasp-mimicking cranefly, ♀s with short ovipositors. Species are known as combe-horns due to the feathery antennae, toothed in ♀s. **HABITAT** Woodlands, where the larvae develop mainly in fallen beech *Fagus*. **SEASON** May to June.

### *Tipula maxima* Giant Cranefly

Wing length: 22–30 mm. Large (body length c.38 mm, leg span c.100 mm), dark pattern on wings. **HABITAT** Mainly woodlands. **SEASON** April to August.

*Ctenophora pectinicornis*

## Family Pediciidae – HAIRY-EYED CRANEFLIES

### *Pedicia rivosa*

Wing length: 20–24 mm. Characteristic wing pattern. **HABITAT** Various, including grasslands. **SEASON** April to September.

*Tipula maxima*

## Family Limoniidae – SHORT-PALPED CRANEFLIES

### *Metalimnobia quadrimaculata*

Wing length: 17–21 mm. Heavily spotted wings. **HABITAT** Woodlands. **SEASON** April to August.

*Pedicia rivosa*

## Family Bibionidae – ST MARK'S FLIES

St Mark's flies are well-known, black hairy flies, from spring (St Marks' Day is on 25 April), sometimes seen in swarms, with legs dangling; ♂s have particularly large eyes. The larvae live in the soil in rotting vegetation.

### *Bibio hortulanus*

Body length: 8–14 mm. ♀ with orange abdomen and red thorax. **HABITAT** Grasslands and others. **SEASON** April to May.

*Metalimnobia quadrimaculata*

### *Bibio marci*

Body length: 10–15 mm. **HABITAT** Grasslands and others. **SEASON** April to June.

*Bibio hortulanus*

## Family Culicidae – MOSQUITOES

Mostly small to medium-sized flies, of which ♀s have piercing mouthparts. Mainly tropical mosquitoes have a bad reputation for being vectors of serious diseases, including malaria. The larvae do well in damper habitats, as they feed on detritus, bacteria and algae in shallow stagnant water. A few species are predators. Adult hosts include vertebrates and large numbers can be a nuisance biting livestock and humans, although it is only the ♀s which feed on blood. By contrast, ♂s drink nectar.

*Bibio marci*

### *Culex pipiens*

Body length: c.6 mm. ♀ with orange abdomen and red thorax. **HABITAT** Various, often with the largest proportion of pools in rural areas; often enters houses. This species is known to be a vector of West Nile virus, first reported in Europe in the 1960s. **SEASON** July to October.

*Culex pipiens*

*Ctenophora pectinicornis* ♀

*Pedicia rivosa*

*Tipula maxima* mating pair, ♀ top

*Metalimnobia quadrimaculata*

*Culex pipiens*

*Bibio hortulanus* ♂ (top), ♀ (bottom) [both SO]

*Bibio marci* mating pair, ♀ top

# Suborder Brachycera

## Family Rhagionidae – SNIPEFLIES

Easily recognisable, small to large flies with long abdomen, legs and wings. The larvae mainly develop as predators in soil and wood detritus. When fresh, the golden hairs of the thorax are conspicuous but they soon rub off.

### *Rhagio scolopaceus* Downlooker Snipefly

Body length: 8–16 mm. Spotted wings. **HABITAT** Woodlands, in characteristic pose upside down on tree trunks. **SEASON** May to August.

## Family Vermileonidae – WORMLION FLIES

Historically included in the Rhagionidae, larvae of this small family are called wormlions (a translation of Vermileo), as they make cone-shaped pits in the ground in sandy areas to attract insects i.e. rather like the unrelated antlions. The trapped insects are eaten.

### *Lampromyia iberica*

Body length: c.13 mm. Pale, wings with sparse brown marks around some veins (the other European species, ***L. funebris*** [not illustrated] is dark). **HABITAT** Open sandy, arid sites, but distribution in Spain rather uncertain. **SEASON** April to June.

## Family Tabanidae – HORSEFLIES

Stout, medium to large flies with large eyes. ♀s have a piercing proboscis and feed on blood of mammals including humans, so it is not surprising they are well represented in areas with plentiful grazing livestock. Sometimes found resting on fences, gates or flowers. The larvae are aquatic, semi-aquatic or live in soil and litter. Parking in a choice spot by vegetation can be productive. The doors can be left open hopefully leading to horseflies flying into the car, which is seen as a large, hot object. The flies can then be placed in a small container, examined and then released.

### *Chrysops caecutiens* Splayed Deerfly

Body length: 9–10 mm. ♀ with stunning eyes; splayed black inverted 'V' mark on 2nd abdominal segment. ♂ abdomen black. **HABITAT** Wet woodlands and shaded wetlands. ♀s feed on the blood of mammals including humans. The larvae feed on decaying vegetation. **SEASON** May to September.

### *Haematopota pluvialis* Notch-horned Cleg

Body length: 8–11.5 mm. Drab brown appearance (♀ eyes pictured left [PC]. A voracious biter, this species is often found to be the culprit. **HABITAT** Various, including coastal areas. **SEASON** May to October.

### *Dasyrhamphis atra*

Body length: 17–19 mm. Large dark species, including wings. The similar ***D. anthracinus*** [not illustrated] has a clear area on wings, also whitish spots on hind part of some abdominal segments. **HABITAT** Grasslands, often resting on vegetation. **SEASON** May to June.

### *Philipomyia aprica*

Body length: c.18 mm. Green-eyed species. Brown hairy thorax, black abdominal bands. **HABITAT** Prefers hills and mountains, often observed nectaring on flowers. **SEASON** June to September.

### *Tabanus sudeticus* Dark Giant Horsefly

Body length: 21–24 mm. Large, dark species, with orange antennae base and black abdominal bands. **HABITAT** Various including woodland edges and mountains. **SEASON** June to September.

*Rhagio scolopaceus*

*Lampromyia iberica*

*Lampromyia funebris*

*Chrysops caecutiens*

*Haematopota pluvialis*

*Dasyrhamphis atra*

*Dasyrhamphis anthracinus*

*Philipomyia aprica*

*Tabanus sudeticus*

*Lampromyia iberica* [SO]

*Rhagio scolopaceus*

*Chrysops caecutiens*

*Dasyrhamphis atra*

*Haematopota pluvialis*

*Philipomyia aprica*

*Tabanus sudeticus*

## Family Stratiomyidae – SOLDIERFLIES

Small to large flies, usually with striking coloration (hence the name soldierflies after brightly coloured ceremonial uniforms of some soldiers). Various habitats from woodland to waterside or coast, on flowers or vegetation. The larvae are aquatic or terrestrial, feeding on algae or decaying vegetable matter. A few larger species are illustrated.

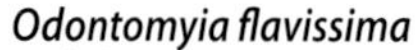

### *Odontomyia flavissima*

Body length: c.10 mm. Conspicuous blue striped eyes; orange and black abdomen. **HABITAT** Wetlands. **SEASON** May to July.

### *Stratiomys longicornis* Long-horned General

Body length: 12.5 mm. Drabber than most species, lacking yellow markings; hairy eyes. **HABITAT** Wetlands, particularly coastal. **SEASON** May to July.

### *Stratiomys potamida* Banded General

Body length: 12.5 mm. One of several bold yellow and black species **HABITAT** Usually seen nectaring on umbellifers or sitting on vegetation in or around wetlands. **SEASON** May to September.

## Family Acroceridae – SMALL-HEADED FLIES

Small-headed Flies are a small family of small, rather strange-looking, hump-backed flies, which are endoparasitoids of spiders.

### *Cyrtus gibbus*

Body length: c.7 mm. Black with bold yellow bands and markings. Covered in fine hairs. **HABITAT** Various where the hosts live, including mountainous areas. **SEASON** June to September.

## Family Bombyliidae – BEE-FLIES

Bee-flies are small to large, broad bee-like insects, often with a long proboscis. They are parasitoids of solitary bees and wasps and sometimes other insects, with offspring eating larvae. Frequently found hovering around nectar sources, resting on vegetation or near bee nesting sites. Whilst some species are very similar, often wing patterns or abdominal markings help with identification.

### *Parageron gratus*

Body length: c.4 mm. ♂ dark with plain wings, ♀ larger with several narrow yellow transverse abdominal bands. **HABITAT** Mountains, for example Sierra Nevada. **SEASON** May to June.

### *Toxophora fasciculata*

Body length: c.7 mm. Recognised by its distinctive shape and long antennae; thorax with long black hairs. **HABITAT** Hot dry areas, often visits flowers including mint *Mentha*. **SEASON** May to September.

### *Bombylius cruciatus*

Body length: 12–15 mm. Abdomen with two transverse whitish bands and darker bands; also ♂ with a longitudinal white line on the thorax, often continuing to abdomen. **HABITAT** Grasslands. **SEASON** May to June.

### *Bombylius discolor* Dotted Bee-fly

Body length: 8–16 mm. Dotted wings, underside of body with yellowish hair. Row of white dots on ♀ abdomen. **HABITAT** Grasslands. **SEASON** March to June.

### *Bombylius fimbriatus*

Body length: 8–12 mm. Dark area near tip of wings, with narrow translucent areas. **HABITAT** Grasslands. **SEASON** March to June.

### *Bombylius medius*

Body length: 8–13 mm. Dotted wings, similar to *B. discolor* but underside of body with black hair. **HABITAT** Grasslands. **SEASON** April to July.

*Odontomyia flavissima*

*Stratiomys longicornis*

*Stratiomys potamida*

*Cyrtus gibbus*

*Parageron gratus*

*Toxophora fasciculata*

*Bombylius cruciatus*

*Bombylius discolor*

*Bombylius fimbriatus*

*Bombylius medius*

*Odontomyia flavissima* [TB]

*Stratiomys longicornis*

*Stratiomys potamida*

*Cyrtus gibbus* [PC]

*Parageron gratus*, ♂ top and ♀ bottom [SO]

*Toxophora fasciculata* [SO]

*Bombylius cruciatus* ♂ (left), ♀ (right) [both SO]

*Bombylius fimbriatus* [SO]

*Bombylius discolor* ♂ (left), ♀ (right) [both PC]

*Bombylius medius* [SO]

### *Anthrax anthrax*
Body length: 7–13 mm. More than two thirds of wing surface darkened; abdomen black with whitish hair patches on abdominal segments 2 and 3, and at tip. **HABITAT** Various, including urban areas; a parasitoid on mason bees *Osmia*, which often nest in walls or wood. **SEASON** May to August.

### *Anthrax binotatus*
Body length: 8–10 mm. Minimal markings on wings, two clear spots near centre. **HABITAT** Grasslands. **SEASON** July to August.

### *Anthrax trifasciatus*
Body length: 6–11 mm. Less than half of wing surface darkened; spotting away from basal area varied, usually with two to three spots (sometimes absent). **HABITAT** Grasslands. **SEASON** June to September.

### *Anthrax virgo*
Body length: 5–9 mm. Small, distinctive area (more than half of wing surface) darkened. **HABITAT** Grasslands. **SEASON** June to July.

### *Balaana grandis*
Body length: 15–18 mm. Large easily recognised species, with several abdominal stripes. Wings with dark brown markings [until recently placed in the genus *Exoprosopa*]. **HABITAT** Grasslands and woodland edge. **SEASON** June to August.

### *Exoprosopa capucina*
Body length: 9–14 mm. Dark pattern reaching hind border of wings. Final abdominal segments pale. **HABITAT** Grasslands, including mountains. **SEASON** May to July.

### *Exoprosopa jacchus*
Body length: 9–15 mm. Similar to *E. capucina* but dark pattern not reaching hind border of wings. **HABITAT** Grasslands. **SEASON** June to September.

*Exoprosopa jacchus* mating pair [SO]

### *Exoprosopa rivularis*
Body length: 11–16 mm. Distinctive dark areas on wings; light brown patches on well banded abdominal segments. **HABITAT** Open areas. **SEASON** May to August.

### *Exoprosopa rutila*
Body length: 12–14 mm. Conspicuous orange areas on upper part of thorax and wings; abdomen black but ♂s with white band and spots. **HABITAT** Various. **SEASON** June to August.

### *Exhyalanthrax muscarius*
Body length: 8–10 mm. White lateral bands on thorax; whitish scutellum. **HABITAT** Various, including coastal sand dunes. **SEASON** May to August.

*Anthrax anthrax*

*Anthrax binotatus*

*Anthrax trifasciatus*

*Anthrax virgo*

*Balaana grandis*

*Exoprosopa capucina*

*Exoprosopa jacchus*

*Exoprosopa rivularis*

*Exoprosopa rutila*

*Exhyalanthrax muscarius*

*Anthrax anthrax* [SO]

*Anthrax binotatus* [SO]

*Anthrax trifasciatus* [SO]

*Anthrax virgo* [SO]

*Balaana grandis*

*Exoprosopa capucina*

*Exoprosopa jacchus* [PC]

*Exoprosopa rivularis* [SO]

*Exoprosopa rutila* [SO]

*Exhyalanthrax muscarius* [SO]

### *Hemipenthes maura*
Body length: 8–14 mm. Dark area extensive, compare pattern with *H. velutina*. Lateral margin of thorax with yellowish or whitish hair. **HABITAT** Woodland edges and others. **SEASON** April to August.

### *Hemipenthes morio*
Body length: 9–14 mm. Dark area extending to nearer tip of wings. **HABITAT** Coastal dunes and inland sandy sites. **SEASON** May to August.

### *Hemipenthes velutina*
Body length: 9–14 mm. Dark area extending to nearer tip of wings compared with *H. morio*; lacks yellowish or whitish hair on lateral margin on thorax. **HABITAT** Coastal sand dunes and inland sandy sites. **SEASON** May to September.

### *Thyridanthrax elegans*
Body length: 6–11 mm. *Thyridanthrax* species have subtle wing pattern differences which help to identify them to species level. Large hyaline panels on wings; one pale abdominal band. **HABITAT** Grasslands. **SEASON** June to August.

### *Thyridanthrax hispanus*
Body length: c.10 mm. Two pale central abdominal bands. Wings dark, minimal hyaline panels. **HABITAT** Grasslands. **SEASON** April to July.

### *Thyridanthrax perspicillaris*
Body length: c.12 mm. Two pale central abdominal bands. Wings dark, with large clear hyaline panels. **HABITAT** Grasslands, a parasitoid of spechid wasps, also grasshopper eggs. **SEASON** July to August.

### *Villa abbadon*
Body length: 5–6.5 mm. Abdomen bright, well banded; hind part of thorax yellowish in centre. **HABITAT** Grasslands.**SEASON** April to August.

### *Villa hottentotta*
Body length: 10–20 mm. Black abdominal banding on sexes differs; one of several similarly marked species. **HABITAT** Grasslands, a parasitoid of spechid wasps. **SEASON** July to August.

### *Villa ixion*
Body length: 7–8 mm. Abdomen with plenty of whitish hair in ♂s. **HABITAT** Grasslands. **SEASON** May to August.

### *Villa melanura*
Body length: 7–8 mm. Distinctive black with orange areas on thorax and laterally on upper abdomen. **HABITAT** Various, including mountainous areas such as Sierra Nevada, Spain. **SEASON** July to August.

The coastal sands and dunes at **Mas Larrieu Reserve Naturelle, Roussillon, France**, are home to many species of bee-fly. [PC]

*Hemipenthes maura*

*Hemipenthes morio*

*Hemipenthes velutina*

*Thyridanthrax elegans*

*Thyridanthrax hispanus*

*Thyridanthrax perspicillaris*

*Villa abbadon*

*Villa hottentotta*

*Villa ixion*

*Villa melanura*

*Hemipenthes maura*

*Hemipenthes morio* [PC]

*Hemipenthes velutina*

*Thyridanthrax elegans*

*Thyridanthrax hispanus* [SO]

*Thyridanthrax perspicillaris* [SO]

*Villa hottentotta* ♂ (left), ♀ (right) [both PC]

*Villa abbadon* [SO]

*Villa ixion* [SO]

*Villa melanura*

## Family Asilidae – ROBBERFLIES

The robberflies are mainly medium to large insects, with stout spiny legs and sharp piercing mouthparts to kill other insects and are often seen paired up, or eating prey. If handled they can deliver a painful bite. The life cycle takes one to three years and, with care, species are usually identifiable in the field. Grasslands or woodland edges are often preferred, where they rest on fences, posts, logs, branches or stones and are therefore likely to be noticed. If an insect passes by, they fly and quickly pounce, then land nearby to devour the catch. The larvae can be found in the soil or rotting wood, mainly feeding on other insect larvae.

### *Antiphrisson trifarius*

Body length: 14–18 mm. Large brown species; one of various similar-looking species. **HABITAT** Grasslands, including mountains. **SEASON** April to August.

### *Dasypogon diadema*

Body length: 18–26 mm. Large black species (legs black or red), although ♀ larger with red legs and abdominal markings and with brown wings. **HABITAT** Various open areas, including mountains. **SEASON** June to August.

### *Asilus crabroniformis* Hornet Robberfly

Body length: 18–28 mm. Large hornet mimic, brown with a yellow tip to its abdomen, hidden by the wings at rest. **HABITAT** Grasslands. ♀s lay eggs in or under the crust of old cattle dung, sometimes of horse or rabbit. The larvae are also predators of dung beetles and other organisms, burying in the soil before pupating. **SEASON** June to September.

### *Laphria bomboides*

Body length: c.18 mm. Bee mimic, first half of thorax with dense golden-yellow hairs; hind part of abdomen covered in white hair. **HABITAT** Open areas close to tree trunks and vegetation. First recorded as new to Spain in 2015 **SEASON** May to September.

### *Laphria flava* Bumblebee Robberfly

Body length: 12–24 mm. Large, orange-brown, furry bee mimic, abdomen covered in dense yellow hair. **HABITAT** Old coniferous woodlands, on stumps or fallen pines in sunny spots; occasionally linked with deciduous trees. **SEASON** May to September.

### *Molobratia teutonus*

Body length: 15–24 mm. Large and colourful, with orange antennae. White patches on abdominal segments. **HABITAT** Various, including mountains and near water. Often rests in seemingly awkward positions on vegetation, with legs outstretched. **SEASON** April to September.

### *Saropogon aberrans*

Body length: c.15 mm. Similar to other *Saropogon* species, but mote white dusting and white hairs on coxa. **HABITAT** Various, including mountains. **SEASON** May to June.

### *Saropogon flavicinctus*

Body length: c.15 mm. Distinctive yellowish-orange marked abdominal segments and legs; green eyes. **HABITAT** Various, including mountains. **SEASON** April to May, perhaps later.

### *Stenopogon costatus*

Body length: 12–15 mm. Tip of abdomen orange; legs orange. **HABITAT** Various, including mountains. **SEASON** June to August.

### *Dioctria atricapilla* Violet Black-legged Robberfly

Body length: 9–12 mm. Bluish-black with yellow halters; ♂s have blue eyes. **HABITAT** Grasslands. **SEASON** May to July, possibly also later.

*Antiphrisson trifarius*

*Dasypogon diadema*

*Asilus crabroniformis*

*Laphria bomboides*

*Laphria flava*

*Molobratia teutonus*

*Saropogon aberrans*

*Saropogon flavicinctus*

*Stenopogon costatus*

*Dioctria atricapilla*

*Antiphrisson trifarius* [SO]

*Dasypogon diadema* ♂

*Asilus crabroniformis*

*Laphria flava* ♀

*Laphria bomboides* [MRo]

*Molobratia teutonus* [PC]

*Saropogon aberrans* [SO]

*Saropogon flavicinctus* [SO]

*Stenopogon costatus*

*Dioctria atricapilla* [PC]

## Family Syrphidae – HOVERFLIES

Hoverflies are a group of small to large sun-loving flies, often black with white or yellow markings on the abdomen; some species mimic bees and wasps and all play an important role in pollination. Walk through grasslands or open woodland in summer and hoverflies will be visiting available flowers for nectar or pollen, or just hovering in the area, defending territories. The larvae of many species are popular with gardeners in that they often feed on aphids, but some are plant eaters or scavengers, a minority aquatic. Hoverflies are one of the most popular groups of flies, but variation can confuse in some species, in addition to species of similar appearance, as it may not be possible to examine the key features in the wild. However, many of Europe's species are quite distinctive and can be identified in the field.

*Chrysotoxum bicinctum*

### *Chrysotoxum bicinctum*

Wing length: 7–10 mm. Two distinctive broad yellow abdominal bands. **HABITAT** Various woodlands and open ground, often visiting umbellifers. **SEASON** Late May to September.

*Chrysotoxum cautum*

### *Chrysotoxum cautum*

Wing length: 10–13 mm. Large *Chrysotoxum*, ♀s with broad abdomen, particularly hairy upper thorax. 1st antennal segment two-thirds length of 2nd segment. **HABITAT** Open scrublands and woodlands. **SEASON** April to July, possibly later.

*Chrysotoxum festivum*

### *Chrysotoxum festivum*

Wing length: 8–12 mm. As with other *Chrysotoxum* species, the elongate antennae projecting forwards. The downturned yellow bars on abdominal segments and orange legs help to identify this species, whose name is rather confused in the literature. **HABITAT** Woodland clearings, around shrubs and flowers. The larvae feed on ant-attended aphids. **SEASON** May to September.

*Chrysotoxum verrnale*

### *Chrysotoxum vernale*

Wing length: 8–10 mm. Similar to *C. festivum*, but yellow abdominal bars are straighter (curved near outer edges in *festivum*). Basal part of fore and mid femora black. **HABITAT** Various woodlands and grasslands. **SEASON** May to August.

*Doros profuges*

### *Doros profuges* Wasp Hoverfly

Wing length: 11–13 mm. Elongate, large wasp-like hoverfly with waisted abdomen, yellow thoracic stripes and narrow yellow abdominal bars; wings with a brown margin. **HABITAT** Woodland edge, possibly on umbellifers or bramble *Rubus* flowers. The larvae may be associated with ant-attended aphids. **SEASON** Late May to June, possibly later.

*Episyrphus balteatus*

### *Episyrphus balteatus* Marmalade Hoverfly

Wing length: 6–10 mm. Rather variable. The double black lines on abdominal segments 3–4 are unique in the only European species of *Episyrphus*. **HABITAT** Various, often abundant on flowers in gardens, grasslands and woodlands. Extremely migratory. **SEASON** All year.

*Eupeodes corallae*

### *Eupeodes corollae*

Wing length: 5–8 mm. Oval abdomen ♂ with quadrate abdominal spots, ♀ with lunules. Lateral edge of abdominal segments yellow. **HABITAT** Open habitats, often breeding in ponds and ditches. **SEASON** All year in far south.

*Leucozona glaucia*

### *Leucozona glaucia*

Wing length: 8–11 mm. Large quadrate spots on 2nd abdominal segment; wings with dark stigma. Scutellum yellow. **HABITAT** Woodlands, often on flowers. **SEASON** Late May to September.

*Scaeva pyrastri*

### *Scaeva pyrastri*

Wing length: 9–12.5 mm. Black and white. **HABITAT** Various, including gardens and grasslands wherever they can find aphids for resulting larvae to feed on. **SEASON** February to November.

*Chrysotoxum bicinctum*

*Chrysotoxum cautum*

*Chrysotoxum festivum* [PC]

*Chrysotoxum verrnale* [PC]

*Doros profuges*

*Episyrphus balteatus*

*Eupeodes corallae*

*Leucozona glaucia* [PC]

*Scaeva pyrastri* [PC]

### *Scaeva selenitica*

Wing length: 10.5–12 mm. Like *S. pyrastri*, but abdominal lunules are yellow and a different shape. **HABITAT** Often in woodlands, including those with predominantly Holm Oak *Quercus ilex*. **SEASON** March to September, from about June in mountains.

*Scaeva selenitica*

### *Syrphus ribesii*

Wing length: 7–11.5 mm. 3rd and 4th abdominal bands are wavy. Hind femora yellow in ♀s (in ♂s on apical third to half) except for black base.

**HABITAT** Various, including gardens, hedgerows, waste ground and woodlands. Likely to be responsible for humming sound as ♂s rest with wings vibrating. The larvae feed on aphids. **SEASON** March to November. **SIMILAR SPECIES** ***S. vitripennis*** [pictured left] (wing length: 7–10 mm) has hind femora mainly black in both sexes. Found in various habitats, including woodlands and gardens, from March to October.

*Syrphus ribesii*

*Syrphus vitripennis*

### *Callicera aurata*

Wing length: 10–12.5 mm. Brassy abdomen (lacks distinct golden hairs), femora black. **HABITAT** Old woodlands, particularly those with beech *Fagus* and oak *Quercus*. **SEASON** Late May to September.

*Callicera aurata*

### *Ferdinandea cuprea*

Wing length: 7.5–11 mm. Abdomen metallic brassy colour. Small spines on all tibiae. **HABITAT** Woodlands, also parks, often on oak *Quercus* trunks or sap runs. **SEASON** March to November.

*Ferninandea cuprea*

### *Rhingia campestris*

Wing length: 6–9.5 mm. Long snout, dark thorax. Abdomen orange with dark central line and lateral margins. **HABITAT** Open woodlands and elsewhere. The larvae develop in cow dung. Adults are often seen on flowers and have amazingly long mouthparts to reach deep tubes in flowers. **SEASON** April to October.

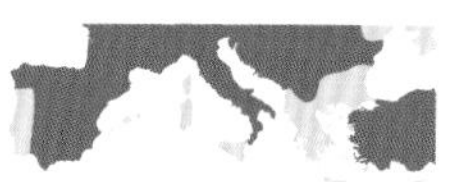
*Rhingia campestris*

### *Rhingia rostrata*

Wing length: 7.5–9.5 mm. Smaller snout than *R. campestris*; abdomen plain orange, or with slight central mark on 2nd segment. **HABITAT** Open woodlands. **SEASON** May to early October.

*Rhingia rostrata*

### *Ceriana vespiformis*

Wing length: 10–11 mm. Wasp-like, like the species name; very long antennae. **HABITAT** Open woodlands and scrub, often associated with oak *Quercus*. Frequently seen on flowers. **SEASON** Late May to September.

*Ceriana vespiformis*

### *Eristalinus aeneus*

Wing length: 6–9.5 mm. Robust-looking species with glossy black or greenish-bronze abdomen. Spotted eyes; upper part of eyes hairy. **HABITAT** Freshwater sites. Rests on vegetation, flowers, rocks and bare ground. **SEASON** April to October.

*Eristalinus aeneus*

### *Eristalinus taeniops* Band-eyed Drone Fly

Wing length: c.8 mm. Conspicuously-banded eyes. **HABITAT** Woodlands, open ground and freshwater sites. Known to visit the edge of streams to drink. **SEASON** April to October.

*Eristalinus taeniops*

*Scaeva selenitica*

*Syrphus ribesii*

*Callicera aurata* [PC]

*Ferninandea cuprea*

*Rhingia campestris*

*Rhingia rostrata*

*Ceriana vespiformis*

*Eristalinus aeneus* [PC]

*Eristalinus taeniops* [PC]

***Eristalis alpina***
Wing length: c.12 mm. Wings with an obvious cloud across middle. Front half of mesonotum greyish. **HABITAT** Woodland edge often by streams or rivers in mountainous areas. Often on waterside umbellifers. **SEASON** Mid May to August.

*Eristalis alpina*

***Eristalis nemorum***
Wing length: 8–10.5 mm. Similar to several *Eristalis* species, but wing stigma sharp-edged. Easy to distinguish in the field as the ♂ hovers above the ♀. This species is listed by some authors as *E. interruptus*. **HABITAT** Wetlands and woodlands, where the larvae often develop in streams and pools, also in waterlogged cow dung. **SEASON** April to September.

*Eristalis nemorum*

***Eristalis pertinax***
Wing length: 8–13 mm. Large, close to *E. tenax*, but fore tarsi orange and basal half of hind tibiae pale. **HABITAT** Wetlands, woodlands and others; usually near streams. **SEASON** February to November.

*Eristalis pertinax*

***Eristalis tenax* Drone Fly**
Wing length: 10–13 mm. Large and variable, close to *E. pertinax*, but fore tarsi and the enlarged and curved hind tibiae are dark. Named 'drone' after its resemblance to ♂ honey bees. **HABITAT** Various, including gardens. **SEASON** All year, but the ♀s may hibernate in crevices and buildings.

*Eristalis tenax*

***Helophilus hybridus***
Wing length: 8.5–11 mm. Distinctive thoracic stripes and yellow and black abdominal markings. Hind tibiae usually with only basal third pale. **HABITAT** Wetlands such as margins of ponds or ditches, where the rat-tailed larvae have been found at the base of bulrushes *Typha*. **SEASON** May to early September.

*Helophilus hybridus*

***Helophilus pendulus***
Wing length: 8.5–11 mm. Distinctive thoracic stripes and yellow and black abdominal markings. Hind tibiae extensively pale. **HABITAT** Wetlands and others. Adults often on flowers, but less common in southern Europe. **SEASON** March to November.

*Helophilus pendulus*

***Milesia crabroniformis***
Wing length: 14–27 mm. Large, with conspicuous thoracic pattern; another hornet mimic. **HABITAT** Woodlands with oak *Quercus* and beech *Fagus*. Adults are sometimes found drinking at stream edges. **SEASON** July to October.

*Milesia crabroniformis*

***Myathropa florea***
Wing length: 7–12 mm. Conspicuous thoracic pattern. **HABITAT** Woodlands and others, where larvae develop in the wet rot-holes of tree trunks, as well as in cow dung and compost heaps. **SEASON** May to October.

*Myathropa florea*

***Spilomyia manicata***
Wing length: 8–16 mm. Large and rather wasp-like. Distinctively marked eyes (pictured left [PC]. **HABITAT** Woodlands. Often on umbellifers, but in decline. **SEASON** Mid June to September.

*Spilomyia manicata*

*Eristalis alpina* [PC]

*Eristalis nemorum* pair, ♂ hovering

*Eristalis pertinax* egglaying

*Eristalis tenax* [PC]

*Helophilus hybridus* [PC]

*Helophilus pendulus* mating pair

*Milesia crabroniformis* [SO]

*Myathropa florea*

*Spilomyia manicata* [PC]

### *Merodon equestris* Large Narcissus Fly

Wing length: 8.5–10 mm. Variable hairy, bumblebee mimic (form *narcissi* pictured left [PC]). **HABITAT** Various, open areas such as grasslands or gardens, with flowers, including the host plant, also woodlands. The larvae attack Liliaciae, Alliaceae and Asparagaceae bulbs, including *Narcissus*, hence they are regarded as a minor pest in commercial bulb fields. Adults often settle on vegetation or bare ground. **SEASON** April to August, the latter month at higher altitudes.

*Merodon equestris*

### *Platynochaetus setosus*

Wing length: 9–12 mm. Large and rather wasp-like. **HABITAT** Oak *Quercus* woodlands and shrublands, adults often settle on dead vegetation or bare ground. **SEASON** March to May.

*Platynochaetus setosus*

### *Arctophila bombiforme*

Wing length: c.10 mm. Bumble bee mimic. **HABITAT** Mountainous areas, often on flowers in subalpine grasslands and near streams and woodland edge. **SEASON** May to August, most likely June to July at higher elevations.

*Arctophila bombiforme*

### *Sericomyia silentis*

Wing length: 9.5–14 mm. Wedge-shaped yellow bars. **HABITAT** Wetlands and woodlands, often on flowers, or resting on vegetation; found in mountainous areas. **SEASON** Late May to early October.

*Sericomyia silentis*

***Volucella*** hoverflies are large bumblebee or wasp mimics, some species with a distinct dark wing cloud. The larvae develop in the nests of social wasps or bumblebees, where they are scavengers or parasites. Adults are often found on flowers. All six European species are illustrated.

### *Volucella bombylans*

Wing length: 8–14 mm. A bumblebee mimic, furry, with various colour forms. **HABITAT** Scrubby grasslands and woodland edges. **SEASON** May to September.

*Volucella bombylans*

### *Volucella elegans*

Wing length: c.15 mm. Yellow and black banded abdomen, with dark wing patches. The black abdominal bands much broader than in *V. zonaria*. **HABITAT** Woodland edges. **SEASON** May to November.

*Volucella elegans*

### *Volucella inanis*

Wing length: 12–14 mm. All abdominal segments with similar markings, black bands narrower than the similar, but larger *V. zonaria* and 2nd abdominal segment in inanis yellow. **HABITAT** Woodland edges. **SEASON** June to September.

*Volucella inanis*

### *Volucella inflata*

Wing length: 11–13 mm. Large orange markings on 2nd abdominal segment. **HABITAT** Woodlands, associated with sap runs on trees. **SEASON** May to September.

*Volucella inflata*

### *Volucella pellucens* Great Pied Hoverfly

Wing length: 10–15 mm. Black, except mostly white 2nd abdominal segment. **HABITAT** Woodland edges. **SEASON** May to October.

*Volucella pellucens*

*Merodon equestris*

*Platynochaetus setosus* [SO]

*Arctophila bombiforme* [PC]

*Sericomyia silentis*

*Volucella bombylans*

*Volucella elegans*

*Volucella inanis*

*Volucella inflata*

*Volucella pellucens*

***Volucella zonaria* Hornet Hoverfly**
Wing length: 15–19 mm. One of Europe's largest hoverflies, a hornet mimic. Yellow and black banded abdomen, 2nd segment chestnut-brown, distinguishing it from *V. inanis*. **HABITAT** Often in gardens and wasteland as well as woodland edge. **SEASON** May to November.

*Volucella zonaria*

***Brachypalpoides lentus***
Wing length: 10–12 mm. Black with a red abdominal belt. **HABITAT** Woodlands, often found in shady spots on or near fallen logs, or in hollows of living oak *Quercus* and beech *Fagus*, where the larvae develop. **SEASON** April to July.

*Brachypalpoides lentus*

***Caliprobola speciosa***
Wing length: 11–12.5 mm. Metallic green abdomen, orange legs and wings. **HABITAT** Old woodlands, often on or near sunlit bases of old beech *Fagus* or oak *Quercus* trees (particularly Cork Oak *Q. suber*) where the larvae feed in rotting heartwood. **SEASON** May to mid July.

*Caliprobola speciosa*

***Pocota personata***
Wing length: 11–13 mm. An amazing bumble bee mimic, but note the small head and short antennae, which easily distinguish them from a bumble bee. **HABITAT** Old woodlands, attracted to beech *Fagus* and poplar *Populus* trunks with rot roles or on flowers. **SEASON** May to early July.

*Pocota personata*

***Syritta pipiens***
Wing length: 5–7 mm. Robust small with swollen hind femora. **HABITAT** Various, including gardens, hedgerows, dry and wet grasslands. Larvae develop in compost or rotting organic matter. **SEASON** All year.

*Syritta pipiens*

## Family Conopidae – THICK-HEADED FLIES
Small to large, slender to stout, flies often wasp-like. Conopids are parasitoids (i.e. killing the host and preventing reproduction) of adult bumble bees and wasps, occasionally solitary bees, the ♀ depositing an egg in the host's abdomen whilst in flight. The larva develops inside and pupates when the host dies. **HABITAT** Wherever the prey lives, although woodland rides and clearings can be productive. Adults look for sunny, warm spots with plenty of nectar sources. They are often seen on flowers, but rarely observed ambushing bumblebees and wasps.

***Conops quadrifasciatus***
Body length: 8–12 mm. Several similar species. Distinctively banded abdomen; legs yellowish brown. **HABITAT** Grasslands, woodlands and others, often on umbellifers and composites. **SEASON** June to September.

*Conops quadrifasciatus*

***Physocephala laticincta***
Body length: c.10 mm. Abdomen black with yellowish bands; femora blackish at base. **HABITAT** Various. **SEASON** June to August.

*Physocephala laticincta*

***Sicus ferrugineus***
Body length: 8–13 mm. Chestnut with a yellow head. **HABITAT** Grasslands and hedgerows. **SEASON** May to September.

*Sicus ferrugineus*

## Family Tephritidae – PICTURE-WINGED FLIES
Small to medium-sized flies often with patterned wings. Tephritid ♀s have a rigid ovipositor to deposit eggs in living plant tissue, the larvae live in the plant and some species induce galls.

***Ceratitis capitata* Mediterranean Fruit Fly**
Body length: 3–5 mm. Unmistakeable. Strongly marked with patterned wings; eyes reddish-purple. **HABITAT** Orchards and gardens where they can be a major pest to fruit crops. ♀s lay eggs into unripened or ripe fruit, where the larvae develop. **SEASON** May to November.

*Ceratitis capitata*

*Volucella zonaria*

*Brachypalpoides lentus*

*Caliprobola speciosa*

*Pocota personata*

*Syritta pipiens*

*Conops quadrifasciatus* ♂

*Physocephala laticincta*

*Sicus ferrugineus* mating pair

*Ceratitis capitata* [NR]

# Suborder Calypterates

## Family Hippoboscidae – FLAT FLIES

A small group of almost flattened, but robust-looking parasitic flies, also known as keds. All are ectoparasites of birds or mammals, feeding on blood, some have reduced wings. A notorious example species is illustrated.

### *Hippobosca equina* Forest Fly

Body length: 6–9 mm. Brown with yellowish markings and some mottling; full-length wings. **HABITAT** Areas with plentiful livestock, mainly horses, but they can survive on some other mammals and possibly birds. Sometimes humans attract them and they land on people. **SEASON** May to October.

## Family Scathophagidae – DUNGFLIES

Small to large, usually slender, with bristles, the long wings often with faint colour or markings.

### *Scathophaga stercoraria* Yellow Dungfly

Body length: 8–10 mm. ♂ golden yellow, ♀ greener and less hairy. **HABITAT** Areas with plentiful livestock, attracted to cow dung in numbers, where they prey mainly on small flies and other insects on dung. **SEASON** March to November.

## Family Fanniidae – LESSER HOUSEFLIES

A group of small to large flies mostly grey or yellowish, originally in the Muscidae. They include a common fly illustrated, which frequently enters houses and circles near the centre of rooms. The larvae feed on decaying matter such as plant material, dung or fungi, also mammal and bird nests.

### *Fannia canicularis* Lesser House Fly

Body length: 3.5–6 mm. Eyes white-bordered, only the ♂ has small orange abdominal patches. The most likely species in the Fannidae to be a vector of myiasis (blowfly strike) in vertebrates. **HABITAT** Various, frequent in houses. **SEASON** May to October.

## Family Muscidae – HOUSEFLIES and ALLIES

A large group of small to large flies usually grey to black, but some metallic green or blue. They include some of the most abundant flies in Europe, particularly those associated with dung. Adults of many species visit flowers for nectar, but some are predators or feed on blood. The larvae can be carnivores, feed on decaying matter such as plant material or dung and in some cases are at least part aquatic. Some muscids are popularly known as houseflies, due to a close association with humans.

### *Mesembrina meridiana*

Body length: 9–12 mm. Black with conspicuous orange wing bases. **HABITAT** Various, particularly near cattle; adults often seen on dung. The larvae develop in dung, feeding on fly larvae. **SEASON** Late April to October.

### *Mesembrina mystacea*

Body length: c.10 mm. Bee-like, with yellowish-brown thorax, orange wing bases and whitish abdominal tip. **HABITAT** Near cattle, sometimes with *M. meridiana* in mountainous areas; adults often seen on dung. **SEASON** June to October.

### *Musca autumnalis* Face Fly

Body length: 7–8 mm. Four black stripes on thorax. Abdomen in ♂ orange with black markings, grey in ♀. **HABITAT** Abundant where there is livestock, Attracted to sweat from animals and humans. The common name derives from this species habit of landing on the face of cattle. **SEASON** March to October.

*Hippobosca equina*

*Scathophaga stercoraria*

*Fannia canicularis*

*Mesembrina meridiana*

*Mesembrina mystacea*

*Musca autumnalis*

*Scathophaga stercoraria* (left), group on dung (right) [PC]

*Hippobosca equina*

*Fannia canicularis* [JG]

*Musca autumnalis*

*Mesembrina meridiana*

*Mesembrina mystacea* [PC]

### *Musca domestica* Common House Fly

Body length: 7–8 mm. Grey to black, thorax with four longitudinal black lines. Brown abdominal patches. **HABITAT** Less common in urban areas than in former times. However, this is a well-known worldwide vector of diseases, breeding in excrement and refuse heaps, then may enter houses, regurgitating stomach contents (with bacteria) on uncovered food. The larvae mature in as little as three weeks. **SEASON** March to October.

### *Stomoxys calcitrans* Stable Fly

Body length: c.8 mm. Grey with four longitudinal stripes along the thorax and dark abdominal spots. **HABITAT** An ideal habitat is stables and barns, where the larvae develop in manure. This species is a well-known biting fly, sucking blood from mammals and humans near livestock (they are a vector of diseases). **SEASON** May to November.

## Family Calliphoridae – BLOWFLIES

Mostly rather stout, small to large flies; blowflies refers to an old English term for meat, with fly eggs on it, said to be 'fly blown.' Some species are metallic, notably bluebottles *Calliphora* species and greenbottles *Lucilia* species, which often bask on walls and fences, entering houses when doors and windows are left open; they will lay c.2,000 eggs on any scraps of meat and fish which may result in an infestation of maggots in the house. They can live for several months, or even a year when overwintering. Many species develop in carrion which they can detect over a considerable distance.

### *Calliphora vicina* Common Bluebottle

Body length: 8–14 mm. Pale brown basicosta (top left of the outstretched wing; black in related species). Hairs on jowls (cheek) black (orange in the similar *C. vomitoria*). **HABITAT** Various, including urban areas, where the larvae develop in fresh carrion, meat and garbage. **SEASON** All year.

### *Calliphora vomitoria* Orange-bearded Bluebottle

Body length: 10–14 mm. Darker appearance in the field than some bluebottles; hairs on cheek orange. **HABITAT** Various. **SEASON** All year.

### *Lucilia caesar* Common Greenbottle

Body length: 8–10 mm. One of various metallic green flies, including some not in the same family. **HABITAT** Various. **SEASON** March to November.

### *Stomorhina lunata*

Body length: 5–9 mm. Boldly striped (including eyes), abdomen yellow and black; could easily be mistaken in the field for a hoverfly. **HABITAT** Grasslands, where they specialise in predating eggs of locusts and grasshoppers. **SEASON** July to October.

## Family Oestridae – WARBLE-FLIES & BOT-FLIES

Small to large robust-looking species; all parasitic on mammals. The best-known species is discussed.

### *Gasterophilus intestinalis* Bot-fly

Body length: 8–18 mm. Brown, rather bee-like; wings with brown patches. **HABITAT** Open areas around livestock, where ♀s lay yellow eggs on the legs and shoulders of horses or donkeys. The resulting larvae burrow their way through the skin (often via the tongue after being licked by the animal) and then into the intestinal tract. They leave via dung, pupating in dung or soil. **SEASON** July to September.

## Family Sarcophagidae – FLESH FLIES

Small to large species; usually stout and bristly, often with a chequered abdomen and never metallic.

### *Sarcophaga carnaria* Flesh Fly

Body length: 8–18 mm. Black-striped species with red eyes. *Sarcophaga* species need to be identified under a microscope. **HABITAT** Various, on or near carrion. ♀s deposit small larvae rather than eggs. **SEASON** April to October.

*Musca domestica*

*Stomoxys calcitrans*

*Calliphora vicina*

*Calliphora vomitoria*

*Lucilia caesar*

*Stomorhina lunata*

*Gasterophilus intestinalis*

*Sarcophaga carnaria*

*Musca domestica* *Stomoxys calcitrans* *Calliphora vicina*

*Calliphora vomitoria* *Lucilia caesar* *Stomorhina lunata*

*Gasterophilus intestinalis* *Sarcophaga carnaria*

## Family Tachinidae – PARASITIC FLIES

Tachinids are small to large, often bristly, flies; the larvae are parasitoids of other insects, mainly caterpillars of butterflies and moths. Eggs are normally laid on or near the host, which the larvae penetrate. Some species can be abundant on umbellifers in late summer. A wide selection of species is illustrated.

*Ectophasia crassipennis*

### *Ectophasia crassipennis*

Body length: 5–9 mm. Black or orange-brown, wings dotted. **HABITAT** Grasslands, often on flowers. **SEASON** May to September. **HOSTS** Bugs.

*Gymnosoma rotundatum*

### *Gymnosoma rotundatum*

Body length: 4.5–8 mm. **HABITAT** Calcareous grasslands, heathlands and woodland edges. **SEASON** June to September. **HOSTS** Bugs.

*Phasia aurigera*

### *Phasia aurigera*

Body length: 8–13 mm. Black thorax with yellow marks, orange abdomen often with black or bluish central line or blotch. **HABITAT** Woodland edges and others, often on flowers. **SEASON** June to October. **HOSTS** Bugs.

*Phasia hemiptera*

### *Phasia hemiptera*

Body length: 8–12.5 mm. The ♂ is much more colourful than the ♀ with a striking metallic blue pattern on the wings, absent in the ♀. **HABITAT** Woodland margins and grasslands, but commoner in central Europe. **SEASON** April to September. **HOSTS** Shieldbugs.

*Phasia pusilla*

### *Phasia pusilla*

Body length: 2–5 mm. **HABITAT** Grasslands. **SEASON** Late May to early September. **HOSTS** Ground bugs.

*Sturmia bella*

### *Sturmia bella*

Body length: c.10 mm. Larva and pupa from a *Vanessa atlalanta* pupa (pictured left). **HABITAT** Grasslands and woodland margins. **SEASON** May to mid October. **HOSTS** Nymphalid butterfly larvae.

*Nowickia ferox*

### *Nowickia ferox*

Body length: 11–15 mm. Black and orange with black legs. **HABITAT** Grasslands and woodland margins. **SEASON** July to September. **HOSTS** Moth larvae.

*Tachina fera*

### *Tachina fera*

Body length: 10–14 mm. Dull black or brown with orange, distinguishing it from the vivid *Nowickia ferox*. **HABITAT** Grasslands and woodland margins. **SEASON** May to September. **HOSTS** Moth larvae.

*Tachina grossa*

### *Tachina grossa*

Body length: 13.5–20 mm. Black with a yellow face; could easily be mistaken for a bumble bee. **HABITAT** Grasslands and woodland margins. **SEASON** July to August. **HOSTS** Moth larvae.

*Trichopoda pennipes*

### *Trichopoda pennipes*

Body length: c.12 mm. Distinctive dark species, with orange abdomen. They often rest with the wings outstetched (pictured right). **HABITAT** Grasslands and gardens; accidentally introduced to southern Europe (initially in Rome) in 1988. **SEASON** May to September. **HOSTS** Larger bugs, including *Nezara viridula*.

*Ectophasia crassipennis* ♂ (left), ♀ (right) [PC]

*Phasia aurigera* [TB]

*Phasia hemiptera* ♂ (left), ♀ (right) [PC]

*Phasia pusilla* [PC]

*Gymnosoma rotundatum* [PC]

*Sturmia bella*

*Nowickia ferox*

*Tachina fera*

*Tachina grossa*

*Trichopoda pennipes* [PC]

# Order MECOPTERA – SCORPIONFLIES

**Southern Europe & Mediterranean: some of Europe's 23 species**

Easy to recognise by their long, downwards pointing beak; species, the ♂ has the genital area swollen and held over its body like a scorpion's tail, hence the common name, although in ♀s the abdomen is tapered at the tip. They are unable to sting, but if handled ♂s will pretend to sting. If disturbed on vegetation they often drop to the ground in order to try to avoid predation. Perhaps most likely to be observed are one of several similar winged scorpionflies belonging to the genus *Panorpa*. There are also several snow fleas, small flightless insects in the genus *Boreus*, active in winter where they are particularly at home in mountainous areas. There is a complete metamorphosis i.e. the life cycle is: egg, larva, pupa and adult. Wing markings may be useful in identification but vary within species so it is sometimes necessary to examine the genitalia. The features on the underside of the genital capsule in ♂s differ in shape (when held forward over the body the underside is upwards and it should be possible to see the calliper shape with a hand lens). ♀s can only be confirmed to species level by specialists examining the shape of the ovipositor under a microscope.
**HABITAT** Grasslands and woodland margins, where they feed on small invertebrates. Some species frequent mountainous areas.

## Family Panorpidae

c.10–15 mm, enlarged genital capsule in ♂s, held upright over the body; winged.

### *Panorpa communis*

♂ genital callipers clearly curved and converging at the tips. **SEASON** May to September.

### *Panorpa germanica*

♂ genital callipers are rather broader and parallel; expanded at the tips. **SEASON** May to September.

### *Panorpa meridionalis*

Base of wings with large black blotch; generally larger bolder spots on wings than other *Panorpa* species. **HABITAT** Includes mountainous areas. **SEASON** May to September.

## Family Boreidae

Small, long ♀ ovipositor, shortened wings and flightless.

### *Boreus hyemalis* Snow Flea

Body length 3-4.5 mm. The ♀ has shortened wings and a distinctive ovipositor, whereas the ♂ has wings modified into stout spines. **HABITAT** Woodlands and others. Eggs are laid in moss and larvae live in a tunnel between moss and substrate, where they feed on small invertebrates. One of several similar species. **SEASON** October to March.

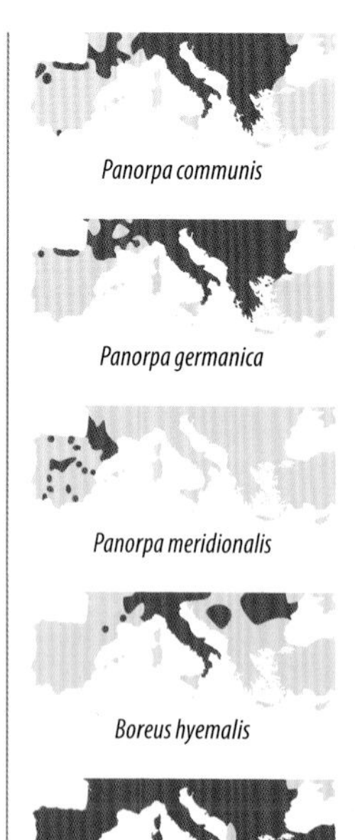

*Panorpa communis*

*Panorpa germanica*

*Panorpa meridionalis*

*Boreus hyemalis*

*Archaeopsylla erinacei*

# Order SIPHONAPTERA – FLEAS

**Southern Europe & Mediterranean: some of Europe's c.260 species**

Wingless, shiny, hairy insects (1–8 mm) with a small, tough, laterally flattened body. Adults have bloodsucking mouthparts. Hind legs are evolved so they are able to jump. The life cycle is: egg, larva, pupa and adult, living as ectoparasites (on the outside) of birds and mammals – only the adults are parasitic and they can survive months without a blood meal. The legless, eyeless larvae feed on organic matter near the host. Fleas are difficult to identify, but are well known for their ability to transit diseases such as plague and typhus; a few also come into contact with people and domestic pets.

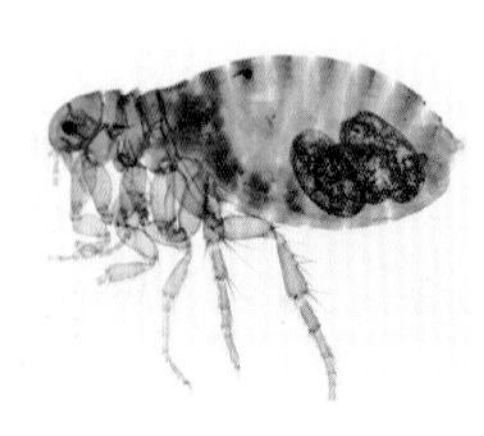

## Family Pulicidae

### *Archaeopsylla erinacei* Hedgehog Flea

Body length: 2–3.5 mm (pictured left [RK]). **HABITAT** On hedgehogs *Erinaceus*, occasionally other mammals, but rarely bites humans. **SEASON** All year.

*Panorpa communis* ♂ (left), ♀ with prey (right)

*Panorpa germanica* ♂ (left & right)

*Panorpa meridionalis* ♂ (left) [FR], ♂ (centre) [SO], ♀ (right)

*Boreus hyemalis* ♂ (left), ♂ teneral (centre), ♀ (right)

# Order TRICHOPTERA – CADDISFLIES

**Southern Europe & Mediterranean: c.1,000 species**

Trichoptera means 'hairy winged' and are a large group of weak-flying freshwater insects, often drab and rather moth-like (forewing length 3 mm to some 30 mm), with wings held over the back. Antennae are long. Many are nocturnal, but some dayfliers are often seen mating, swarming around lakes, ponds or streams with aquatic or marginal vegetation. Mating and egglaying usually takes place soon after emergence. There is a complete metamorphosis: egg, larva, pupa and adult. Nearly all species have aquatic larvae which have jaws for biting and chewing, most living in transportable cases. However, three small species in Europe are fully terrestrial including ***Enoicyla pusilla*** [family Limnephilidae] (larva pictured left); this species is unusual in having a wingless ♀. Adult caddisflies are usually on or near waterside vegetation, and are attracted to lights, in some cases well away from water. Whilst some species only live a few days and rarely feed, others including *Glyphotaelius* exploit temporary pools, ditches and marshes that dry up over summer, living as adults from spring until autumn, feeding on nectar of umbellifers and other flowers. Several species are illustrated from a selection of the families (often distinguished by subtle differences in wing venation), but often species with a similar appearance can confuse identification and it is necessary to examine genitalia in some species. Several scientists are studying Trichoptera in Europe, hence caddisflies are better known than many other small insect orders.

*Enoicyla pusila*

*Philopotamus montanus*

*Brachycentrus subnubilus*

*Anabolia nervosa*

*Limnephilus lunatus*

*Limnephilus marmoratus*

*Limnephilus rhombicus*

*Limnephilus sparsus*

## Family Philopotamidae – BAG-MAKING CADDIS

***Philopotamus montanus*** **Yellow-spotted Sedge**

Forewing length: 8–13 mm. Forewing brown with yellow spots; rather variable. **HABITAT** Fast flowing streams and stony rivers. **SEASON** March to October.

## Family Brachycentridae – BRACHYCENTRIDS

***Brachycentrus subnubilus*** **Grannom**

Forewing length: 7–14 mm. Forewing grey with yellowish markings. **HABITAT** Fast rivers and streams; a day flier. **SEASON** March to June.

## Family Limnephilidae – LIMNEPHILIDS

***Anabolia nervosa*** **Brown Sedge**

Forewing length: 10–15 mm. Dark reddish-brown forewing with two pale spots near hind margin. **HABITAT** Large streams, rivers, lakes and ponds. **SEASON** July to October.

***Limnephilus lunatus*** **Cinnamon Sedge**

Forewing length: 10–15 mm. Tip of forewing with pale crescent-shaped marking, bordered by dark line. **HABITAT** Ponds, lakes, streams and pools. **SEASON** May to November.

***Limnephilus marmoratus*** **Cinnamon Sedge**

Forewing length: 12–17 mm. Wings strongly marked. **HABITAT** Ponds, lakes and pools. **SEASON** May to October.

***Limnephilus rhombicus***

Forewing length: 14–19 mm. Forewing with large pale rhomboid-like central mark. **HABITAT** Ponds, lakes, marshes and rivers. **SEASON** April to September.

***Limnephilus sparsus***

Forewing length: 10–13 mm. Forewing dark brown with white spots. **HABITAT** Temporary pools and marshes. **SEASON** May to October.

*Philopotamus montanus*

*Brachycentrus subnubilus*

*Anabolia nervosa*

*Limnephilus lunatus*

*Limnephilus marmoratus*

*Limnephilus rhombicus*

*Limnephilus sparsus*

Larva *Limnephilus* sp. [PC]

***Chaetopteryx villosa***
Forewing length: 6–12 mm. Broad brown forewing, with long bristles. **HABITAT** Rivers and streams. **SEASON** August to November.

***Glyphotaelius pellucidus* Mottled Sedge**
Forewing length: 12–17 mm. Forewing with excised outer margin. Pattern varies in the sexes as shown, which only applies to a few caddisfly species. **HABITAT** Woodlands, near streams and pools. **SEASON** May to October.

*Glyphotaelius pellucidus* ♀

***Halesus radiatus* Caperer**
Forewing length: 17–23 mm. Dark speckling on forewing, forming a distinctive pattern. **HABITAT** Rivers and small rivers and streams. **SEASON** August to November.

## Family Sericostomatidae – SERICOSTOMATIDS

***Sericostoma personatum* [Welshman's Button]**
Forewing length: 9–16 mm. Reddish-brown. **HABITAT** Rivers, streams and stony lakes. **SEASON** May to September.

## Family Odontoceridae – ODONTOCERIDS

***Odontocerum albicorne* Silver Sedge or Grey Sedge**
Forewing length: 12–18 mm. Wings brown with paler areas. Distinctive toothed antennae. **HABITAT** Stony streams and rivers; less common in northern Europe. **SEASON** May to September.

## Family Leptoceridae – LONG-HORNED CADDIS

***Athripsodes albifrons* Brown Silverhorn**
Forewing length: 6–9 mm. Forewing brown with four white marks; head with patch of white hairs. Distinctive black and white antennae. **HABITAT** Rivers and streams. **SEASON** May to September.

***Athripsodes bilineatus***
Forewing length: 7–10 mm. Similar to *A. albifrons*, but head black. **HABITAT** Rivers, streams and lakes. **SEASON** May to August.

***Mystacides azureus* Black Silverhorn**
Forewing length: 6–9 mm. Bluish-black, with large maxillary palps and red eyes; antennae white. Angular shape at rest. **HABITAT** Streams, rivers, lakes and large ponds. **SEASON** May to September.

*Chaetopteryx villosa*

*Glyphotaelius pellucidus*

*Halesus radiatus*

*Sericostoma personatum*

*Odontocerum albicorne*

*Athripsodes albifrons*

*Athripsodes bilineatus*

*Mystacides azureus*

*Chaetopteryx villosa* mating pair

*Glyphotaelius pellucidus* ♂

*Halesus radiatus*

*Sericostoma personatum*

*Odontocerum albicorne*

*Athripsodes albifrons*

*Athripsodes bilineatus*

*Mystacides azureus* [PC]

# Order LEPIDOPTERA – BUTTERFLIES & MOTHS

**Southern Europe & Mediterranean: most of Europe's c.8,500 species (c.430 butterfles and c.8,070 moths)**

This group of insects range from 17–102 mm in wingspan in southern Europe and have two pairs of wings in adults, usually covered in scales. The adult mouthparts are adapted into a slender proboscis (tongue) for feeding on nectar, coiled up under the head when not in use. One of the commonest questions asked is 'what is the difference between butterflies and moths?' Many moths are nocturnal, but there are some very colourful dayflying species, and others may be disturbed during the day. The antennae of butterflies are narrow-stemmed, with a club at the tip. Moth antennae are much more variable, usually hairline or feathery. Burnet moths *Zygaena* species do, however, have thickened, rather clubbed antennae. When resting, butterflies hold their wings together above the body, whereas most moths tend to hold their wings flat. The life cycle is complete metamorphosis; egg, larva (caterpillar), pupa (chrysalis) and adult. Butterflies and moths have always been the most popular group of insects to study. Wingspan measurements are based on European works which can be several millimetres less than wingspan as recorded in the UK for the same species. Measurements are normally taken from wing tip to wing tip but can vary, depending how specimens are set (the main reference for butterfly measurements in this book is Leraut's *Butterflies of Europe* (2016) which includes recent changes in classification).

**HABITAT** Grasslands, gardens and woodlands to coastal sites, often visiting flowers or vegetation. Some of the best sites are non-intensive forms of land management such as areas of moderate livestock grazing. The larvae feed on leaves of their foodplants, with several of the blue butterflies enjoying a complex relationship with ants; some feed on ant larvae in later stages of their development.

**HOTSPOTS** Numerous sites, including National Parks. For butterfly species richness (figures in parentheses), these countries feature high on any list: Italy (260), France (260), Spain (239), Greece (232) and Bulgaria (216). A useful commentary on richness of countries features here www.bc-eig.org.uk/countries.html. Some of the author's favourite sites include the French Pyrenees, with up to 200 species in the Midi-Pyrénées, and Picos de Europa in northern Spain, with 136 species. The Italian Alps also tend to be the best sites in Italy. Some entomologists only study moths, but many butterfly enthusiasts progress to also watching and photographing day-flying moths. Several natural history tour operators in Europe feature moths. One stunning tourist site worth visiting is the so-called 'Valley of the butterflies' 26 km from Rhodes town on the Greek Island of Rhodes. Visit during late May to September where an incredible sight awaits – *Euplagia quadripunctaria* moths may be spotted sheltering from the summer heat, resting on rocks and occasionally flying.

**The French Pyrenees** various butterflies frequent different altitudes in the mountains, in this case not far from the well known mountain pass Col du Tourmalet (2,115 m.), one of the most famous climbs on the Tour de France.

**'Valley of the butterflies' Rhodes, Greece** where the incedible sight of *Euplagia quadripunctaria* Jersey Tiger moths sheltering from the heat on the cool rocks in the valley awaits the visitor. [SR]

*Aporia crataegi* (Pieridae) group at mud puddle

*Meltaea phoebe* (Nymphalidae) mating pair

A parasitised fritillary (Nymphalidae) larva

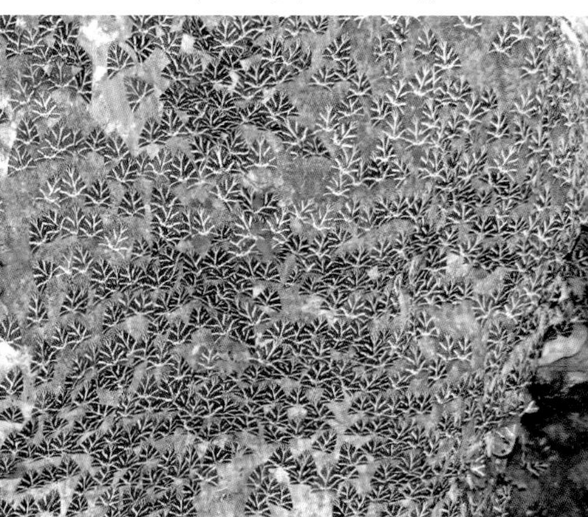

*Euplagia quadripunctaria* (Erebidae) moths in the 'Valley of the butterflies' [SR]

*Endromis versicolora* (Endromidae) egglaying

*Thaumetopoea pitycampa* (Notodontidae) web on pine

# BUTTERFLIES

The beautiful, sun-loving butterflies have always fascinated people and there are several identification books to choose from, more recently apps and DVDs. Europe's butterflies has been well studied and whilst there has been a serious decline in many species in Britain, this is less noticeable in Europe at this stage, although a study in 2010 showed that 9% of species are threatened and 10% Near Threatened, mostly in southern Europe. The whole area is densely populated, particularly in coastal areas with potential for more habitat loss or more intensive agriculture, always of concern to conservationists. Other risks include abandonment, isolation or inappropriate management and to, a lesser extent, collecting. The flight periods provided are a guide only, as in warm years, butterflies may fly earlier than normal and have an additional brood. In mountainous parts of southern Europe, butterflies appear later than at lower altitudes and may have various slightly different forms.

## Family Papilionidae – FESTOONS, APPOLOS & SWALLOWTAILS

The large tailed 'Swallowtail' butterfly is familiar to many, one of 12 colourful European species, some lacking tails. The tails and eye-spots nearby can sometimes fool birds into thinking these are the head and it is not uncommon to see them missing one or both tails!

### *Zerynthia cerisy* Eastern Festoon

Wingspan: 45–62 mm. Pale yellow with black spots and markings, also several red spots on tailed hindwings. Less heavily marked than related *Zerynthia* species, although ♀s have more extensive black markings. **HABITAT** Various grasslands, including mountain slopes up to 1,200 m. Larvae feed on *Aristolochia*. **SEASON** March to June.

### *Zerynthia cretica* Cretan Festoon

Wingspan: 45–50 mm. Like *Z. cerisy*, but no hindwing tail and red spots in ♂s are faint or missing. **HABITAT** Bushy habitats, agricultural land and mountain slopes to 1,000 m., only in Crete. Larvae feed on *Aristolochia*. **SEASON** March to early June.

### *Zerynthia polyxena* Southern Festoon

Wingspan: 40–56 mm. Yellow (sometimes pale) with black spots and markings, also dependant on subspecies, a variable number of red spot on hindwings. **HABITAT** Bushy habitats, hills up to 1,700 m. Larvae feed on *Aristolochia*. **SEASON** February to early July.

### *Zerynthia rumina* Spanish Festoon

Wingspan: 37–50 mm. Yellow with black spots and markings; transparent spot near forewing tip (lacking in *Z. polyxena*). Red spots on forewings and hindwings. **HABITAT** Grasslands with scrub and woodland edge, up to 1,500 m. Larvae feed on *Aristolochia*. Little overlap with *Z. polyxena*. **SEASON** March to May.

### *Parnassius apollo* Apollo

Wingspan: 62–95 mm. Large partly transparent, white butterfly, with large black spots and two red black-ringed spots on hindwings. Various forms include subspecies *nevadensis* (orange spots) in Sierra Nevada, Spain. **HABITAT** Rocky mountain slopes, often 1,000 to 2,500 m. Larvae feed on stonecrop *Sedum* and houseleek *Sempervivum*. This enigmatic species is protected in most countries. **SEASON** May to August, usually July to August in mountains.

### *Parnassius corybas* Small Apollo

Wingspan: 57–68 mm. Variable, sometimes like a smaller version of *P. apollo*, but antennae are black and white striped (plain grey in *P. apollo*), other forms have red marks on the forewings. Formerly misidentified as *P. phoebus*. **HABITAT** Mountain slopes, often 1,600 to 2,800 m. Larvae feed on Yellow Mountain-saxifrage *Saxifraga azioides* and others. **SEASON** July to August.

### *Driopa mnemosyne* Clouded Apollo

Wingspan: 50–64 mm. Rather plain, outer margin of forewings blackish, partly transparent; otherwise whitish with two black spots. Formerly in the genus *Parnassius*. **HABITAT** Mountain slopes, often 1,000 to 2,000 m., meadows, woodland edge. Larvae feed on *Cordyalis*. **SEASON** Late April to July.

*Zerynthia cerisy*

*Zerynthia cretica*

*Zerynthia polyxena*

*Zerynthia rumina*

*Parnassius apollo*

*Parnassius corybas*

*Driopa mnemosyne*

*Zerynthia cerisy* ♂ (left & right) [both MS]

*Zerynthia cretica* ♀ [TB]

*Zerynthia polyxena* ♀ (left & right)

*Zerynthia rumina*

*Parnassius corybas* ♀ [KB]

*nassius apollo* ♂ (top) [JAs], ♂ (bottom left) [MS], ♀ subsp. *nevadensis* (bottom right)

*Driopa mnemosyne* ♂ [KB]

### *Iphiclides podalirius* Scarce Swallowtail

Wingspan: 50–90 mm. Large pale yellow and black butterfly with long tails. The more whitish ***Iphicles feisthamelii* Southern Scarce Swallowtail** (Iberia) is often regarded as a subspecies of *podalirius*, although it was established again as a valid species in 2015. **HABITAT** Various, to above 2,000 m., including slopes, parks and gardens. The larvae (pictured left) feed on *Prunus* species, *Crataegus* and others. Although adults fly fast, photographers can easily obtain images of them nectaring, flying to puddles and in orchards. This species is well known for hill-topping, where several may congregate around the highest point. **SEASON** March to October, in two to three generations.

*Iphiclides podalirius*

*Iphicles feisthamelii*

### *Papilio alexanor* Southern Swallowtail

Wingspan: 50–75 mm. Vivid yellow and black butterflies with large tails. Red eyes and base of hindwings, which have some bluish areas. **HABITAT** Rocky hillsides, including calcareous areas to 2,400 m. The larvae feed on various umbellifers, with a rather limited distribution range. **SEASON** April to July.

*Papilio alexanor*

### *Papilio hospiton* Corsican Swallowtail

Wingspan: 60–72 mm. Yellow and black butterfly with short tails but similar to *P. machaon*. **HABITAT** Various open grassy slopes in Corsica and Sardinia to 2,000 m. The larvae (pictured left [WW]) feed on umbellifers, particularly *Ferula communis*. **SEASON** Mid May to July.

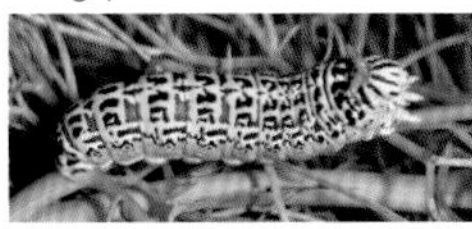

*Papilio hospiton*

### *Papilio machaon* Swallowtail

Wingspan: 60–93 mm. Unmistakable large yellow and black butterfly with large tails; also with black veins on wings. **HABITAT** Often dry cultivated land, but populations further north invariably seek wetter habitats. Occurs at high altitude during migration. The larvae (pictured left) feed on various umbellifers. Adults fly fast and may seem elusive, but there are plenty of times when photographers can easily obtain images of them nectaring or flying to puddles. This species is well known for hill-topping. **SEASON** March to September, in two generations.

*Papilio machaon*

## Family Hesperiidae – SKIPPERS

Small moth-like species with hairy bodies and a large gap between the bases of the antennae, generally regarded as 'primitive' butterflies. Fast moving in flight, a pose uniquely adopted by several species in this family, is to rest with the fore and hindwings held at different angles. Several species are very similar and need critical examination of upperside and underside. The larvae feed on low growing plants or grasses.

### *Erynnis tages* Dingy Skipper

Wingspan: 24–34 mm. Dark brown with grey patches; wings edged with white spots; easily mistaken for a day-flying moth. **HABITAT** Various grasslands, including calcareous, up to 2,000 m., where the larvae feed on legumes such as *Lotus*. Often basks on bare ground or stones. **SEASON** Late April to mid June, then often 2nd generation July to August.

*Erynnis tages*

### *Carcharodus alceae* Mallow Skipper

Wingspan: 22–32 mm. Brown with pink or purple tinge. **HABITAT** Various grasslands including slopes, also some wooded areas to 2,000 m. The larvae feed on mallow *Malva* and others. **SEASON** March to October.

*Carcharodus alceae*

### *Carcharodus baeticus* Southern Marbled Skipper

Wingspan: 24–29 mm. Greyish brown. See subtle differences by comparing with *C. lavatherae*. **HABITAT** Rocky slopes to 1,600 m., also sand dunes. **SEASON** May to September.

*Carcharodus baeticus*

*Iphiclides podalirius* ♀

*Iphicles feisthamelii* (left) [PC], (right)

*Papilio alexanor* [PS]

*Papilio hospiton* [WW]

*Papilio machaon* (left), (right) [PC]

*Erynnis tages* [PC]

*Carcharodus alceae*

*Carcharodus baeticus*

*Carcharodus flocciferus*

**Carcharodus flocciferus Tufted Marbled Skipper**
Wingspan: 23–31 mm. Greyish-brown, with dark patches and some whitish marks. **HABITAT** Grasslands, often in mountainous areas to 2,000 m. The larvae mainly feed on *Stachys*. **SEASON** May to August.

*Carcharodus lavatherae*

**Carcharodus lavatherae Marbled Skipper**
Wingspan: 27–35 mm. Brownish, with whitish marks on forewings and notably across centre of hindwings, much more extensive than in other *Carcharodus* species. **HABITAT** Grasslands, often in calcareous areas and mountains to 1,600 m., where the larvae feed on *Lavatera* and *Stachys*. **SEASON** Mid May to July.

*Spialia phlomidis*

**Spialia phlomidis Persian Skipper**
Wingspan: 25–30 mm. Dark brown, with a number of often large whitish marks; with a series of submarginal spots. **HABITAT** Grasslands, often rocky slopes to 2,200 m., where the larvae feed on *Convolvulus*. **SEASON** Mainly June to July.

*Spialia sertorius*

**Spialia sertorius Red Underwing Skipper**
Wingspan: 17–24 mm. Dark brown with scattered white spots. Easily recognised in the field by its reddish underside, with large white spots. **HABITAT** Grasslands to 1,600 m., where the larvae feed on Salad Burnet *Poterium sanguisorba*. **SEASON** April to August in two generations. **SIMILAR SPECIES** *S. rosae* (Spain) now split from *S. sertorius*.

*Muschampia proto*

**Muschampia proto Sage Skipper**
Wingspan: 28–30 mm. Grey or brownish with white spots. Underside brownish (pictured left). **HABITAT** Hot stony or calcareous grasslands with sparse vegetation to 1,800 m., where the larvae feed on *Phlomis*. There are sometimes few other butterflies flying in the selected habitat. **SEASON** June to August.

*Muschampia tessellum*

**Muschampia tessellum Tessellated Skipper**
Wingspan: 29–40 mm. Grey or brownish with row of submarginal white spots. Underside brownish. **HABITAT** Grassland slopes with scrub to 2,000 m., where the larvae feed on *Phlomis*. **SEASON** April to August.

*Pyrgus alveus*

**Pyrgus alveus Large Grizzled Skipper**
Wingspan: 27–30 mm. Greyish brown with variable white spots. Usually one of the largest *Pyrgus* species and can be confused with other related species; size difference noticeable when at mud puddles with other species. **HABITAT** Grasslands or clearings, favours mountainous areas 1,000 to 2,000 m., where the larvae feed on rock-rose *Helianthemum* and cinquefoil *Potentilla*. **SEASON** May to August.

*Pyrgus armoricanus*

**Pyrgus armoricanus Oberthür's Grizzled Skipper**
Wingspan: 23–26 mm. Greyish brown with a number of white spots. Easily confused with other related species and requires close perusal of the markings. **HABITAT** Rocky grasslands to 1,600 m., where the larvae often feed on cinquefoil *Potentilla*. **SEASON** May to October.

*Pyrgus folquieri*

**Pyrgus folquieri Foulquier's Grizzled Skipper**
Wingspan: 26–30 mm. Greyish brown with various white spots. Could be confused with other related species, although it has a limited distribution range. **HABITAT** Mountainous areas, often 1,000 to 1,700 m., where the larvae often feed on cinquefoil *Potentilla*. **SEASON** Mid July to August.

*Carcharodus flocciferus*

*Carcharodus lavatherae*

*Spialia phlomidis* [KB]

*Spialia sertorius* (left & right)

*Muschampia proto*

*Muschampia tessellum* [KB]

*Pyrgus alveus* (left & right)

*Pyrgus armoricanus* [MS]

*Pyrgus folquieri* (left & right) [both KB]

**_Pyrgus cacaliae_ Dusky Grizzled skipper**
Wingspan: 26–31 mm. Dark brown, forewings with small white spots, so unlikely to be confused with related species. **HABITAT** Mountainous areas, often 1,000 to 1,800 m., where the larvae mainly feed on cinquefoil *Potentilla*. **SEASON** July to August.

*Pyrgus cacaliae*

**_Pyrgus carthami_ Safflower Skipper**
Wingspan: 26–33 mm. Brownish grey, with grey hair at wing base; one of the larger *Pyrgus*. Wings with white spots, including on outer margin of hindwing. **HABITAT** Grasslands, often 600 to 1,800 m., where the larvae feed on cinquefoil *Potentilla* and others. **SEASON** May to August.

*Pyrgus carthami*

**_Pyrgus cinarae_ Sandy Grizzled Skipper**
Wingspan: 26–32 mm. Easily recognised by large white markings on wings. **HABITAT** Rocky grasslands and woodland clearings to 2,300 m., where the larvae feed on Sulphur Cinquefoil *Potentilla recta*. **SEASON** July to early August.

*Pyrgus cinarae*

**_Pyrgus cirsii_ Cinquefoil Skipper**
Wingspan: 24–29 mm. Brownish grey, c-shaped central white spot, beneath which white spots are joined together (except high altitudes in part of its range in France and Italy) to form a sinuous mark. **HABITAT** Grasslands, including mountainous slopes 600 to 2,500 m., where the larvae feed on cinquefoil *Potentilla*. **SEASON** Mid July to early September.

*Pyrgus cirsii*

**_Pyrgus malvae_ Grizzled Skipper**
Wingspan: 18–24 mm. Dark brown to black with plentiful white spots, including submarginal. **HABITAT** Grasslands, including rocky slopes to 2,500 m., as well as woodland clearings. The larvae feed on strawberry *Fragaria*, cinquefoil *Potentilla* and bramble *Rubus*. **SEASON** March to September, but most likely April to June.

*Pyrgus malvae*

**_Pyrgus malvoides_ Southern Grizzled Skipper**
Wingspan: 20–26 mm. Regarded by some authors as a subspecies of *P. malvae* although genitalia differ. **HABITAT** Grasslands to 1,800 m. **SEASON** April to August.

*Pyrgus malvoides*

**_Pyrgus serratulae_ Olive Skipper**
Wingspan: 24–26 mm. Dark brown with white spots on wings, underside olive green. **HABITAT** Grasslands, often 1,000 to 2,600 m., where the larvae feed on cinquefoil *Potentilla*. **SEASON** May to July.

*Pyrgus serratulae*

**_Pyrgus sidae_ Yellow-banded Skipper**
Wingspan: 72–35 mm. As in various species, dark brown with white spots on wings, but easily recognised by its size and two black-edged yellow bands on the underside. **HABITAT** Grasslands to 1,800 m., where the larvae feed on Sulphur Cinquefoil *Potentilla recta*. **SEASON** May to July.

*Pyrgus sidae*

**_Heteropterus morpheus_ Large Chequered Skipper**
Wingspan: 27–35 mm. Dark brown with a few white or yellow spots on forewings. Underside yellow with large black-bordered white spots. **HABITAT** Damp grasslands up to 1,000 m., where the larvae feed on various tall grasses. **SEASON** June to July.

*Heteropterus morpheus*

*Pyrgus cacaliae* (top & bottom) [both KM]

*Pyrgus carthami* (top & bottom)

*Pyrgus cinarae* (top) [TN], (bottom) [KB]

*Pyrgus cirsii* [KB]

*Pyrgus malvae* (left & right)

*Pyrgus malvoides*

*Pyrgus serratulae* (left & right) [both KB]

*Pyrgus sidae* (left & right) [both MS]

*Heteropterus morpheus*

**_Carterocephalus palaemon_ Chequered Skipper**
Wingspan: 22–30 mm. Dark brown with yellowish spots. **HABITAT** Woodland edges and clearings and damp grasslands up to 1,800 m. The larvae feed on various grasses. **SEASON** May to June, usually July in mountains.

*Carterocephalus palaemon*

**_Thymelicus acteon_ Lulworth Skipper**
Wingspan: 21–27 mm. Small, dark species with dusting of golden scales. **HABITAT** Grasslands to 2,500 m., where the larvae feed on grasses. **SEASON** May to September.

*Thymelicus acteon*

**_Thymelicus lineola_ Essex Skipper**
Wingspan: 21–30 mm. Easily confused with some other *Thymelicus* species, but the antennal tip (pictured left) is black underneath. **HABITAT** Grasslands to 2,200 m., where the larvae feed on grasses. **SEASON** May to August.

*Thymelicus lineola*

**_Thymelicus sylvestris_ Small Skipper**
Wingspan: 21–29 mm. Attractive small golden-coloured skipper, only the ♂ has conspicuous black scent scales on the forewings. The antennal tip is orange underneath. **HABITAT** Grasslands up to 2,300 m., where the larvae feed on various grasses. **SEASON** May to September.

*Thymelicus sylvestris*

**_Hesperia comma_ Silver-spotted Skipper**
Wingspan: 24–34 mm. Bright with distinctive silvery white underside spots. **HABITAT** Grasslands, often calcareous up to 2,500 m., where the larvae feed on grasses. **SEASON** July to September.

*Hesperia comma*

**_Ochlodes sylvanus_ Large Skipper**
Wingspan: 23–36 mm. Dark brown with orange, also yellowish spots, ♂with large sex brand, but lacks the silvery-white underside spots. **HABITAT** Grasslands up to 1,800 m., where the larvae feed on various grasses. **SEASON** May to August.

*Ochlodes sylvanus*

**_Gegenes nostrodamus_ Mediterranean Skipper**
Wingspan: 29–36 mm. Dark brown with elongate forewings, only ♀s with pale forewing spots. Underside brown with small spots. **HABITAT** Rocky areas. **SEASON** April to October.

*Gegenes nostrodamus*

**_Gegenes pumilio_ Pygmy Skipper**
Wingspan: 30–34 mm. Dark brown, only ♀s with pale forewing spots. Underside brown with small spots. **HABITAT** Rocky areas up to 1,800 m. **SEASON** April to November.

*Gegenes pumilio*

**_Borbo borbonica_ Zeller's Skipper**
Wingspan: 28–30 mm. Dark brown with golden scales when fresh; conspicuous white forewing spots. **HABITAT** Rocky areas and others with bushes, on or near coast. **SEASON** June to November (all year in certain sites).

*Borbo borbonica*

**_Pelopidas thrax_ Millet Skipper**
Wingspan: 33–42 mm. Dark brown with whitish forewing spots. Underside plain, except ♀s with small whitish spots. **HABITAT** Agricultural and others, often coastal areas where the larvae feed on Millet *Panicum miliaceum*. **SEASON** May to October.

*Pelopidas thrax*

*arterocephalus palaemon* ♂ (top), (bottom)

*Thymelicus acteon* ♂ (top), (bottom)

*Thymelicus lineola* ♂ (top), (bottom)

*Thymelicus sylvestris* ♂

*Hesperia comma* ♂ (left) [PC], (right)

*Ochlodes sylvanus* ♂ (left & right)

*Gegenes pumilio* [SR]

*Gegenes nostrodamus*

*Borbo borbonica* [DBC]

*Pelopidas thrax* [SR]

## Family Pieridae – WHITES & YELLOWS

This family includes the familiar 'Cabbage' whites, regarded by many as pests.

*Leptidea duponcheli*

### *Leptidea duponcheli* Eastern Wood White

Wingspan: 30–37 mm. White with forewing tips black or faint black-smudged. Tip of antenna dark, including underside. **HABITAT** Rocky woodland edges and grasslands, often below 1,200 m., where the larvae feed on legumes *Lathyrus* and *Lotus*. **SEASON** Mid April to August in two generations.

*Leptidea juvernica*

*Leptidea reali*

### *Leptidea juvernica* Cryptic Wood White [Williams' Wood White]

Wingspan: 33–39 mm. White, with black or grey tip, more extensive than in *L. sinapsis*. **HABITAT** Woodland edges and clearings where the larvae feed on legumes *Lathyrus* and *Lotus*. **SEASON** May to June. **SIMILAR SPECIES** ***L. reali*** **Réal's Wood White** ([not illustrated] wingspan: 35–38 mm). Separated from *L. juvernica* in 2011 by molecular analysis. Not readily distinguishable in the field from the more widespread *L. sinapis*. A south-west European species found in humid to wet grasslands from April to August.

*Leptidea sinapis*

### *Leptidea sinapis* Wood White

Wingspan: 32–43 mm. Delicate-looking white butterfly with narrow black or grey, rounded wingtips. Tip of antenna black, underside white. **HABITAT** Woodland edges and others, including rocky areas up to 2,300 m. The slow, fluttering flight of the most widespread *Leptidea* species is conspicuous. This species takes mineral salts from puddles and nectars on flowers, including larval foodplants *Lathyrus*, *Lotus*, *Trifolium* and *Vicia*. **SEASON** May to August in two generations.

*Anthocharis cardamines*

### *Anthocharis cardamines* Orange-tip

Wingspan: 29–52 mm. Orange-tipped (♂ only). ♀ (pictured left) could be mistaken for a *Pieris* species but are easily recognised at rest with wings closed. **HABITAT** Various grasslands and woodland edges up to 2,300 m., where they are often seen fluttering near foodplants (various Brassicaceae). **SEASON** April to June, later in mountains.

*Anthocharis euphenoides*

### *Anthocharis euphenoides* Provence Orange-tip

Wingspan: 31–42 mm. Orange-tipped with inner border black (bolder in yellow-winged ♂; wings are white in ♀). **HABITAT** Grasslands and light woodland glades up to 1,800 m. **SEASON** March to June.

*Anthocharis gruneri*

### *Anthocharis gruneri* Gruner's Orange-tip

Wingspan: 26–34 mm. Similar to *A. cardamines*, but ♂ slightly yellowish. Black suffused area near black spot. **HABITAT** Grasslands including mountains and light woodland glades up to 2,300 m. **SEASON** March to June, but mainly April to May.

*Colotis evagore*

### *Colotis evagore* Desert Orange-tip

Wingspan: 30–36 mm. White, forewing black and orange tipped with further distinctive black markings and margins (more extensive in ♀), also on the hindwings. **HABITAT** Rocky grasslands and others on and near the coast, up to 400 m., where the larvae feed on *Capparis*. **SEASON** February to October.

*Euchloe ausonia*

### *Euchloe ausonia* Eastern Dappled White

Wingspan: 34–45 mm. Dappled white. **HABITAT** Open rocky grasslands and agricultural land up to 1,600 m., with Brassicaceae. Little overlap with closely related species. **SEASON** March to July, in two generations.

*Leptidea duponcheli* [TN]

*Leptidea juvernica*

*Leptidea sinapis*

*Anthocharis cardamines* ♂

*Anthocharis gruneri* ♂ (left) [KB], (right) [MS]

*Anthocharis euphenoides* ♂ (left & centre), ♀ (right)

*Colotis evagore* ♂ (left & right) [both SO]

*Euchloe ausonia* [MS]

***Euchloe belemia* Green-striped White**
Wingspan: 32–42 mm. Similar upperside to other *Euchloe* species, but distinctive striped underside. **HABITAT** Open grasslands and agricultural land up to 1,500 m., with Brassicaceae. **SEASON** February to early June, in two generations.

*Euchloe belemia*

***Euchloe crameri* Western Dappled White**
Wingspan: 40–48 mm. Similar to *E. ausonia*. **HABITAT** Rocky grasslands and agricultural land up to 2,000 m., with Brassicaceae. Western distribution. **SEASON** February to July, in two generations.

*Euchloe crameri*

***Euchloe penia* Eastern Greenish Black-tip**
Wingspan: 33–37 mm. Yellow, forewings with black markings. **HABITAT** Rocky, often mountainous areas up to 2,500 m., with Brassicaceae. **SEASON** March to August.

*Euchloe penia*

***Aporia crataegi* Black-veined White**
Wingspan: 47–76 mm. White with bold black veins. **HABITAT** Various mainly open habitats including orchards, up to 2,600 m., where the larvae feed on *Prunus* and others. **SEASON** April to July.

*Aporia crataegi*

***Pieris brassicae* Large White**
Wingspan: 48–70 mm. Usually larger than other *Pieris* species. Bold black patch from the wing tip to outer edge of wing (black at side as well as top). In addition, the ♀ has two rounded spots on the forewings. **HABITAT** Mainly open habitats including gardens, up to 2,600 m., where the larvae can be a pest on *Brassica* and others. **SEASON** February to November.

*Pieris brassicae*

***Pieris bryoniae* Mountain Green-veined White**
Wingspan: 38–44 mm. Wings with distinctive heavy suffusion. **HABITAT** Mountainous areas, typically 800 to 2,700 m., on Brassicaceae. **SEASON** May to September.

*Pieris bryoniae*

***Pieris krueperi* Krueper's Small White**
Wingspan: 42–50 mm. Forewings with addition black mark. **HABITAT** Rocky grasslands up to 2,000 m., on Brassicaceae. **SEASON** March to October.

*Pieris krueperi*

***Pieris mannii* Southern Small White**
Wingspan: 35–41 mm. Forewings with black tip more extensive than in the similar *P. rapae*. **HABITAT** Rocky grasslands and others up to 2,000 m., on Brassicaceae. **SEASON** April to August.

*Pieris mannii*

***Pieris rapae* Small White**
Wingspan: 38–57 mm. Usually smaller than *P. brassicae*, with a smaller, often fainter grey to black patch on the wing tip only along the top edge. **HABITAT** Various open habitats including gardens, up to 3,000 m., where the larvae can be a pest on *Brassica* and others. **SEASON** February to October.

*Pieris rapae*

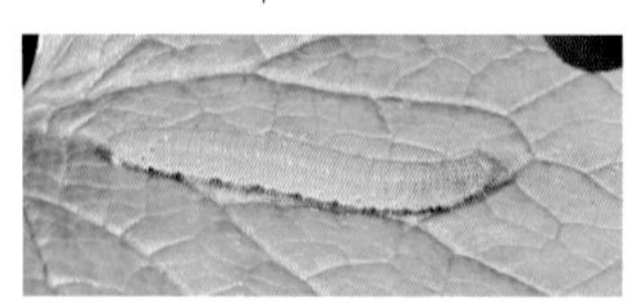

***Pieris napi* Green-veined White**
Wingspan: 32–57 mm. Underside with distinctive green-veined wings. **HABITAT** Grasslands, up to 2,000 m., on Brassicaceae (larva pictured left). **SEASON** March to November.

*Pieris napi*

*Euchloe belemia*

*Euchloe crameri* (left & right)

*Euchloe penia* [TN]

*Aporia crataegi* (left & right)

*Pieris brassicae* ♂

*Pieris bryoniae* ♀ [KM]

*Pieris krueperi* [MS]

*Pieris mannii* group [KB]

*Pieris rapae*

*Pieris napi* ♀

**_Pontia daplidice_ Bath White**
Wingspan: 31–52 mm. Dappled black, white and grey. **HABITAT** Grasslands, up to 3,000 m., on Brassicaceae (larva pictured below). Technically, this species is western, the eastern lookalike being ***P. edusa*** [not pictured] (distinguishable only by molecular analysis), with some overlap in range. **SEASON** April to October.

*Pontia daplidice*

*Pontia edusa*

**_Colias alfacariensis_ Berger's Clouded Yellow**
Wingspan: 40–52 mm. Dull lemon underside. The upperside is distinctive, much more extensive black edge on the hindwings of *C. croceus*, but they rest with wings closed. ♀s could be confused with form *helice* but most closely resemble *C. hyale*. **HABITAT** Rocky and calcareous grasslands, up to 2,600 m., where the larvae mainly feed on Horseshoe Vetch *Hippocrepis comosa*. The black spots on the larvae readily distinguish them from larvae of other *Colias* species. **SEASON** May to October.

*Colias alfacariensis*

**_Colias aurorina_ Greek Clouded Yellow**
Wingspan: 44–55 mm. ♂s deep orange with a noticeable purple reflection. **HABITAT** Rocky mountainous areas with low scrub, 500 to 3,000 m., where the larvae mainly feed on *Astracantha*. **SEASON** May to August.

*Colias aurorina*

**_Colias croceus_ Clouded Yellow**
Wingspan: 39–56 mm. Bright orange and yellow with black border (upperside rarely seen in the wild). Yellow, tinged with green on the underside. ♀ form *helice* is not uncommon and this has the ground colour creamy white. **HABITAT** Grasslands up to 3,000 m., often flying fast. The larvae mainly on various legumes, including clover *Trifolium*. **SEASON** March to November.

*Colias croceus*

**_Colias hyale_ Pale Clouded Yellow**
Wingspan: 33–62 mm. Similar to *C. alfacariensis* but with forewing tip slightly pointed, virtually impossible to distinguish from it in the field. **HABITAT** Grasslands up to 1,800 m., particularly fields with plentiful medick *Medicago* and clover *Trifolium*. **SEASON** May to September.

*Colias hyale*

**_Colias phicomone_ Mountain Clouded Yellow**
Wingspan: 38–48 mm. Greenish yellow, dusted with grey. **HABITAT** Mountainous areas typically 900 to 2,500 m., where the larvae mainly feed on various legumes. **SEASON** June to August, sometimes a small brood later, or emerges in May at lower altitudes.

*Colias phicomone*

**_Gonepteryx cleopatra_ Cleopatra**
Wingspan: 47–68 mm. Forewings pale green (in ♂s with large orange patch). **HABITAT** Open woodlands and scrub to 1,600 m., where the larvae feed on buckthorn *Rhamnus*. **SEASON** May to hibernation about August. Sometimes therefore seen early in the year.

*Gonepteryx cleopatra*

**_Gonepteryx rhamni_ Brimstone**
Wingspan: 47–74 mm. Unmistakeable sulphur yellow ♂ (the ♀ is greenish white) with hooked wingtips. **HABITAT** Woodlands, gardens and scrub to 2,000 m., where the larvae feed on buckthorn *Rhamnus*. **SEASON** May to hibernation about September. Sometimes therefore seen early in the year from February.

*Gonepteryx rhamni*

*Pontia daplidice* ♂ (left), ♀ (right) [PC]

*Colias alfacariensis* ♂

*Colias croceus* ♂ (left), ♀ (centre) [PC], ♀ form *helice*

*Colias aurorina* ♂ [MS]

*Colias hyale* [PE]

*Colias phicomone* [PC]

*Gonepteryx cleopatra* ♂ (left), ♀ (right)

*Gonepteryx rhamni* ♂

## Family Nymphalidae – NYMPHALIDS, FRITILLARIES & BROWNS

The Family includes some spectacular species well known even to casual observers. Graylings and some others are likely to be seen on bare ground and, when landing, quickly tuck the forewings down so the eye-spots are hidden. If disturbed, the forewings are raised revealing the eye-spots, which may startle a potential predator. In the past the Milkweed butterflies and browns were treated as distinct families Danaidae and Satyridae.

### *Libythea celtis* Nettle-tree Butterfly

Wingspan: 35–43 mm. Brown with large orange spots, easily recognised by wing shape and snout. **HABITAT** Woodlands and other areas foodplants occur, up to 2,000 m., where the larvae feed on *Celtis* spp. **SEASON** June to August, also after hibernation in March.

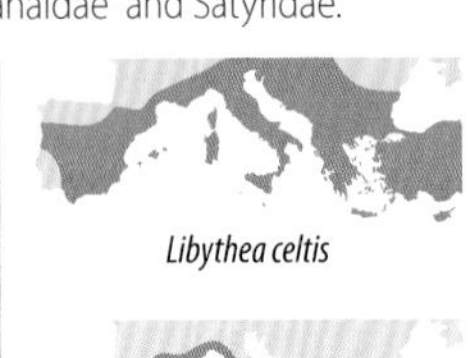

*Libythea celtis*

### *Danaus chrysippus* Plain Tiger

Wingspan: 60–80 mm. Orange with black tips and borders. **HABITAT** Coastal grasslands, gardens and parks where the larvae feed on milkweeds, particularly *Asclepias curassavica*. A known migrant species. **SEASON** May to October.

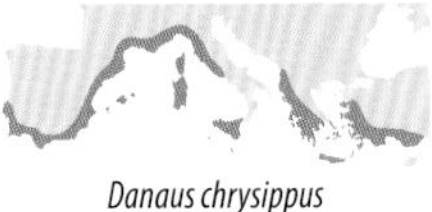

*Danaus chrysippus*

### *Danaus plexippus* Monarch

Wingspan: 89–102 mm. Unmistakeable large orange butterflies, with black veins and borders. **HABITAT** Grasslands, gardens and parks where the larvae feed on milkweeds, particularly *Asclepias curassavica*. The larvae sport warning colours derived from milkweeds, indicating to potential predators that they are poisonous. Numbers vary and are often modest. However, they were abundant in southern Spain in September 2016, often flying in towns; some of these then migrate to other countries in Europe. **SEASON** May to October.

*Danaus plexippus*

### *Charaxes jasius* Two-tailed Pasha

Wingspan: 75–80 mm. Dark brown with broad orange borders. Hindwing with two tails. **HABITAT** Various scrubby habitats and gardens to 1,300 m., where the larvae often feed on Strawberry-tree *Arbutus unedo*. Adults are fast fliers, often resting on tree trunks, on the foodplant, or flying to over-ripe fruit. In the Alameda, Gibraltar Botanic Gardens, the larvae also feed on *Osyris quadripartita*. **SEASON** May to October in two generations.

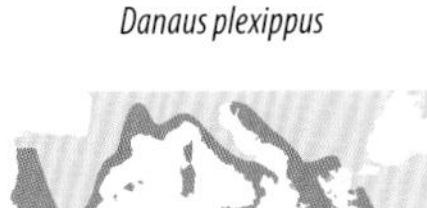

*Charaxes jasius*

### *Kirinia climene* Lesser Lattice Brown

Wingspan: 46–48 mm. ♂ forewing orange with brown borders and small eye spot. Underside with small black spots. **HABITAT** Woodland edges to 2,000 m., where the larvae often feed on course grasses. Adults often rest on tree trunks. **SEASON** June to August.

*Kirinia climene*

### *Kirinia roxelana* Lattice Brown

Wingspan: 58–62 mm. Underside with large black ringed spots and wavy lines. **HABITAT** Open woodlands and grasslands to 2,000 m., where the larvae feed on various grasses. Adults often rest on tree trunks or in bushes. **SEASON** May to September.

*Kirinia roxelana*

### *Lasiommata maera* Large Wall

Wingspan: 38–49 mm. ♂ darker brown than *P. megera*. **HABITAT** Woodlands and grasslands to 2,500 m., where the larvae feed on various grasses. **SEASON** Late April to September.

*Lasiommata maera*

### *Lasiommata megera* Wall

Wingspan: 38–47 mm. Golden upperside with conspicuous eye-spots, and a zig-zag pattern on the underside. **HABITAT** Various, often rocky grasslands with some bare ground and ideally walls to 3,000 m., where the larvae feed on various grasses. **SEASON** April to October.

*Lasiommata megera*

### *Lasiommata petropolitana* Northern Wall Brown

Wingspan: 36–42 mm. ♂ dark brown, forewings with three dark bars, absent in the similar *P. maera*. **HABITAT** Woodlands and grasslands to 2,300 m., where the larvae feed on various grasses. **SEASON** Late April to September.

*Lasiommata petropolitana*

*Danaus chrysippus* ♂

*Danaus plexippus* ♂

*Libythea celtis* [KB]

*Charaxes jasius*

*Kirinia climene* [TN]

*Kirinia roxelana* [MS]

*Lasiommata megera* ♂

*Lasiommata petropolitana* [KB]

*Lasiommata maera* ♂ (left), ♀ (centre), ♀ (right) [PC]

***Lopinga achine*** **Woodland Brown**
Wingspan: 40–46 mm. Dark brown, with large yellow-ringed black eye-spots on both upperside and underside. **HABITAT** Woodlands to 1,500 m., including damp meadows nearby, where the larvae feed on various grasses. **SEASON** June to July.

*Lopinga achine*

***Parage aegeria*** **Speckled Wood**
Wingspan: 35–42 mm. Dark brown with orange spots (some populations in northern Europe, including Britain, have yellow spots). **HABITAT** Woodlands, open areas including gardens and parks to 2,500 m., where the larvae feed on various grasses. **SEASON** Late February to October.

*Parage aegeria*

***Coenonympha arcania*** **Pearly Heath**
Wingspan: 29–36 mm. Orange. Hindwings with orange-ringed black eye-spots and a broad white band. **HABITAT** Grasslands including woodland clearings to 2,300 m. The larvae feed on various grasses. **SEASON** May to September.

*Coenonympha arcania*

***Coenonympha dorus*** **Dusky Heath**
Wingspan: 28–34 mm. Orange. Hindwings with several orange-ringed black eye-spots. **HABITAT** Rocky grasslands including woodland clearings to 1,700 m. The larvae feed on various grasses. **SEASON** June to August.

*Coenonympha dorus*

***Coenonympha gardetta*** **Alpine Heath**
Wingspan: 23–30 mm. Greyish-brown bands. Underside of hindwings with black eye-spots on a whitish band. **HABITAT** Subalpine grasslands. **SEASON** June to August.

*Coenonympha gardetta*

***Coenonympha glycerion*** **Chestnut Heath**
Wingspan: 27–32 mm. Orange. Hindwings with small yellow-ringed black eye-spots and white patches. **HABITAT** Grasslands to 3,000 m. The larvae feed on various grasses. **SEASON** June to August.

*Coenonympha glycerion*

***Coenonympha oedippus*** **False Ringlet**
Wingspan: 29–35 mm. Orange. Hindwings with larger yellow-ringed black eye-spots and white streak. **HABITAT** Wetlands to 700 m. The larvae feed on grasses. **SEASON** June to July.

*Coenonympha oedippus*

***Coenonympha orientalis*** **Balkan Heath**
Wingspan: 30–32 mm. Orange. Hindwings with small yellow-ringed black eye-spots and a white band. **HABITAT** Grassland slopes and woodland clearings to 2,100 m. The larvae feed on various grasses. **SEASON** June to August.

*Coenonympha orientalis*

***Coenonympha pamphilus*** **Small Heath**
Wingspan: 22–33 mm. Small, almost plain, pale orange species. **HABITAT** Grasslands to 2,700 m. The larvae feed on various grasses. **SEASON** Late February to October.

*Coenonympha pamphilus*

***Coenonympha rhodopensis*** **Eastern Large Heath**
Wingspan: 32–34 mm. Hindwings with small yellow-ringed black eye-spots and a white, almost central mark. **HABITAT** Mountainous areas 750 to 2,500 m. **SEASON** June to August.

*Coenonympha rhodopensis*

*Parage aegeria* ♂ (left & centre), ♀ (right) [PC]

*Lopinga achine*

*Coenonympha arcania*

*Coenonympha dorus*

*Coenonympha gardetta* [PC]

*Coenonympha glycerion* [MS]

*Coenonympha oedippus*

*Coenonympha orientalis* [KB]

*Coenonympha pamphilus*

*Coenonympha rhodopensis* [MS]

**_Erebia aethiops_ Scotch Argus**
Wingspan: 35–52 mm. Dark brown with distinctly spotted orange bands. Hindwings of underside with bands (pictured left). **HABITAT** Mountainous areas including forest clearings, all *Erebia* larvae feed on grasses. **SEASON** Late June to September.

**_Erebia cassioides_ Common Brassy Ringlet**
Wingspan: 27–32 mm. Dark brown with a distinct brassy sheen. Underside of hindwings silvery grey (pictured left [KB]). **HABITAT** Rocky mountainous areas 1,600 to 2,600 m. **SEASON** Late June to September. **SIMILAR SPECIES** ***Erebia arvernensis*** (parts of France, north Spain, Italy, Switzerland) [not illustrated] now split from *E. cassiodes*, likewise *E. neleus* (Greece, Bulgaria *et al*).

**_Erebia epiphron_ Mountain Ringlet**
Wingspan: 29–42 mm. Usually small, dark brown with distinctly spotted orange bands, including underside, but variable. **HABITAT** Damp mountainous areas up to 3,000 m. **SEASON** Late June to early August.

**_Erebia euryale_ Large Ringlet**
Wingspan: 36–40 mm. Dark brown with orange band on both wings; eye-spots small. **HABITAT** Mountainous areas 650 to 2,500 m. **SEASON** Late June to August.

**_Erebia gorge_ Silky Ringlet**
Wingspan: 30–37 mm. Dark brown, shiny, with broad orange band. Underside of hindwings greyish brown (pictured left [KB]). **HABITAT** Rocky mountainous areas to 2,500 m. **SEASON** Late June to August.

**_Erebia hispania_ Spanish Brassy Ringlet**
Wingspan: 31–36 mm. Similar to *E. cassioides*. **HABITAT** Rocky mountainous areas 1,800 to 2,900 m, only plentiful in Sierra Nevada, Spain. **SEASON** Mid June to August. **SIMILAR SPECIES** ***Erebia rondoui* Pyrenees Brassy Ringlet** (pictured left [PC]) is found at 1,300 to 2,900 m on alpine grasslands in the Pyrenees from July to August.

**_Erebia lefebvrei_ Lefèbvre's Ringlet**
Wingspan: 36–41 mm. Dark brownish black with orange band in ♀. Conspicuous black-ringed white spots. **HABITAT** Rocky mountainous areas 1,700 to 2,700 m. **SEASON** Late June to August.

**_Erebia ligea_ Arran Brown**
Wingspan: 38–42 mm. Brown with broad orange bands on wings. Underside with white streak. **HABITAT** Mountainous areas to 2,500 m. **SEASON** June to August.

**_Erebia melampus_ Lesser Mountain Ringlet**
Wingspan: 27–30 mm. Dark brown with broad orange band. **HABITAT** Mountainous areas 800 to 2,400 m. **SEASON** July to mid September.

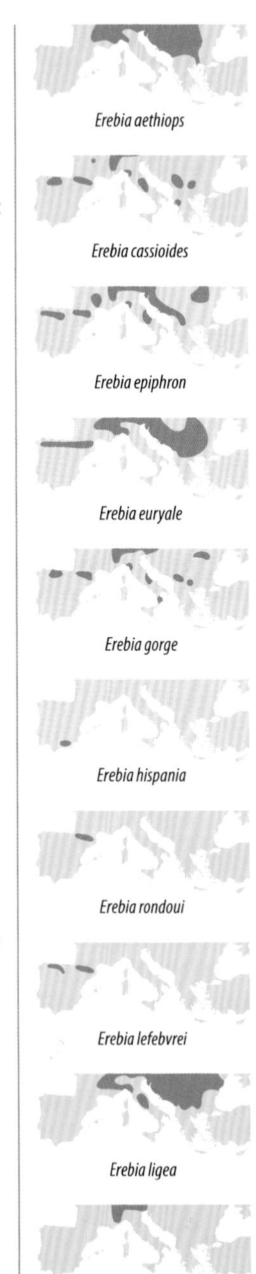

*Erebia aethiops* ♂

*Erebia cassioides* ♂ [KB]

*Erebia epiphron*

*Erebia euryale* ♂

*Erebia gorge* [KB]

*Erebia ligea* [MS]

*Erebia hispania* ♀ (left & right)

*Erebia melampus* [KB]

*Erebia lefebvrei* ♂ (left) [PC], ♀ (centre & right)

**_Erebia meolans_ Piedmont Ringlet**
Wingspan: 36–14 mm. Brown, two uneven apical eye-spots, sometimes another tiny spot; underside with orange band. **HABITAT** Mountainous areas, mostly 600 to 2,000 m. **SEASON** Late May to mid August.

*Erebia meolans*

**_Erebia oeme_ Bright-eyed Ringlet**
Wingspan: 34–40 mm. Brown, orange of wings variable. Vernacular name originates from bright eye-spot pupils, larger on underside than other *Erebia* (mating pair pictured left). **HABITAT** Mountainous areas, mostly 1,500 to 2,100 m. **SEASON** Mid June to early August.

*Erebia oeme*

**_Erebia ottomana_ Ottoman Brassy Ringlet**
Wingspan: 32–40 mm. Dark brown with broad orange band, forewings with two eye spots touching. **HABITAT** Mountainous areas 650 to 2,500 m. **SEASON** July.

*Erebia ottomana*

**_Erebia pharte_ Blind Ringlet**
Wingspan: 32–38 mm. Brown, with orange band (no spots). **HABITAT** Mountainous areas 1,000 to 2,500 m. **SEASON** July to August.

*Erebia pharte*

**_Erebia triaria_ de Prunner's Ringlet**
Wingspan: 39–45 mm. Similar to *E. meolans*, but three apical eye spots in a straight line. **HABITAT** Mountainous areas to 2,500 m. **SEASON** Late April to mid July.

*Erebia triaria*

**_Aphantopus hyperantus_ Ringlet**
Wingspan: 30–42 mm. Dark brown upperside with indistinct eye spots; could be confused with *Maniola jurtina*, but the underside has conspicuous yellow ringed eye-spots (absent in some specimens). **HABITAT** Woodlands including mountainous areas to 2,000 m., where the larvae feed on various tall grasses. **SEASON** June to August.

*Aphantopus hyperantus*

**_Maniola jurtina_ Meadow Brown**
Wingspan: 36–46 mm. ♂ dark brown (underside pictured left), ♀ with orange patches. **HABITAT** Various grasslands, where the larvae eat grasses. **SEASON** May to September.

*Maniola jurtina*

**_Maniola megala_ Turkish Meadow Brown**
Wingspan: 36–46 mm. Darker brown than close relatives, ♂ underside of hindwings with two to six larger eye-spots. **HABITAT** Rocky grasslands including in woodlands to 500 m., where the larvae eat grasses. Restricted to Lesbos and Turkey, overlapping with the similar paler *M. telmessia*. **SEASON** May to September.

*Maniola megala*

**_Maniola telmessia_ Aegean Meadow Brown**
Wingspan: 33–42 mm. Dark brown with orange patch, ♀ with much more orange. **HABITAT** Grasslands to 2,000 m., where the larvae eat grasses. **SEASON** April to September.

*Maniola telmessia*

*Erebia meolans* (left) [PC], right

*Erebia oeme* ♀

*Erebia ottomana* [TN]

*Erebia pharte* (left & right) [both KB]

*Erebia triaria* ♀

*Aphantopus hyperantus* (left & right)

*Maniola jurtina* ♂

*Maniola megala* ♀ [SR]

*Maniola telmessia* ♂ [MS]

***Proterebia phegea*** **Dalmatian Ringlet**
Wingspan: 35–46 mm. Dark brown, with several large rings on both wings. Underside of hindwings with pale veins (pictured left [KB]). **HABITAT** Grassy, rocky slopes to 1,500 m or so, where the larvae feed on Sheep's Fescue *Festuca ovina*. **SEASON** April to May.

*Proterebia phegea*

***Pyronia bathseba*** **Spanish Gatekeeper**
Wingspan: 34–40 mm. Orange with dark brown borders, ♂ with more extensive brown area at base of both wings than other *Pyronia* species. Underside with a distinctive whitish band, surrounded by eye-spots. **HABITAT** Light woodlands and rocky scrub 300 to 1,700 m. The larvae in the genus *Pyronia* feed on various grasses. **SEASON** May to July.

*Pyronia bathseba*

***Pyronia cecilia*** **Southern Gatekeeper**
Wingspan: 30–32 mm. Bright orange, large forewing eye-spot, similar to *P. tithonus*. **HABITAT** Rocky grasslands, often below 1,200 m., but in the mountains up to 2,300 m. **SEASON** May to September.

*Pyronia cecilia*

***Pyronia tithonus*** **Gatekeeper**
Wingspan: 34–40 mm. Orange upperside, eye-spot moderate size. ♂ forewings with a broad sex brand (pictured right). **HABITAT** Grasslands to 2,300 m., including damp sites, but mostly at lower altitudes. **SEASON** June to September.

*Pyronia tithonus*

***Melanargia galathea*** **Marbled White**
Wingspan: 45–50 mm. Black and white or cream pattern. ♀ underside yellowish (pictured left). **HABITAT** Various grasslands to 2,000 m. The larvae in the genus *Melanargia* feed on grasses. **SEASON** June to August.

*Melanargia galathea*

***Melanargia ines*** **Spanish Marbled White**
Wingspan: 41–54 mm. Innermost white forewing patch with strong black bar. Underside of hindwing with five large eye-spots. **HABITAT** Rocky grasslands to 1,500 m or more. **SEASON** Late March to June.

*Melanargia ines*

***Melanargia lachesis*** **Iberian Marbled White**
Wingspan: 43–47 mm. Upperside with plenty of white areas. **HABITAT** Grasslands to 2,000 m. **SEASON** June to early August.

*Melanargia lachesis*

***Melanargia larissa*** **Balkan Marbled White**
Wingspan: 43–45 mm. Easily recognised by suffused dark markings. **HABITAT** Various rocky grasslands to 2,200 m. **SEASON** May to mid August.

*Melanargia larissa*

***Melanargia russiae***
**Esper's Marbled White**
Wingspan: 43–55 mm. Innermost white forewing patch with black central stripe (♂ underside pictured left [TN]). **HABITAT** Grasslands including mountainous areas to 1,800 m. **SEASON** Late June to August.

*Melanargia russiae*

*Proterebia phegea* [KB]

*Pyronia bathseba* ♂ (left), ♀ (right)

*Pyronia cecilia* ♀ (left), ♂ (right)

*Pyronia tithonus*

*Melanargia galathea* ♂ [PC]

*Melanargia ines* ♂ (left), ♀ (right)

*Melanargia lachesis* ♂ [PC]

*Melanargia larissa* [MS]

*Melanargia russiae* [KB]

### *Arethusana boabdil* Southern False Grayling

Wingspan: 37–49 mm. Brown with orange bands, similar in appearance to *Hipparchia semele* and other species. However, the underside of the forewings has one black spot (two in *H. semele*); conspicuous white-veined hindwings. **HABITAT** Lightly wooded areas and rocky grasslands, including mountainous areas to 1,700 m. The larvae feed on grasses. **SEASON** June to September.

*Arethusana boabdil*

### *Brintesia circe* Great Banded Grayling

Wingspan: 48–80 mm. Dark brown to black with broad white bands on both wings; underside of hindwings with broad white band and shorter, partial inner band. **HABITAT** Woodland clearings and grasslands to 2,000 m. The larvae feed on grasses. **SEASON** Late May to September.

*Brintesia circe*

*Brintesia circe* in flight, **Jujols Reserve Naturelle, eastern Pyrenees, Roussillon, France**: the broad white bands on the wings are visible when the butterfly takes flight. [LC]

### *Chazara briseis* Hermit

Wingspan: 45–71 mm. Dark brown with cream band. **HABITAT** Rocky grasslands to 2,400 m. The larvae feed on grasses. **SEASON** July to August.

*Chazara briseis*

### *Hipparchia hermione* Rock Grayling

Wingspan: 51–63 mm. Dark brown with pale band incorporating two eye-spots. Very similar to *H. fagi* and others, genitalia differ. **HABITAT** Rocky grasslands to 1,600 m. The larvae of this and other *Hipparchia* species feed on various grasses. **SEASON** July to August.

*Hipparchia hermione*

### *Hipparchia fagi* Woodland Grayling

Wingspan: 51–63 mm. Dark brown with pale band. **HABITAT** Woodland edges and clearings to 2,400 m. **SEASON** May to October.

*Hipparchia fagi*

### *Hipparchia fatua* Freyer's Grayling

Wingspan: 47–60 mm. Fore wing upperside and underside with two white dots between eye-spots. **HABITAT** Rocky areas, including woodlands and gardens to 2,000 m. **SEASON** July to September.

*Hipparchia fatua*

### *Hipparchia fidia* Striped Grayling

Wingspan: 51–68 mm. Upperside and underside of forewings with two large white dots between eye-spots. Underside of hindwings with characteristic stripes. **HABITAT** Rocky sites with sparse woodlands to 2,200 m. **SEASON** Late June to August.

*Hipparchia fidia*

### *Hipparchia mersina* Samos Grayling

Wingspan: 45–50 mm. Underside of hindwings greyish brown. **HABITAT** Rocky grasslands to 2,000 m where it is restricted to the Greek islands of Lesbos and Samos, but also in Turkey. **SEASON** Mid May to November.

*Hipparchia mersina*

### *Hipparchia semele* Grayling

Wingspan: 40–59 mm. Orange and brown upperside, mottled grey underside. **HABITAT** Grasslands including in woodlands, to 2,000 m. **SEASON** Late June to August.

*Hipparchia semele*

*Brintesia circe*

*Chazara briseis* [TN]

*Arethusana boabdil*

*Hipparchia hermione*

*Hipparchia fagi*

*Hipparchia fatua* [SR]

*Hipparchia fidia*

*Hipparchia mersina* [MS]

*Hipparchia semele* (top) [PC], (bottom)

***Hipparchia statilinus* Tree Grayling**
Wingspan: 42–55 mm. Underside of forewings with two large yellow-ringed eye-spots, with two small white dots in between. **HABITAT** Rocky grassland in mixed woodlands to 2,000 m. **SEASON** July to September.

*Hipparchia statilinus*

***Hipparchia syriaca* Eastern Rock Grayling**
Wingspan: 50–58 mm. Underside of forewings with broad whitish or yellowish band. **HABITAT** Mountainous mixed woodlands and grassy areas to 1,800 m. **SEASON** May to September.

*Hipparchia syriaca*

***Hipparchia volgensis* Delattin's Grayling**
Wingspan: 46–56 mm. Rather similar to *H. semele* but does not overlap in range. **HABITAT** Sparse pine woodlands, rocky grasslands, and others to 1,700 m, often resting on tree trunks. **SEASON** Late May to September.

*Hipparchia volgensis*

***Minois dryas* Dryad**
Wingspan: 44–63 mm. Dark brown, forewings with two large black eye-spots with blue pupils. **HABITAT** Woodland clearings and rocky sites to 2,200 m. **SEASON** July to August.

*Minois dryas*

***Pseudochazara anthelea* White-banded Grayling**
Wingspan: 44–55 mm. Striking whitish banded species, underside much paler than related species. **HABITAT** Light woodlands and rocky slopes, often on calcareous soil, 500 to 2,400 m. **SEASON** Late May to August.
**SIMILAR SPECIES** ***Pseudochazara amalthea*** (Greece, Bulgaria *et al*) [not illustrated] now split from *P. anthelea.*

*Pseudochazara anthelea*

***Pseudochazara cingowskii* Macedonian Grayling**
Wingspan: 50–54 mm. Forewings with two small white dots between eye-spots. **HABITAT** Rocky slopes with sparse vegetation on calcareous soil, 1,000 to 1,200 m, restricted to the Prilep area, Macedonia. **SEASON** July to August.

*Pseudochazara cingowskii*

***Pseudochazara williamsi* Nevada Grayling**
Wingspan: 41–51 mm. Similar to *H. semele*, with which it may fly with, but noticeably paler. Regarded by some authors as a subspecies of the Asian *P. hippolyte.* **HABITAT** Rocky mountainous sites 1,400 to 2,700 m, with its stronghold in Sierra Nevada, Spain. **SEASON** Late June to July.

*Pseudochazara williamsi*

***Satyrus actaea* Black Satyr**
Wingspan: 42–55 mm. Dark brown ♂ (pictured left), usually lighter in ♀ (♂ often black). **HABITAT** Rocky grasslands or margins of lightly woodlands, often 1,000 to 2,000 m. **SEASON** June to August.

*Satyrus actaea*

***Satyrus ferula* Great Sooty Satyr**
Wingspan: 47–57 mm. Dark brown or black ♂, lighter in ♀. with orange patch surrounding eye-spots. **HABITAT** Rocky grasslands 400 to 2,200 m., they sometimes rest with wings open, unlike many related species. **SEASON** Mid June to August.

*Satyrus ferula*

*Hipparchia statilinus*

*Hipparchia syriaca* [SR]

*Hipparchia volgensis* [KB]

*Minois dryas* ♀ [KB]

*Pseudochazara anthelea* ♂ [MS]

*Pseudochazara cingowskii* [TN]

*Pseudochazara williamsi*

*Satyrus actaea* ♂ (left), ♀ (right)

*Satyrus ferula* ♂ (left), ♂ (centre) [PC], ♀ (right)

**_Boloria dia_ Weaver's Fritillary**
Wingspan: 29–35 mm. Orange with black spots (♂ pictured right); hindwing underside with a violet tinge. **HABITAT** Woodland clearings and grasslands to 2,000 m. **SEASON** Late April to early September, in one or two generations.

*Boloria dia*

**_Boloria euphrosyne_ Pearl-bordered Fritillary**
Wingspan: 31–42 mm. Orange with black spots, sometimes confused with *B. selene*, but on the underside, the hindwings pattern in particular is rather different, with only one silver spot in the central band. **HABITAT** Woodland clearings and grasslands to 2,000 m, where the larvae of this and other *Boloria* species, feed on *Viola* leaves and flowers. **SEASON** Late April to July with a partial second brood July to September.

*Boloria euphrosyne*

**_Boloria graeca_ Balkan Fritillary**
Wingspan: 33–37 mm. Orange with less black than other *Boloria* species. **HABITAT** Various mainly mountainous areas 750 to 2,500 m. **SEASON** June to August.

*Boloria graeca*

**_Boloria pales_ Shepherd's Fritillary**
Wingspan: 34–37 mm. Distinctive hindwing shape. **HABITAT** Alpine and subalpine meadows 2,200 to 2,700 m. **SEASON** Late June to August.

*Boloria pales*

**_Boloria selene_ Small Pearl-bordered Fritillary**
Wingspan: 30–40 mm. Orange with black spots, most easily distinguished from *B. euphrosyne* by the greater colour contrast on the underside, including hindwings with several whitish blotches (only two in *euphrosyne*, excluding margins. **HABITAT** Often damp woodland edges or clearings, or some grasslands to 2,200 m. **SEASON** May to August.

*Boloria selene*

**_Issoria lathonia_ Queen of Spain Fritillary**
Wingspan: 36–46 mm. Orange with black spots. Underside with large silver spangles. **HABITAT** Various to 3,000 m., where the larvae feed on *Viola*. **SEASON** May to October.

*Issoria lathonia*

**_Brenthis daphne_ Marbled Fritillary**
Wingspan: 38–47 mm. Orange with black spots, margin with large spots. On the underside, the outer part of hindwings is purple-tinged. **HABITAT** Woodland edges and bushy grasslands, occasionally at higher ground to 2,000 m. The larvae feed on bramble *Rubus*. **SEASON** Late May to July.

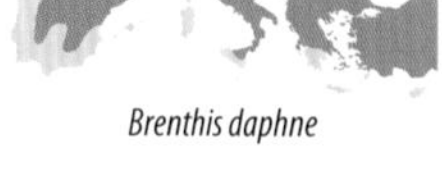

*Brenthis daphne*

**_Brenthis ino_ Lesser Marbled Fritillary**
Wingspan: 35–42 mm. Orange with black spots, margin black. Outer part of hindwings with a yellow underside. **HABITAT** Woodland edges and marshy grasslands to 2,000 m. The larvae feed on various Rosaceae. **SEASON** June to mid August.

*Brenthis ino*

*Brenthis ino* ♀

*Boloria dia* ♀ (top), ♂ (bottom)

*Boloria euphrosyne* (top & bottom)

*Boloria graeca* (top & bottom) [both KB]

*Boloria pales* (top & bottom) [both KB]

*Boloria selene* (top & bottom)

*Issoria lathonia* (top & bottom)

*Brenthis daphne* ♂ (left & right)

*Brenthis ino* ♂

*Argynnis adippe*

*Argynnis aglaja*

*Argynnis niobe*

*Argynnis pandora*

*Argynnis paphia*

*Neptis rivularis*

*Neptis sappho*

### *Argynnis adippe* High Brown Fritillary

Wingspan: 46–62 mm. Easily mistaken in flight with other fritillaries, although the underside of *A. adippe* has large silver spots (lacking in form *cleodoxa*). *A. adippe* has red-ringed spots (mating pair pictured right [PC]) absent in *A. aglaja* where the hindwings are flushed with green. **HABITAT** Woodland clearings and others, often at higher altitudes to 2,300 m where the larvae feed on *Viola*. **SEASON** June to August.

### *Argynnis aglaja* Dark Green Fritillary

Wingspan: 44–61 mm. Large orange species with black spots; underside with basal half of the hindwings containing silver spots. Underside conspicuously green-flushed. **HABITAT** Woodland clearings and others to 2,500 m where the larvae feed on *Viola*. **SEASON** June to August.

### *Argynnis niobe* Niobe Fritillary

Wingspan: 45–52 mm. Easily mistaken for *A. adippe* (silver spots on hindwings lacking in form *eris* [♂ pictured right]). Like, *A. adippe*, hindwing with red-ringed spots. Look also for a small black dot near the base of the hindwings in *A. niobe*. **HABITAT** Grasslands and woodlands to 2,400 m. The larvae feed on *Viola*. **SEASON** June to mid August.

### *Argynnis pandora* Cardinal

Wingspan: 60–75 mm. The largest European fritillary is greenish brown with a distinctive pale green, silver-striped hindwings. **HABITAT** Woodland clearings and grasslands to 2,000 m or so, where they often seek out thistles to nectar on. The larvae feed on *Viola*. **SEASON** June to October.

### *Argynnis paphia* Silver-washed Fritillary

Wingspan: 54–70 mm. Large tawny species with black spots and bars in the ♂; underside greenish with silver streaks. ♀ darker. **HABITAT** Woodland clearings and margins to 2,300 m. The larvae feed on *Viola*. **SEASON** June to early September.

### *Neptis rivularis* Hungarian Glider

Wingspan: 50–52 mm. Black with white band. **HABITAT** Woodland clearings to 1,600 m. The larvae feed on *Spiraea* and others. **SEASON** Late May to August.

### *Neptis sappho* Common Glider

Wingspan: 50–56 mm. Black with two white bands on hindwings (underside pictured left [KB]). **HABITAT** Woodland clearings and others to 1,500 m. The larvae feed on *Lathyrus*. **SEASON** May to September in two generations.

*Argynnis adippe* ♂

*Argynnis aglaja* ♂

*Argynnis niobe* ♀

*Argynnis paphia* ♂ (left), ♂s (right)

*Neptis rivularis* [KB]

*Argynnis pandora* ♂ (left), ♀ (right)

*Neptis sappho* [KB]

### *Limenitis camilla* White Admiral

Wingspan: 44–60 mm. Sooty brown with white band and markings on the upperside; tawny orange with grey and white markings on the underside. **HABITAT** Open woodlands to 1,600 m., where the larvae feed on honeysuckle *Lonicera*. **SEASON** May to September in up to two generations.

### *Limenitis populi* Poplar Admiral

Wingspan: 63–75 mm. Black with white band, orange markings and bluish sheen. Underside mainly orange (pictured left [MS]). **HABITAT** Woodlands, sometimes mixed, up to 2,000 m where the larvae mainly feed on Aspen *Populus tremula*. **SEASON** Late May to July.

### *Limenitis reducta* Southern White Admiral

Wingspan: 40–55 mm. Black with a bluish tinge. White markings on forewings and band on hindwings. Underside brown with whitish areas (pictured left). **HABITAT** Woodland clearings and others, to 2,000 m where the larvae mainly feed on honeysuckle *Lonicera*. **SEASON** April to October in up to three generations.

### *Apatura ilia* Lesser Purple Emperor

Wingspan: 52–64 mm. Brown with orange-ringed black spots on fore and hindwings. ♂s iridescent purple. Form *clytie* is light brown. **HABITAT** Woodland clearings and others, to 1,300 m where the larvae feed on poplar *Populus* and willow *Salix*. **SEASON** Late May to August if two generations.

### *Apatura iris* Purple Emperor

Wingspan: 60–75 mm. Stunning, ♂s flash every shade of purple in the sun, on the upperside, but at certain angles look like the brown ♀s, with whitish markings. Unlike *A. ilia*, only the hindwings have a black spot. The underside is paler brown, with darker areas, white markings and a large black ring, with brown border on the forewings. **HABITAT** Woodland clearings and others, to 1,500 m where the larvae feed on willow *Salix*. For much of the time they are elusive, staying in the tree-tops, perhaps on oak *Quercus*. **SEASON** Mid June to mid August.

### *Araschnia levana* Map

Wingspan: 30–38 mm. Orange with black and a few white spots in spring, the summer form *prorsa* is black and white. Characteristic map-like underside. **HABITAT** Various woodlands to 1,700 m, where the larval foodplant, nettle *Urtica* grows. **SEASON** April to August, sometimes a later generation.

*Araschnia levana* form *prorsa* [both KB]

### *Vanessa atalanta* Red Admiral

Wingspan: 46–66 mm. Black with red band and white markings. **HABITAT** Various to 2,500 m, the larvae feed on species of Urticaceae. **SEASON** May to October and in March to April after hibernation.

### *Vanessa cardui* Painted Lady

Wingspan: 46–62 mm. Rosy-orange, the black wing tips marked with white. **HABITAT** Various to 3,000 m, the larvae feed on various plants, including thistles *Carduus* and *Cirsium*. **SEASON** March to October.

*Limenitis camilla*

*Limenitis populi*

*Limentis reducta*

*Apatura ilia*

*Apatura iris*

*Araschnia levana*

*Vanessa atalanta*

*Vanessa cardui*

*Limenitis camilla* | *Limenitis populi* [MP] | *Limentis reducta* [TB]

*Apatura ilia* ♂ (left & centre), ♂ form *clyte* (right) [KB]

*Apatura iris* ♂ (left) [PE], (right) [KB]

*Araschnia levana* ♀ [PE] | *Vanessa atalanta* | *Vanessa cardui*

***Aglais io* Peacock**
Wingspan: 45–62 mm. Easily recognised by the bold eye-spots. The underside is black. **HABITAT** Various to 2,500 m., the larvae mainly feed on Common Nettle *Urtica dioica*. **SEASON** June to October in one generation. They hibernate and re-appear from March.

*Aglais io*

***Aglais urticae* Small Tortoiseshell**
Wingspan: 40–53 mm. Bright orange ground-colour, with marginal blue spots. The black and white underside is quite a contrast. **HABITAT** Open areas to 3,000 m., where the larvae feed on nettle *Urtica*. **SEASON** March to October, the early specimens having hibernated.

*Aglais urticae*

***Nymphalis antiopa* Camberwell Beauty**
Wingspan: 50–76 mm. Maroon with a cream border and blue marginal spots (underside pictured left [TN]). **HABITAT** Woodlands, gardens and parks to 2,500 m., where the larvae mainly feed on willow *Salix*. **SEASON** April to September, the early specimens having hibernated.

*Nymphalis antiopa*

***Nymphalis polychloros* Large Tortoiseshell**
Wingspan: 56–68 mm. There are four black spots on the forewing, central area separating it from the smaller and brighter *Aglais urticae*. **HABITAT** Woodland edges and others to 2,500 m., where the larvae feed on poplar *Populus*, willow *Salix*, elm *Ulmus* and others. **SEASON** March to August, the early specimens having hibernated. Fresh adults hatch from late June.

*Nymphalis polychloros*

***Polygonia c-album* Comma**
Wingspan: 40–52 mm. Easily recognised by its ragged wing margins and the white comma on the underside (pictured right). **HABITAT** Woodlands and others to 2,000 m., where the larvae feed on various plants, including willow *Salix* and nettle *Urtica*. **SEASON** March to October, the early specimens having hibernated. Fresh adults hatch in June.

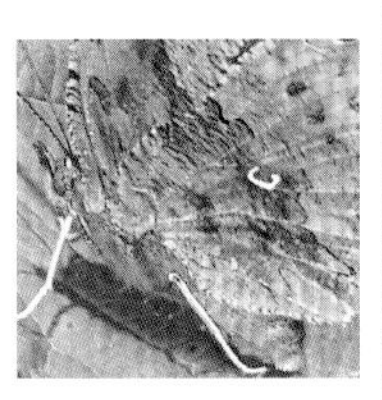

*Polygonia c-album*

***Polygonia egea* Southern Comma**
Wingspan: 38–49 mm. Black spots much smaller than in *P. c-album*. **HABITAT** Grasslands including rocky slopes and river valleys to 2,500 m., where the larvae mainly feed on Eastern Pellitory-of-the-wall *Parietaria officinalis*. **SEASON** March to October, the early specimens having hibernated. Fresh adults hatch in May.

*Polygonia egea*

***Euphydryas aurinia* Marsh Fritillary**
Wingspan: 29–43 mm. Brightly chequered in orange, brown and yellow. **HABITAT** Wetlands and dry grasslands to 2,000 m., where the larvae mainly feed on Devil's-bit Scabious *Succisa pratensis*. **SEASON** May to July. **SIMILAR SPECIES** ***Euphydryas beckeri*** (Spain, Portugal) [not illustrated] has been split from *E. aurinia*.

*Euphydryas aurinia*

***Euphydryas cynthia* Cynthia's Fritillary**
Wingspan: 32–40 mm. Distinctive white bands on both wings. **HABITAT** Grassy mountainous slopes 900 to 3,000 m., where the larvae mainly feed on Alpine Plantain *Plantago alpina* and Long-spurred Pansy *Viola calcarata*. **SEASON** Late June to August.

*Euphydryas cynthia*

***Melitaea aetherie* Aetherie Fritillary**
Wingspan: 40–44 mm. Orange with black markings, ♂s with zigzag submarginal line. **HABITAT** Grasslands to 1,100 m., where the larvae feed on *Centaurea*. **SEASON** Mid April to May, 2nd generation in September in Sicily.

*Melitaea aetherie*

*Aglais io*

*Aglais urticae* (left & right)

*Nymphalis antiopa* [KB]

*Nymphalis polychloros* (left & right)

*Polygonia c-album*

*Polygonia egea* (left & right)

*Euphydryas aurinia* (top & bottom)

*Euphydryas cynthia* (top & bottom) [both KB]

*Melitaea aetherie* (top & bottom) [both MS]

### *Melitaea athalia* Heath Fritillary

Wingspan: 31–40 mm. Orange with dark brown bands. **HABITAT** Grasslands and woodlands to 2,300 m., where the larvae feed on various plants. **SEASON** May to July. **SIMILAR SPECIES** ***M. nevadensis* Oberthür's Fritillary**, of which *M. celadussa* is considered to be a synonym. Flies up to 2,600 m.

*Melitaea athalia*

*Melitaea nevadensis*

### *Melitaea cinxia* Glanville Fritillary

Wingspan: 27–41 mm. Orange or brown, with dark brown lines. **HABITAT** Grasslands to 3,000 m., where the larvae mainly feed on plantain *Plantago* and speedwell *Veronica*. **SEASON** May to September, with two generations in the south.

*Melitaea cinxia*

### *Melitaea deione* Provençal Fritillary

Wingspan: 32–44 mm. ♀s often with pale yellow bands. Easily confused with related species in the field and requires careful examination of markings. Various subspecies and forms. **HABITAT** Grasslands, often hillsides and woodland edges to 1,500 m., where the larvae feed on snapdragon *Antirrhinum*, foxglove *Digitalis*, toadflax *Linaria* and others. **SEASON** May to June, also August to September.

*Melitaea deione*

### *Melitaea diamina* False Heath Fritillary

Wingspan: 32–37 mm. Forewings with little orange spotting. Note also dark areas on underside of hindwings. Noticeably darker than *M. athalia* in the field. **HABITAT** Grasslands, sometimes damper areas to 2,500 m., where the larvae often feed on valerian *Valeriana*. **SEASON** May to July, sometimes a later generation.

*Melitaea diamina*

### *Melitaea didyma* Spotted Fritillary

Wingspan: 31–41 mm. Bright orange and well spotted (sexes rather different), with a characteristic shape. **HABITAT** Grasslands, mainly below 1000 m, but sometimes in rocky areas to 2,400 m., where the larvae feed on various low-growing plants. **SEASON** May to September in two generations.

*Melitaea didyma*

### *Melitaea parthenoides* Meadow Fritillary

Wingspan: 29–35 mm. More orange but also paler than most Fritillaries, and more lightly marked. **HABITAT** Woodland edges mainly below 1,000 m., but sometimes higher altitudes, where the larvae feed on plantain *Plantago*. **SEASON** May to September in up to two generations.

*Melitaea parthenoides*

### *Melitaea phoebe* Knapweed Fritillary

Wingspan: 36–43 mm. Large central marginal lunule on forewings. Band on underside of hindwings with orange spots. **HABITAT** Grasslands and light woodlands to 1,700 m., where the larvae mainly feed on *Centaurea*. **SEASON** Mid April to September in two generations.

*Melitaea phoebe*

### *Melitaea trivia* Lesser Spotted Fritillary

Wingspan: 28–36 mm. Similar to *M. didyma*, but with submarginal crescent-shaped markings. **HABITAT** Grasslands to 1,700 m., where the larvae feed on mullein *Verbascum*. **SEASON** May to September, mainly in two generations.

*Melitaea trivia*

## Family Riodinidae – METALMARKS

There is one small European uncertain representative of this family from the tropics, originally thought to be a fritillary and more recently placed with the Lycaenidae.

### *Hamearis lucina* Duke of Burgundy

Wingspan: 23–34 mm. Easily recognised by orange spots on a brown background. **HABITAT** Woodlands, including clearings to 1,900 m., where the larvae feed on *Primula*. **SEASON** Late April to September in up to two generations.

*Hamearis lucina*

*Melitaea athalia* ♂

*Melitaea nevadensis* ♀

*Melitaea cinxia*

*Melitaea deione* (top & bottom) [both SO]

*Melitaea diamina* (top & bottom)

*Melitaea parthenoides* ♀ (top & bottom)

*Melitaea didyma* ♂ (left), ♀ (centre) [PC], ♀ (right)

*Melitaea phoebe* ♂

*Melitaea trivia* [MS]

*Hamearis lucina* ♂

## Family Lycaenidae – HAIRSTREAKS, COPPERS & BLUES

A colourful range of small butterflies, ♀s often much drabber than the showy ♂s. The larvae of some mainly blue species are reliant on ants in the latter part of their development.

### *Lycaena alciphron* Purple-shot Copper

Wingspan: 27–33 mm. ♂ with purple flush, less so in subspecies. **HABITAT** Grasslands to 2,500 m., where the larvae feed on dock *Rumex*. **SEASON** Mid June to August.

*Lycaena alciphron*

### *Lycaena candens* Balkan Copper

Wingspan: 34–35 mm. ♂ with purple sheen on black borders. Subtle differences in both sexes with the similar *L. hippothoe* (although range does not overlap). **HABITAT** Grasslands, including damp areas from 800 to 2,500 m., where the larvae feed on Common Sorrel *Rumex acetosa*. **SEASON** June to August.

*Lycaena candens*

### *Lycaena dispar* Large Copper

Wingspan: 33–41 mm. ♂ orange with black borders; hindwings with weak orange submarginal band (♀ underside pictured left). **HABITAT** Wetlands to 1,000 m., where the larvae feed on dock *Rumex*. **SEASON** Late May to September.

*Lycaena dispar*

### *Lycaena hippothoe* Purple-edged Copper

Wingspan: 27–33 mm. ♂ with purple sheen on black borders. Subtle differences in both sexes with the similar *L. candens*, ♂ underside of hindwings with weak orange submarginal band (pictured left). **HABITAT** Grasslands, including damp areas to 2,500 m., where the larvae feed on dock *Rumex*. **SEASON** June to August.

*Lycaena hippothoe*

### *Lycaena ottomana* Grecian Copper

Wingspan: 28–30 mm. ♂ orange with black borders and black spots on forewings. **HABITAT** Grasslands and woodland clearings to 2,200 m., where the larvae mainly feed on Common Sorrel *Rumex acetosella*. **SEASON** March to September.

*Lycaena ottomana*

### *Lycaena phlaeas* Small Copper

Wingspan: 20–32 mm. Shining coppery forewings with black spots; outer margins brown (♀ underside pictured left). **HABITAT** Grasslands to 3,100 m., where the larvae feed on dock *Rumex*. **SEASON** April to November, in up to three to four generations.

*Lycaena phlaeas*

### *Lycaena thersamon* Lesser Fiery Copper

Wingspan: 28–31 mm. ♂ orange with narrow black borders. **HABITAT** Grasslands, often mountainous areas to 2,500 m., where the larvae feed on Knotgrass *Polygonum aviculare* and others. **SEASON** May to August, possibly later.

*Lycaena thersamon*

### *Lycaena tityrus* Sooty Copper

Wingspan: 22–28 mm. ♂ sooty brown, ♀ with brown with orange areas and black spots (♀ underside pictured left [PC]. **HABITAT** Grasslands to 2,500 m., where the larvae feed on dock *Rumex*. **SEASON** May to September.

*Lycaena tityrus*

### *Lycaena virgaureae* Scarce Copper

Wingspan: 23–32 mm. ♂ bright copper with narrow black borders; distinctive underside. **HABITAT** Grasslands, including damp areas, usually 1,000 to 2,000 m., where the larvae feed mainly on Common Sorrel *Rumex acetosa* and Sheep's Sorrel *R. acetosella*. **SEASON** Late June to August.

*Lycaena virgaureae*

*Lycaena candens* ♂ [MS]

*Lycaena alciphron* ♂ (top & bottom)

*Lycaena dispar* ♂ [MS] (top), ♀ (bottom)

*Lycaena ottomana* ♂ [KB]

*Lycaena hippothoe* ♂ (top), ♀ (bottom)

*Lycaena phlaeas* ♂

*Lycaena thersamon* (left) [MS], (right) [KB]

*Lycaena tityrus* ♂ (top), ♀ (bottom)

*Lycaena virgaureae* ♂ (top) [KB], ♂ (bottom)

**_Thecla betulae_ Brown Hairstreak**
Wingspan: 30–40 mm. ♂ dark brown with wing-tails orange, ♀ with distinctive orange band on forewings. **HABITAT** Semi-open woodlands and others to 1,700 m where the larvae feed on *Prunus*. **SEASON** Late June to September.

*Thecla betulae*

**_Quercusia quercus_ Purple Hairstreak**
Wingspan: 29–35 mm. ♂s have a purple sheen which is restricted to the base of the forewings in ♀s, otherwise purplish-black). The underside is silvery-grey, markings reduced in form *ibericus* from Iberia. This species has been placed by some authors in the genus *Favonius*. **HABITAT** Woodlands, gardens and parks, occasionally even in the mountains, where the larvae feed on various oaks *Quercus* spp. **SEASON** June to September.

*Quercusia quercus*

**_Laeosopis roboris_ Spanish Purple Hairstreak**
Wingspan: 28–33 mm. Black with purple basal patch. The underside (no tail) is brownish-grey with and orange submarginal band. **HABITAT** Open woodlands, gardens and parks up to 1,900 m., where the larvae feed on ash *Fraxinus*. **SEASON** May to July.

*Laeosopis roboris*

**_Tomares ballus_ Provence Hairstreak**
Wingspan: 22–30 mm. Brown, except ♀s with orange patches. Underside of hindwings with a distinctive large green base. **HABITAT** Grasslands to 1,300 m., where the pink larvae mainly feed on various Fabaceae. **SEASON** February to April.

*Tomares ballus*

**_Callophrys rubi_ Green Hairstreak**
Wingspan: 20–26 mm. Chocolate brown with green underside, sometimes with a line of white spots. **HABITAT** Various to 2,300 m where the larvae feed on a wide range of plants, including *Genista* spp., also shrubs. **SEASON** March to June, also later in some areas.

*Callophrys rubi*

**_Satyrium acaciae_ Sloe Hairstreak**
Wingspan: 23–31 mm. Greyish-brown. Underside of hindwings with a dark-edged, fairly straight white streak. Grey spot near tail. **HABITAT** Bushy hills and woodland clearings to 2,300 m., where the larvae feed on Blackthorn *Prunus spinosa* and others. **SEASON** Late May to July.

*Satyrium acaciae*

**_Satyrium esculi_ False Ilex Hairstreak**
Wingspan: 23–33 mm. Dark brown, although there is a ♀ orange form. Underside of hindwings with weak white line. Orange lunules with black border only on inner side. **HABITAT** Sparse woodlands and rocky hills to 1,300 m., where the larvae feed on oak *Quercus*. **SEASON** Late May to August.

*Satyrium esculi*

**_Satyrium ilicis_ Ilex Hairstreak**
Wingspan: 28–34 mm. Dark brown, amount of orange suffusion varies in ♀s. Underside of hindwings with wavy white line. Similar to *S. esculi* but orange lunules with black border on both sides. **HABITAT** Woodlands and bushy places to 2,600 m., where the larvae feed on oak *Quercus*. **SEASON** Late May to July.

*Satyrium ilicis*

**_Satyrium spini_ Blue-spot Hairstreak**
Wingspan: 25–34 mm. Dark brown, underside with white streak on both wings and distinctive blue spot near tails. **HABITAT** Woodlands and bushy grasslands to 1,600 m., where the larvae feed mainly on various buckthorn *Rhamnus* spp. **SEASON** May to July.

*Satyrium spini*

**_Satyrium w-album_ White-letter Hairstreak**
Wingspan: 28–32 mm. Dark brown with conspicuous white 'W'-shaped lines on the underside, also orange lunules. **HABITAT** Woodland edges, parks and gardens to 1,600 m., where the larvae mainly feed on elm *Ulmus*.. **SEASON** June to July. **SIMILAR SPECIES _S. pruni_ Black Hairstreak** [not illustrated or mapped] has black spots on the underside of hindwings which readily distinguish it from *S. w-album*. The larvae feed mainly on *Prunus*.

*Satyrium w-album*

*Thecla betulae* [KB]

*Quercusia quercus* ♀ (left), ♂ form *ibericus* (right)

*Laeosopis roboris* (left & right) [both KB]

*Tomares ballus* [KB]

*Callophrys rubi* [KB]

*Satyrium acaciae* [KB]

*Satyrium esculi*

*Satyrium ilicis*

*Satyrium spini*

*Satyrium w-album* [TB]

**_Lampides boeticus_ Long-tailed Blue**
Wingspan: 23–36 mm. ♂ bluish-mauve. Underside brownish with white lines; two eye-spots near long tail. **HABITAT** Grasslands, gardens and parks. Even reaches mountainous areas to 2,000 m. The larvae feed on various legumes. **SEASON** February to November.

*Lampides boeticus*

**_Cacyreus marshalli_ Geranium Bronze**
Wingspan: 21–26 mm. ♂ Brown with brown and white fringes. Underside brownish with whitish streaks. **HABITAT** Mainly gardens and parks where the larvae feed on *Pelargonium* and *Geranium*. **SEASON** May to October.

*Cacyreus marshalli*

**_Leptotes pirithous_ Lang's Short-tailed Blue**
Wingspan: 21–27 mm. ♂ bluish, ♀ with brown margins and black spots. Underside brown wavy with white lines. **HABITAT** Grasslands, including cultivated areas to 2,300 m. The larvae feed on various low-growing plants including Lucerne *Medicago sativa*. **SEASON** February to October.

*Leptotes pirithous*

**_Zizeeria knysna_ African Grass Blue**
Wingspan: 18–22 mm. ♂ violet-blue with wide black border, ♀ brown with some blue at base. Greyish-brown, heavily spotted underside. **HABITAT** Grasslands to 1,500 m. **SEASON** Late February to October, multi-brooded.

*Zizeeria knysna*

**_Cupido alcetas_ Provençal Short-tailed Blue**
Wingspan: 20–26 mm. ♂ violet-blue with narrow black border, ♀ brown. Short-tailed. **HABITAT** Woodland edges, often near streams at low altitudes. **SEASON** May to September.

*Cupido alcetas*

**_Cupido argiades_ Short-tailed Blue**
Wingspan: 20–32 mm. ♀ brown, with some blue. Similar to *C. alcetas* but underside with one to three orange spots near tail. **HABITAT** Grasslands, including cultivated areas and woodland edges to 1,000 m. The larvae feed on legumes. **SEASON** April to August, in two generations.

*Cupido argiades*

**_Cupido decoloratus_ Eastern Short-tailed Blue**
Wingspan: 24–25 mm. ♂ blue with narrow black border; forewings with almost central black spot, ♀ brown. Underside of hindwing with black lunule near tail. **HABITAT** Woodland edges and grasslands to 1,000 m. The larvae feed on Fabaceae *Medicago*, *Trifolium* and *Vicia* spp. **SEASON** May to September, in two to three generations.

*Cupido decoloratus*

**_Cupido lorquinii_ Lorquin's Blue**
Wingspan: 19–28 mm. ♂ blue with sooty black border (a mountain subspecies is brown), ♀ brown. Similar to *C. minimus*. **HABITAT** Rocky grasslands to 2,000 m. The larvae feed on Kidney Vetch *Anthyllis vulneraria*. **SEASON** Mid April to mid June.

*Cupido lorquinii*

**_Cupido minimus_ Small Blue**
Wingspan: 19–26 mm. Dark brown with a dusting of silvery-blue in fresh ♂s. The underside is silvery-grey with tiny black dots (not in a straight line) with very thin white surround. **HABITAT** Grasslands, often calcareous, to 2,800 m. The larvae feed mainly on Kidney Vetch *Anthyllis vulneraria*. **SEASON** April to September, in two generations.

*Cupido minimus*

**_Cupido osiris_ Osiris Blue**
Wingspan: 22–28 mm. ♂ violet-blue Similar to *C. minimus* but spots almost straight on underside of forewings. **HABITAT** Rocky often calcareous grasslands, 500 to 1,800 m. The larvae feed on Kidney Vetch *Anthyllis vulneraria* and *Onobrychis* spp. **SEASON** May to August.

*Cupido osiris*

*Lampides boeticus* ♂

*Cacyreus marshalli*

*Leptotes pirithous* ♀ [PC]

*Zizeeria knysna* ♂ (top) [SR], (bottom)

*Cupido alcetas* ♀ (top), ♂ (bottom)

*Cupido argiades* ♂ (top & bottom)

*Cupido decoloratus* ♂ [KB]

*Cupido lorquinii* ♂ (left), ♀ (right)

*Cupido minimus* (left & right)

*Cupido osiris* [KB]

***Celastrina argiolus*** **Holly Blue**
Wingspan: 21–32 mm. ♂shiny blue upperside with narrow black margins, much broader in the ♀. Underside silvery blue with only black spots. **HABITAT** Woodlands, grasslands, gardens and parks to c.2,000 m. The larvae feed on various plants. **SEASON** March to September.

*Celastrina argiolus*

***Pseudophilotes abencerragus*** **False Baton Blue**
Wingspan: 18–22 mm. ♂violet-blue with wide black margins, as well a black spot. ♀ brown. Both sexes will bold brown and white chequered fringes. The genus *Pseudophilotes* is regarded by some authors as a subgenus of *Scolitantides*. **HABITAT** Open woodlands or scrubby areas to 1,500 m. The larvae feed on *Cleonia lusitanica*. **SEASON** April to May.

*Pseudophilotes abencerragus*

***Pseudophilotes baton*** **Baton Blue**
Wingspan: 19–28 mm. Similar to *P. abencerragus*, ♂ pale blue. Underside of hindwings with orange spots. **HABITAT** Grasslands with scrub to 2,000 m. The larvae feed on thyme *Thymus* and others. **SEASON** April to September.

*Pseudophilotes baton*

***Pseudophilotes bavius*** **Bavius Blue**
Wingspan: 20–25 mm. similar to *P. baton*, hindwings with orange submarginal lunules on upper and underside. **HABITAT** Calcareous grasslands 600 to 1,500 m. The larvae feed on sage *Salvia* spp. **SEASON** Mid May to June.

*Pseudophilotes bavius*

***Pseudophilotes panoptes*** **Panoptes Blue**
Wingspan: 20–22 mm. Similar to *P. abencerragus*, ♂ pale blue with black margin, and underside of hindwings lacks or has indistinct orange submarginal spots. **HABITAT** Grasslands with scrub to 2,000 m. The larvae mainly feed on thyme *Thymus*. **SEASON** April to August.

*Pseudophilotes panoptes*

***Pseudophilotes vicrama*** **Eastern Baton Blue**
Wingspan: 20–24 mm. similar to *P. baton*, but Eastern distribution. **HABITAT** Grasslands to 1,900 m. The larvae feed on thyme *Thymus* and others. **SEASON** April to October in two generations (one at higher altitude).

*Pseudophilotes vicrama*

***Scolitantides orion*** **Chequered Blue**
Wingspan: 24–28 mm. ♂ dark blue, underside whitish. **HABITAT** Various, often calcareous sites including rocky hills to 1,100 m. The larvae feed on stonecrop *Sedum* spp. **SEASON** May to July, with a possible later generation.

*Scolitantides orion*

***Glaucopsyche iolas*** **Iolas Blue**
Wingspan: 32–39 mm. Large, ♂ pale violet-blue, narrow dark borders (broad in ♀). **HABITAT** Rocky calcareous slopes to 1,800 m. The larvae feed on Bladder Senna *Colutea arborescens* which have bladder-like seed pods, also related species. **SEASON** May to June, with a possible later generation.

*Glaucopsyche iolas*

***Glaucopsyche melanops*** **Black-eyed Blue**
Wingspan: 21–28 mm. ♂ violet-blue with brown borders, less blue ♀s; underside with large black spots on forewings. **HABITAT** Grasslands, open woodlands to 1,200 m. The larvae feed on legumes. **SEASON** April to May. **SIMILAR SPECIES** ***G. alexis*** **Green-underside Blue** (pictured left [JA]) hindwings have a greenish flush at base (underside).

*Glaucopsyche melanops*

*Glaucopsyche alexis*

*Celastrina argiolus* ♀

*Pseudophilotes abencerragus* ♀ (left & right) [both KB]

*Pseudophilotes baton* ♂

*Pseudophilotes bavius* ♂ (left & right) [both MS]

*Pseudophilotes panoptes* ♂ [SO]

*Pseudophilotes vicrama* ♂ [KB]

*Glaucopsyche iolas* [MS]

*Glaucopsyche melanops* ♀

*Scolitantides orion* ♀ (top & bottom)

**_Phengaris alcon_ Alcon Blue**
Wingspan: 29–35 mm. ♂ pale violet-blue, narrow black borders (broad in ♀). **HABITAT** Various wetlands, also at higher altitudes to 2,300 m in mountains. The larvae mainly feed on Marsh Gentian *Gentiana pneumonanthe* and related species; later stages on *Myrmica ruginodis* ant larvae. **SEASON** Mid June to mid August.

*Phengaris alcon*

**_Phengaris arion_ Large Blue**
Wingspan: 29–40 mm. Blue, with variable number of black markings. Underside with bluish-green flush at base of hindwings. **HABITAT** Various grasslands to 2,000 m. The larvae mainly feed on thyme *Thymus* but live in *Myrmica sabuleti* ant nests from 3rd instar. **SEASON** June to early August.

*Phengaris arion*

**_Phengaris nausithous_ Dusky Large Blue**
Wingspan: 34–36 mm. Rather darker than *P. agrion* ♂ with broad borders. ♀s brown. Underside lacking submarginal spots. **HABITAT** Various wetlands 600 to 1,600 m. The larvae mainly feed on Great Burnet *Sanguisorba officinalis*; later stages develop in *Myrmica rubra* ant nests. **SEASON** Late June to mid August.

*Phengaris nausithous*

**_Kretania hespericus_ Spanish Zephyr Blue**
Wingspan: 23–29 mm. Bright blue ♂. **HABITAT** Grasslands, such as open woodlands, 600 to 1,500 m. The larvae feed on *Astragalus* spp. **SEASON** May to June.

*Kretania hespericus*

**_Kretania sephirus_ Zephyr Blue**
Wingspan: 27–32 mm. Blue ♂ with narrow black borders, margin of hindwings black-spotted. **HABITAT** Rocky or sandy grasslands, clearings in woodlands to 2,600 m. The larvae feed on *Astragalus* spp. **SEASON** Mid May to July.

*Kretania sephirus*

**_Plebejus argus_ Silver-studded Blue**
Wingspan: 18–27 mm. Blue with broad black borders in the ♂, dark brown, with a variable number of orange spots around the edges in the ♀. The underside is greyish with blue at base, margin of hindwings shiny blue in centre of spots and orange lunules (mating pair pictured left). **HABITAT** Various grasslands, including wet areas to 2,400 m. The larvae mainly feed on legumes, later stages develop in *Lasius* ant nests. **SEASON** May to August.

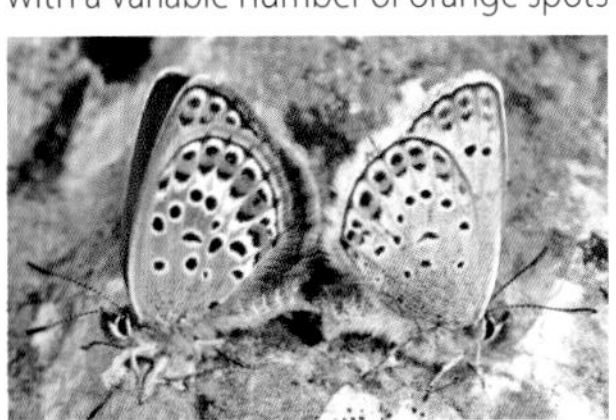

*Plebejus argus*

**_Plebejus argyrognomon_ Reverdin's Blue**
Wingspan: 24–29 mm. Violet-blue ♂ with narrow black borders. ♀ dark brown, with a variable number of submarginal orange spots. Distinctive underside, margin with shiny blue in centre of spots and orange lunules (pictured right). **HABITAT** Various grasslands and woodland edge to 1,900 m. The larvae feed on *Astragalus* spp., Crown Vetch *Securigera varia* and others. **SEASON** May to July, later in some areas.

*Plebejus argyrognomon*

**_Plebejus idas_ Idas Blue**
Wingspan: 21–30 mm. Blue with narrow black borders in the ♂, compared to *P. argus*. **HABITAT** Dry and wet grasslands to 2,500 m. **SEASON** May to August.

*Plebejus idas*

**_Eumedonia eumedon_ Geranium Argus**
Wingspan: 24–31 mm. Dark brown with white fringes. Underside of hindwings with distinctive white streak. **HABITAT** Grasslands and woodland edges, often mountainous areas to 2,400 m, on crane's-bill *Geranium* spp. **SEASON** June to August.

*Eumedonia eumedon*

*Phengaris alcon* ♂ (top & bottom) [both KB]

*Phengaris arion* (top) [JM], ♂ (bottom)

*Phengaris nausithous* ♂ (top & bottom) [both KB]

*Kretania hespericus* ♂ [MS]

*Kretania sephirus* ♂s [KB]

*Plebejus argus* ♂

*Plebejus argyrognomon* ♂

*Plebejus idas* ♂

*Eumedonia eumedon*

**_Agriades optilete_ Cranberry Blue**
Wingspan: 22–28 mm. Violet-blue ♂ with narrow black borders. ♀ dark brown. Margin of hindwings (underside) with margin shiny blue in centre of spots and orange lunules. **HABITAT** Wetlands including bogs, mainly 1,500 to 2,800 m. The larvae feed on *Vaccinium* spp and others. **SEASON** Mid June to July.

*Agriades optilete*

**_Agriades orbitulus_ Alpine Blue**
Wingspan: 21–26 mm. Blue ♂ with narrow black border. Distinctive white-spotted underside. **HABITAT** Alpine grasslands, sometimes damp areas 800 to 3,200 m. The larvae feed on Alpine Milk-vetch *Astragalus alpinus*. **SEASON** June to August.

*Agriades orbitulus*

**_Agriades pyrenaicus_ Gavarnie Blue**
Wingspan: 21–24 mm. Greyish. Underside of forewings with large black spots, hindwing white-spotted. **HABITAT** Rocky calcareous alpine slopes, 1,800 to 2,200 m. The larval foodplants include Rock-jasmine *Androsace villosa*. **SEASON** June to early August.

*Agriades pyrenaicus*

**_Aricia agestis_ Brown Argus**
Wingspan: 22–28 mm. Dark brown with orange spots around the edges of the wings. Underside greyish-brown with orange marginal spots and a number of white-ringed black spots. Closest to *A. artaxerxes*. **HABITAT** Rocky calcareous grasslands to 1,800 m. The larvae feed on stork's-bill *Erodium*, crane's-bill *Geranium* and others. **SEASON** April to October. **SIMILAR SPECIES _A. cramera_ Southern Brown Argus** (Iberia and adjoining France, also Sardinia) (pictured left) is now split from *A. agestis*.

*Aricia agestis*

**_Aricia anteros_ Blue Argus**
Wingspan: 24–32 mm. Pale blue ♂ with greyish borders. **HABITAT** Mountainous areas to 2,500 m. The larvae feed on crane's-bill *Geranium*. **SEASON** May to September.

*Aricia anteros*

**_Aricia artaxerxes_ Mountain Argus** [Northern Brown Argus]
Wingspan: 23–31 mm. ♂ with orange submarginal lunules only on forewings (sometimes lacking). **HABITAT** Calcareous grasslands usually 1,000 to 2,000 m. **SEASON** June to August.

*Aricia artaxerxes*

**_Aricia morronensis_ Spanish Argus**
Wingspan: 22–30 mm. Dark brown with chequered fringes. Black central forewing spot can be white-ringed and on the underside is the largest black spot. Subspecies *ramburi* (Sierra Nevada) is illustrated. **HABITAT** Rocky slopes 900 to 2,700 m. The larvae feed on stork's-bill *Erodium*. **SEASON** June to August.

*Aricia morronensis*

**_Aricia nicias_ Silvery Argus**
Wingspan: 22–27 mm. Silvery blue ♂ with broad black borders. **HABITAT** Damper grasslands and clearings, typically 1,000 to 2,300 m. The larvae feed on crane's-bill *Geranium*. **SEASON** July to August.

*Aricia nicias*

**_Cyaniris semiargus_ Mazarine Blue**
Wingspan: 22–33 mm. Deep blue ♂ with narrow black borders; easily recognised by black veins. Greyish-brown underside black-spotted. In subspecies *helena* (Greece) there are orange submarginal marks on the hindwings. *Cyaniris* is regarded by some authors as a subgenus of *Polyommatus*. **HABITAT** Various dry and damp grasslands to 2,300 m. The larvae mainly feed on Red Clover *Trifolium pratense*. **SEASON** May to early August, sometimes with a later generation.

*Cyaniris semiargus*

*Agriades optilete* ♂ [KB]

*Agriades pyrenaicus* (left & right) [both JAs]

*Agriades orbitulus* ♂ [KB]

*Aricia agestis*

*Aricia anteros* ♂ [MS]

*Aricia artaxerxes* ♀

*Aricia nicias* ♂ (left & right) [both KB]

*Aricia morronensis*

*Cyaniris semiargus* ♂ (left), ♀ (right) [PC]

**_Polyommatus admetus_ Anomalous Blue**
Wingspan: 26–33 mm. Brown including fringes. Underside yellowish-brown. **HABITAT** Calcareous grasslands and clearings, typically 400 to 1800 m. The larvae feed on *Onobrychis* spp. **SEASON** Mid June to September.

*Polyommatus admetus*

**_Polyommatus amandus_ Amanda's Blue**
Wingspan: 29–36 mm. Large, blue ♂ with suffused dark border or at least veins, particularly on forewings; underside pale. **HABITAT** Various grasslands and clearings to 2,500 m. The larvae often feed on *Vicia* spp. **SEASON** Late May to early August.

*Polyommatus amandus*

**_Polyommatus aroaniensis_ Grecian Anomalous Blue**
Wingspan: 28–32 mm. Both sexes brown. Underside yellowish-brown, hindwings with weak white stripe, if present at all. **HABITAT** Rocky calcareous grasslands and scrub, 400 to 2,000 m., mostly below 1,500 m. The larvae feed on *Onobrychis arenaria*. **SEASON** Late June to early August.

*Polyommatus aroaniensis*

**_Polyommatus daphnis_ Meleager's Blue**
Wingspan: 28–36 mm. Blue ♂ with narrow black borders, ♀ typical form with much blue and broad dark brown border. Hindwings scalloped in both sexes. **HABITAT** Rocky calcareous grasslands near woodland to 2,300 m. The larvae feed on various Lamiaceae. **SEASON** Mid June to August.

*Polyommatus daphnis*

**_Polyommatus dolus_ Furry Blue**
Wingspan: 27–34 mm. Silvery-white ♂ with narrow brown borders and veins. **HABITAT** Grasslands 500 to 1,500 m. The larvae feed on *Onobrychis* spp. **SEASON** Mid July to August.

*Polyommatus dolus*

**_Polyommatus dorylas_ Turquoise Blue**
Wingspan: 25–31 mm. Turquoise blue ♂ with narrow black borders and white fringes. Underside pale, rather distinctive. **HABITAT** Various grasslands and clearings, typically 400 to 1,800 m. The larvae feed on *Onobrychis* spp. **SEASON** June to September.

*Polyommatus dorylas*

**_Polyommatus eros_ Eros Blue**
Wingspan: 23–30 mm. Blue ♂ with broad black borders and white fringes. **HABITAT** Various rocky and sandy grasslands typically 1,200 to 2,100 m. The larvae feed on *Genista depressa* and others. **SEASON** Mid June to early September.

*Polyommatus eros*

**_Polyommatus escheri_ Escher's Blue**
Wingspan: 27–33 mm. Blue ♂ with narrow black borders and white fringes. ♀ dark brown with orange lunules. **HABITAT** Rocky calcareous grasslands mainly 500 to 2000 m. The larvae feed on milk-vetch *Astragalus*. **SEASON** June to August.

*Polyommatus escheri*

**_Polyommatus fulgens_ Catalonian Furry Blue**
Wingspan: 23–30 mm. Silvery-blue ♂ with narrow brown borders (underside pictured left [KB]). ♀ brown with darker border and veins. **HABITAT** Grasslands 900 to 1,200 m. The larvae feed on Sainfoin *Onobrychis viciifolia*. **SEASON** July to August.

*Polyommatus fulgens*

**_Polyommatus golgus_ Nevada Blue**
Wingspan: 22–29 mm. Blue ♂ with black borders and white fringes. ♀ dark brown with orange submarginal lunules. **HABITAT** Mountainous rocky calcareous areas 1,900 to 3,000 m.; restricted to Sierra Nevada. The larvae feed on Kidney Vetch *Anthyllis vulneraria*. **SEASON** Late June to July.

*Polyommatus golgus*

*Polyommatus admetus* [KB]

*Polyommatus amandus* ♂

*Polyommatus aroaniensis* [KB]

*Polyommatus daphnis* ♀ (left) [KB], mating pair – ♂ on right (right) [MS]

*Polyommatus dolus* [KB]

*Polyommatus dorylas* ♂ (left & right)

*Polyommatus eros* ♂ [KB]

*Polyommatus escheri* ♂

*Polyommatus fulgens* ♂ [KB]

*Polyommatus golgus* ♂

**_Polyommatus icarus_ Common Blue**
Wingspan: 23–36 mm. Violet-blue ♂ with plain fringes. ♀ dark brown, variable with a lot, little or no blue (pictured left). **HABITAT** Various, mainly grasslands to 3,000 m. The larvae feed on legumes. **SEASON** Late March to October. **SIMILAR SPECIES** ***P. celina*** (Spain, Portugal & Italy) is now split from *P. icarus.*

*Polyommatus icarus*

**_Polyommatus nivescens_**
**Mother-of-pearl Blue**
Wingspan: 25–33 mm. shining light grey ♂ with dark borders. ♀ dark brown with orange submarginal lunules. **HABITAT** Rocky grassland slopes, usually 1,000 to 1,900 m in Spain, with erroneous reports in France. The larvae feed on Kidney Vetch *Anthyllis vulnerania.* **SEASON** Late May to early August.

*Polyommatus nivescens*

**_Polyommatus ripartii_ Ripart's Anomalous Blue**
Wingspan: 26–33 mm. Both sexes brown including fringes. Underside yellowish-brown with a central white stripe. **HABITAT** Grasslands to 2,500 m. The larvae feed on *Onobrychis* spp. **SEASON** Late June to August.

*Polyommatus ripartii*

**_Polyommatus thersites_ Chapman's Blue**
Wingspan: 24–35 mm. Rather like *P. icarus*, but the underside of forewings lacks a basal black spot usually present in *icarus*. The ♂ of *thersites* also has a dark central forewing patch. **HABITAT** Grasslands to 2,100 m. The larvae feed on *Onobrychis* spp. **SEASON** May to August.

*Polyommatus thersites*

**_Neolysandra coelestina_ Pontic Blue**
Wingspan: 22–26 mm. Dark blue ♂ with broad black borders. **HABITAT** Usually calcareous grasslands to 1,900 m. The larvae mainly feed on Tufted Vetch *Vicia cracca.* **SEASON** June to July.

*Neolysandra coelestina*

**_Lysandra albicans_ Spanish Chalkhill Blue**
Wingspan: 28–36 mm. Large, whitish ♂. **HABITAT** Various grasslands and clearings, 500 to 2,000 m. The larvae feed on Horseshoe Vetch *Hippocrepis comosa.* **SEASON** Mid June to August.

*Lysandra albicans*

**_Lysandra bellargus_ Adonis Blue**
Wingspan: 26–34 mm. Iridescent cobalt blue ♂ with chequered fringes, ♀ dark brown. **HABITAT** Various calcareous grasslands to 2,000 m. The larvae feed on legumes, later develop in ant nests. **SEASON** April to September.

*Lysandra bellargus*

**_Lysandra coridon_ Chalkhill Blue**
Wingspan: 27–36 mm. Silvery-blue ♂ with broad brown borders and chequered wing fringes (there are various subspecies). **HABITAT** Calcareous grasslands to 2,000 m. The larvae foodplants include Horseshoe Vetch *Hippocrepis comosa.* **SEASON** Late June to September.

*Lysandra coridon*

**_Tarucus balkanicus_ Little Tiger Blue**
Wingspan: 18–20 mm. ♂ pale blue. The ♀ is partly greyish-brown. Underside white with black markings and lines and a few blue spots on tailed hindwings. **HABITAT** Rocky grasslands. The larvae feed on Jerusalem Thorn *Paliurus spina-christi.* **SEASON** March to September.

*Tarucus balkanicus*

**_Turanana taygetica_ Odd-spot Blue**
Wingspan: 18–22 mm. Large central submarginal odd black spot on underside of forewings. **HABITAT** Alpine calcareous grasslands 950 to 2,400 m. The larvae feed on Prickly Thrift *Acantholimon echinus.* **SEASON** May to September.

*Turanana taygetica*

*Polyommatus icarus* ♂

*Polyommatus nivescens* ♂ [SO]

*Polyommatus thersites* ♂ [MS]

*Polyommatus ripartii* (left) [KB], (right [TN]

*Neolysandra coelestina* ♂ [KB]

*Lysandra albicans* ♂

*Lysandra bellargus* ♂ (left), ♀ (right)

*Lysandra coridon* ♂

*Tarucus balkanicus*

*Turanana taygetica* ♂ [KB]

# MOTHS

The mainly nocturnal moths are one of the most popular insect groups in Europe, particularly the larger, macro moths. Some people regularly moth trap in their gardens, which result in a wide range of species, where over 100 species a night is not unusual. Permission is needed to run moth traps from the relevant authorities in some countries, including Spain, although check around lights in towns and there are sometimes many moths resting on walls around lights. Why are moths attracted to light? The main theory is that they use the moon to navigate at night and are confused by bright lights. Some of these species are just passing through on migration. Day-flying moths are more likely to be noticed by the public, these are often colourful, such as burnet moths. Photographs of a selection of moths are provided in this book, including selected colourful caterpillars (larvae). Note that seasons vary widely for species and early months may only relate to the far south.

## Family Brahmaeidae – BRAHMIN MOTHS

A small family of moths, these include species in the genus Lemonia, which some authors regard as belonging to a separate family, the Lemoniidae.

### *Lemonia philopalus* Iberian Patrician

Wingspan: 50–60 mm. Brown with pale borders and veins. **HABITAT** Grasslands. The larvae on hawkweed *Hieracium*, sowthistle *Sonchus* and dandelion *Taraxacum*. Restricted to Iberia. **SEASON** October to February.

## Family Hepialidae – SWIFT MOTHS

A primitive family of moths, the swifts are characterised by short antennae and elongated wings held tight against the body when resting. They do not feed as adults; the larvae feed on plant roots.

### *Korscheltellus lupulina* Common Swift

Wingspan: 25–40 mm. Brown with pale markings. **HABITAT** Grasslands and gardens. **SEASON** May to July.

## Family Cossidae – LEOPARD & GOAT MOTHS

Large and distinctive moths with wings held at a sharp angle to the body, which do not feed as adults. Larvae live in host plants.

### *Cossus cossus* Goat Moth

Wingspan: 60–96 mm. Greyish-brown with cross-lines. **HABITAT** Woodland edges, gardens and other mainly damper sites. The larvae develop in trunks of oak *Quercus* and other trees, taking a few years to develop. **SEASON** May to July.

### *Zeuzera pyrina* Leopard Moth

Wingspan: 35–78 mm. Whitish with six black spots on the thorax and blackish spotting on the wings. **HABITAT** Open woodlands and other areas. The larvae develop in trunks and branches of various trees and can be a pest on fruit trees. **SEASON** May to October.

### *Dyspessa ulula*

Wingspan: 18–28 mm. Yellowish-brown. **HABITAT** Garrigues and unmanaged grasslands where the larvae develop in garlics and onions *Allium* spp.. **SEASON** April to July.

## Family Castniidae – CASTNIID MOTHS

A small family of mainly Neotropical day-flying moths with wings with clubbed antennae and bright hindwings.

### *Paysandisia archon* Palm Moth

Wingspan: 90–110 mm. Brownish forewings, hindwings bright orange with black band and white spots. **HABITAT** Where palms grow (day flying). Accidental introduction to France in the 1990s (a native of Argentina and Uruguay), spreading, particularly along the Mediterranean coast. The larvae develop in the stems and trunks of palms. **SEASON** June to September.

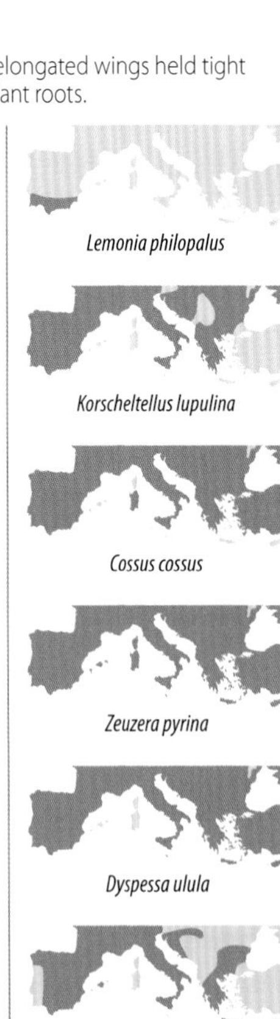

*Lemonia philopalus* [PH]

*Korscheltellus lupulina* ♂

*Cossus cossus* (left), larva (right)

*Zeuzera pyrina*

*Dyspessa ulula*

*Paysandisia archon* [PC]

## Family Sesiidae – CLEARWING MOTHS

The Sesiidae fly in sunny weather and the maggot-like larvae are mainly found in branches or trunks of host plants. Often attractive, these wasp-mimicking day-fliers typically tend to be seen only occasionally on flowers or vegetation in Europe. Keen moth enthusiasts use pheromone baits to attract ♂s.

**_Sesia apiformis_ Hornet Moth**
Wingspan: 31–48 mm. Large, hornet-like. **HABITAT** Light woodlands, parks and others. The larvae develop in poplar *Populus* trunks, with tell-tale exit holes near the base. **SEASON** May to August.

**_Paranthrene tabaniformis_ Dusky Clearwing**
Wingspan: 20–38 mm. Characteristic dark forewings. **HABITAT** Open woodlands with poplar *Populus*. **SEASON** May to August.

**_Synanthedon vespiformis_ Yellow-legged Clearwing**
Wingspan: 16–27 mm. Four yellow abdominal bands; legs also mainly yellow. **HABITAT** Woodlands and parks, associated with oak *Quercus* and others. **SEASON** May to October.

**_Synanthedon tipuliformis_ Currant Clearwing**
Wingspan: 11–21 mm. Yellow collar and yellow lines around thorax; three to four narrow yellow bands of abdomen, of which tip is black. **HABITAT** Gardens and wherever currants are grown. **SEASON** May to August.

**_Bembecia ichneumoniformis_ Six-belted Clearwing**
Wingspan: 12–29 mm. Six narrow yellowish abdominal bands. **HABITAT** Open areas, where the larvae develop in roots. **SEASON** June to September.

**_Pyropteron chrysidiformis_ Fiery Clearwing**
Wingspan: 17–26 mm. Vivid orange or red forewings. **HABITAT** Grasslands, associated with dock *Rumex*. **SEASON** May to August.

**_Pyropteron triannuliforme_**
Wingspan: 11–26 mm. Black with yellow longitudinal stripes on thorax and abdomen; also narrow white bands on abdomen. **HABITAT** Rocky and sandy sites, where the larvae feed on dock *Rumex* roots. **SEASON** May to August.

**_Chamaesphecia tenthrediniformis_**
Wingspan: 12–21 mm. Colourful black and yellow species. **HABITAT** Grasslands and woodland edges. The larvae feed on spurge *Euphorbia* roots. **SEASON** April to June.

## Family Limacodidae – SLUG MOTHS

A mostly tropical family, some having slug-like larvae.

**_Apoda limacodes_ Festoon**
Wingspan: 20–32 mm. Orange-brown with curved cross-lines; the ♂ rests with the abdomen upturned. **HABITAT** Woodlands and parks. The larvae feed on oak *Quercus*, hornbeam *Carpinus* and beech *Fagus*. **SEASON** June to July.

**_Hoyosia codeti_ Codet's Shield Moth**
Wingspan: 20–26 mm. Brown with faint cross-line. **HABITAT** Woodlands. **SEASON** May to October.

*Sesia apiformis*

*Paranthrene tabaniformis*

*Synanthedon vespiformis*

*Synanthedon tipuliformis*

*Bembecia ichneumoniformis*

*Pyropteron chrysidiformis*

*Pyropteron triannuliforme*

*Chamaesphecia tenthrediniformis*

*Apoda limacodes*

*Hoyosia codeti*

*Sesia apiformis* ♀ [KB]

*Paranthrene tabaniformis* [TN]

*Synanthedon tipuliformis* ♂

*Bembecia ichneumoniformis* mating pair

*Pyropteron chrysidiformis* ♀

*Synanthedon vespiformis* ♀

*Pyropteron triannuliforme* [TN]

*Chamaesphecia tenthrediniformis*

*Apoda limacodes*

*Hoyosia codeti*

## Family Zygaenidae – FORESTER & BURNET MOTHS

Attractive day-flying moths with club-shaped antennae, often seen on flowers, sometimes in groups on a single flowerhead. The burnet moths require close examination of the forewing pattern, which is variation in some species across a wide geographical range. In rare cases, the usually red coloration is yellow.

**_Adscita statices_ Forester**
Wingspan: 24–29 mm. Green. **HABITAT** Various sandy or calcareous grasslands to 1,500 m. The larvae feed on dock *Rumex*. **SEASON** May to August.

**_Zygaena carniolica_ Crepuscular Burnet**
Wingspan: 28–35 mm. Wide variation, but distinctive forewing pattern. **HABITAT** Sunny calcareous hillsides to 1,500 m., sometimes coniferous woodlands. The larvae feed on legumes *Anthyllis*, *Dorycnium*, *Lotus* and *Onobrychis* species. **SEASON** July to September.

**_Zygaena ephialtes_ Billowing Burnet**
Wingspan: 32–35 mm. Bluish-black, forewing with 5 to 6 spots, including two red or yellow basal spots with corresponding red or yellow ring on abdomen Antennae tip white. **HABITAT** Up to mid mountainous slopes. The larvae feed on Crown Vetch *Securigera varia*. **SEASON** July to August.

**_Zygaena fausta_ Chalk Burnet**
Wingspan: 21–32 mm. Variable, but rather distinctive forewing pattern. **HABITAT** Sunny limestone hillsides, woodland edges, the larvae (pictured left) on *Coronilla* species. **SEASON** June to October.

**_Zygaena filipendulae_ Six-spot Burnet**
Wingspan: 25–40 mm. Forewing with six red spots. **HABITAT** Various grasslands, including damp areas. **SEASON** June to August. **SIMILAR SPECIES _Z. anthyllidis_ Pyrenean Burnet** (wingspan: 30–38 mm [not mapped]) found in the central and eastern Pyrenees on rocky mountain slopes at 1,700 to 2,800 m, has a red band on abdomen and collar. The larvae feed on Alpine Bird's-foot-trefoil *Lotus alpinus*.

**_Zygaena lavandulae_ Broom Burnet**
Wingspan: 31–33 mm. White collar. **HABITAT** Grasslands. The larvae feed on *Dorycnium pentaphyllum* and *Anthyllis cytisoides*. **SEASON** May to July.

**_Zygaena lonicerae_ Narrow-bordered Five-spot Burnet**
Wingspan: 30–46 mm. Forewing with five red spots, narrower and marginally more pointed than in the similar **_Z. trifolii_ Five-spot Burnet** (pictured right [not mapped]). **HABITAT** Various, from open woodlands, coastal areas and calcareous grasslands to 2,000 m. **SEASON** Late June to August.

**_Zygaena loti_ [Slender Scotch Burnet]**
Wingspan: 26–31 mm. Rather variable. **HABITAT** Grasslands, including hillsides and woodland clearings. **SEASON** May to August in one or two broods.

**_Zygaena osterodensis_ Woodland Burnet**
Wingspan: 30–34 mm. Red forewing patches form two parallel stripes. **HABITAT** Shaded woodlands to 1,800 m. The larvae feed on *Vicia* and *Lathyrus*. **SEASON** June to July.

**_Zygaena purpuralis_ Transparent Burnet**
Wingspan: 30–39 mm. Red streaks on forewings. **HABITAT** Various including alpine meadows to 2,000 m or so. The larvae feed on thyme *Thymus*. **SEASON** Late May to August.

*Adscita statices*

*Zygaena carniolica*

*Zygaena ephialtes*

*Zygaena fausta*

*Zygaena filipendulae*

*Zygaena lavandulae*

*Zygaena lonicerae*

*Zygaena loti*

*Zygaena osterodensis*

*Zygaena purpuralis*

*Adscita statices*

*Zygaena carniolica* [PC]

*Zygaena ephialtes* [PC]

*Zygaena fausta*

*Zygaena filipendulae*

*Zygaena anthyllidis*

*Zygaena lavandulae*

*Zygaena loti* mating pair

*Zygaena lonicerae*

*Zygaena osterodensis*

*Zygaena purpuralis*

## Family Drepanidae – HOOK-TIPS, LUTESTRINGS and ALLIES

A family sharing the same type of hearing organs. Many species have hooked forewing tips.

***Watsonalla binaria* Oak Hook-tip**
Wingspan: 19–35 mm. Orange-brown, hindwings paler. **HABITAT** Woodlands and parks. The larvae mainly feed on oak *Quercus*. **SEASON** June to September.

*Watsonalla binaria*

***Watsonalla uncinula* Spiny Hook-tip**
Wingspan: 18–35 mm. Orange-brown. **HABITAT** Woodlands. **SEASON** All year.

*Watsonalla uncinula*

***Cilix glaucata* Chinese Character**
Wingspan: 16–27 mm. Whitish with dark markings; resembles a bird dropping. There are three similar species in Spain. **HABITAT** Woodlands and others. The larvae mainly feed on *Prunus*. **SEASON** March to September.

*Cilix glaucata*

***Thyatira batis* Peach Blossom**
Wingspan: 30–44 mm. Dark brown with pink-blotched forewings. **HABITAT** Woodlands. The larvae feed on bramble *Rubus*. **SEASON** April to September.

*Thyatira batis*

***Habrosyne pyritoides* Buff Arches**
Wingspan: 32–44 mm. Unique patterned forewings. **HABITAT** Woodlands and gardens. The larvae feed on bramble *Rubus*. **SEASON** June to October.

*Habrosyne pyritoides*

## Family Lasiocampidae – EGGAR MOTHS

Large-bodied moths with broad wings.

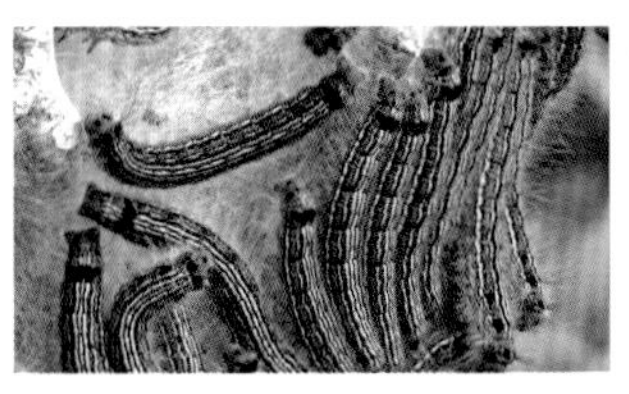

***Malacosoma neustria* Lackey**
Wingspan: 25–41 mm. Yellowish to reddish-brown, forewings with two cross-lines. **HABITAT** Woodlands, gardens and parks. The larvae (pictured left) feed on hawthorn *Crataegus*, fruit and other trees and bushes. **SEASON** May to September.

*Malacosoma neustria*

***Lasiocampa quercus* Oak Eggar**
Wingspan: 45–90 mm. Brown or buff. **HABITAT** Open areas including woodlands. The larvae (below left) feed on bramble *Rubus* and others. **SEASON** Late May to September.

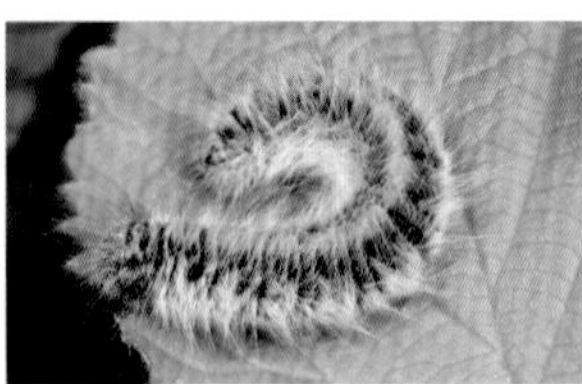

*Lasiocampa quercus*

***Lasiocampa trifolii* Grass Eggar**
Wingspan: 35–65 mm. Reddish brown, narrower pale lines on forewings than *L. quercus*. **HABITAT** Open areas. The larvae (above right) feed on grasses and other plants. **SEASON** June to October, can be earlier in the year.

*Lasiocampa trifolii*

***Macrothylacia rubi* Fox Moth**
Wingspan: 48–75 mm. Reddish-brown to grey. **HABITAT** Open sites including woodlands. The larvae (pictured left) feed on bramble *Rubus*, heather *Calluna* and others. **SEASON** May to July.

*Macrothylacia rubi*

*Watsonalla binaria* *Watsonalla uncinula* *Cilix glaucata*

*Thyatira batis*

*Habrosyne pyritoides*

*Malacosoma neustria* ♂ colour forms

*Lasiocampa trifolii* ♂ [KT]

*Lasiocampa quercus* ♂ (left), ♀ (right)

*Macrothylacia rubi* ♂

***Dendrolimus pini*** **Pine-tree Lappet**
Wingspan: 45–80 mm. distinctively banded. **HABITAT** Coniferous woodlands, where the larvae feed on pine *Pinus*. **SEASON** June to September.

*Dendrolimus pini*

***Euthrix potatoria*** **Drinker**
Wingspan: 40–70 mm. Reddish-brown or yellowish patches, cross-line on forewing runs to the wing tip. **HABITAT** Wetlands and others, where the larvae feed on grasses and reeds. **SEASON** Late June to mid August.

*Euthrix potatoria*

***Phyllodesma kermesifolia*** **Lajonquière Lappet**
Wingspan: 34–44 mm. Dark brown. **HABITAT** Open woodlands mainly in Iberia. The larvae feed on oak *Quercus*. **SEASON** February to June, possibly also later, up to August.

*Phyllodesma kermesifolia*

***Phyllodesma tremulifolia*** **Aspen Lappet**
Wingspan: 30–48 mm. Reddish brown. **HABITAT** Open woodlands. The larvae feed on hawthorn *Crataegus*, *Prunus* and others. **SEASON** Late April to August.

*Phyllodesma tremulifolia*

***Gastropacha quercifolia*** **Lappet**
Wingspan: 56–88 mm. Purplish-brown with scalloped outer wing edge when at rest, snout conspicuous, with part of hindwing exposed. **HABITAT** Woodlands, where the larvae feed on oak *Quercus*, poplar *Populus* and birch *Betula*. **SEASON** May to August.

*Gastropacha quercifolia*

***Streblote panda*** **Blueberry Lappet**
Wingspan: 30–70 mm. Orange to dark brown. **HABITAT** Woodlands and more open areas, where the larvae feed on various plants. **SEASON** May to September, possibly also earlier and later.

*Streblote panda*

***Odonestis pruni*** **Plum Lappet**
Wingspan: 30–60 mm. Yellowish-brown. **HABITAT** Woodlands, where the larvae mainly feed on *Prunus*, other trees and bushes. **SEASON** May to August, possibly later to October.

*Odonestis pruni*

***Trichiura ilicis*** **Holm Oak Eggar**
Wingspan: 19–30 mm. Brownish, forewings with darker broad band bordered by black (pictured right [PH]). **HABITAT** Woodlands, where the larvae feed on oak *Quercus*. **SEASON** December to April.

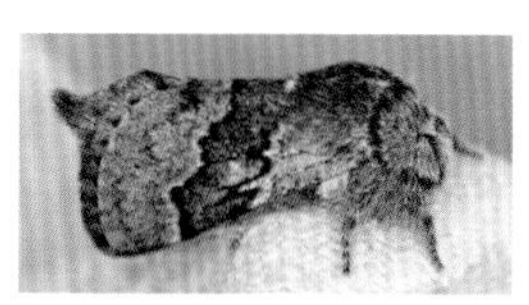

*Trichiura ilicis*

## Family Endromidae – KENTISH GLORY & ALLIES
A small family, with only two Palaearctic species,

***Endromis versicolora*** [Kentish Glory]
Wingspan: 45–89 mm. Attractive bold wing patterns, ♂ darker. **HABITAT** Woodlands, where the larvae mainly feed on birch *Betula*. **SEASON** March to May.

*Endromis versicolora* ♂

*Endromis versicolora*

*Dendrolimus pini* ♂ [RC]

*Streblote panda* ♂

*Phyllodesma kermesifolia*

*Phyllodesma tremulifolia*

*Gastropacha quercifolia* [KB]

*Euthrix potatoria* ♂

*Odonestis pruni* ♂

## Family Saturniidae – EMPEROR MOTHS [SILKMOTHS]

Medium to large moths, the wings often with bold eye-spots. The cocoons of some species are used to make silk.

### *Saturnia pavonia* Emperor Moth

Wingspan: 40–90 mm. Greyer than *S. pyri* and much smaller. **HABITAT** Various including grasslands up to 2,000 m, heathlands and woodland edge. The larvae (pictured left) feed on bramble *Rubus*, heather *Calluna* and many others. **SEASON** March to June.

### *Saturnia pavoniella* Southern Emperor Moth

Wingspan: 45–95 mm. Similar to *S. pavonia* but larger and paler. **HABITAT** Open areas. The larvae feed on various trees and bushes. **SEASON** Late February to June.

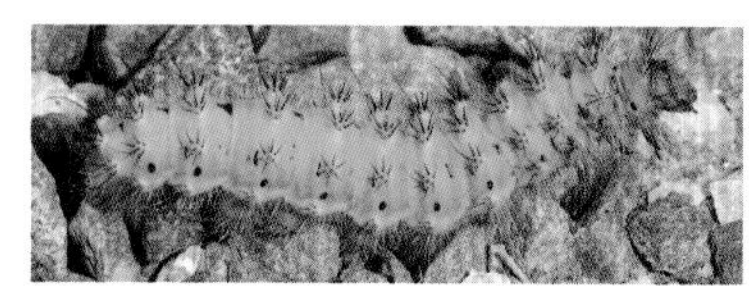

### *Saturnia pyri* Giant Peacock Moth

Wingspan: 87–166 mm. Impressive large, dark species with pale borders. **HABITAT** Open areas with scattered trees. The larvae (pictured left) feed on Walnut *Juglans regia*; fruit trees pear *Pyrus*, apple *Malus* and others. **SEASON** Mid March to June, sometimes later.

### *Samia cynthia* Diana's Silkmoth

Wingspan: 113–125 mm. Large, greenish ground colour. **HABITAT** Urban areas and valleys at low altitudes where the main larval foodplant Tree-of-Heaven *Ailanthus* is established. An introduced species from China. **SEASON** May to June, September.

*Samia cynthia* ♂ (left), larva (below) [both ARP]

### *Aglia tau* Tau Emperor

Wingspan: 60–84 mm. Rather variable, normal form yellowish-orange, a dark brown or black form *melaina* is associated with cooler, mountainous areas. **HABITAT** Woodlands, where the larvae mainly feed on beech *Fagus*. ♂s are fast day-fliers. **SEASON** Late March to early June.

### *Graellsia isabellae* Spanish Moon Moth

Wingspan: 65–100 mm. Pale green with reddish brown borders and veins. **HABITAT** Mature coniferous woodlands, 500 to 1,800 m. The larvae feed on Scots Pine *Pinus sylvestris* and Black Pine *P. nigra*. **SEASON** March to early July.

*Graellsia isabellae* larva [ARP]

*Saturnia pavonia*

*Saturnia pavoniella*

*Saturnia pyri*

*Samia cynthia*

*Aglia tau*

*Graellsia isabellae*

*Saturnia pavonia* ♂

*Saturnia pavoniella* ♂

*Saturnia pyri* ♂

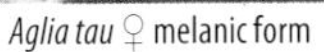

*Aglia tau* ♀ melanic form

*Graellsia isabellae* ♂ [ARP]

## Family Sphingidae – HAWK-MOTHS

Medium to large moths, the wings narrow and tapering for powerful flight. Some species have a long proboscis to gather nectar from flowers in flight, others do not feed. The larvae of many species have a distinctive horn.

### *Mimas tiliae* Lime Hawk-moth

Wingspan: 60–80 mm. Green with dark olive-green central blotches. A reddish-brown form *brunnea* is sometimes seen. **HABITAT** Woodlands to 1,500 m. The larvae feed on lime *Tilia* and elm *Ulmus*. **SEASON** May to August.

*Mimas tiliae*

### *Smerinthus ocellata* Eyed Hawk-moth

Wingspan: 70–95 mm. Forewings pinkish-brown to dark brown or black; the hindwings are pink with bold eye-spots. **HABITAT** Various including damper sites, orchards and gardens to 2,000 m. The larvae feed on apple *Malus*, poplar *Populus* and willow *Salix*. **SEASON** March to August.

*Smerinthus ocellata*

### *Laothoe populi* Poplar Hawk-moth

Wingspan: 70–100 mm. Grey with chestnut-brown patch on the hindwings. At rest the hindwings project well in front of the forewings. **HABITAT** Woodlands, open damp areas, parks and gardens to 1,600 m. The larvae feed on poplar *Populus* and willow *Salix*. **SEASON** April to September.

*Laothoe populi*

### *Agrius convolvuli* Convolvulus Hawk-moth

Wingspan: 95–130 mm. Grey with hindwings and abdomen pink-banded. **HABITAT** Open areas including agricultural areas and gardens but in many areas apart from the far south of Europe, these moths are migrating north from northern Africa. Adults nectar at night by hovering over tubular flowers such as *Nicotiana*. Larvae (pictured left} often feed on *Convolvulus*, **SEASON** April to November.

*Agrius convolvuli*

### *Acherontia atropos* Death's-head Hawk-moth

Wingspan: 90–130 mm. Bluish-black, some dark brown streaks with hindwings yellow and black, the abdomen yellow with black bands and a blue central longitudinal broad line. Skull-like mark usually present on thorax. **HABITAT** Open areas including agricultural sites. As well as seeking foodplant flowers for nectar, adults may be seen around bee hives, which they enter to feed on honey. Larvae feed on Solanaceae, such as potato. **SEASON** March to October.

*Acherontia atropos*

### *Sphinx ligustri* Privet Hawk-moth

Wingspan: 90–120 mm. Dark brown with paler areas on the forewings; hindwings and abdomen pink and black banded. **HABITAT** Open areas including woodlands to 1,500 m. The larvae feed on privet *Ligustrum*, ash *Fraxinus* and others. **SEASON** April to May, also August.

*Sphinx ligustri*

### *Sphinx maurorum* Southern Pine Hawkmoth

Wingspan: 70–80 mm. Grey with black streaks on the forewings. **HABITAT** Coniferous woodlands where the larvae feed on pine *Pinus*. **SEASON** Mainly mid July to early August. **SIMILAR SPECIES** ***S. pinastri* Pine Hawk-moth** (wingspan: 70–96 mm [not pictured]) is often larger with different genitalia and is found in open coniferous or mixed woodlands to 1,600 m. Little overlap with *S. maurarum*.

*Sphinx maurorum*

*Sphinx pinastri*

### *Hemaris tityus* Narrow-bordered Bee Hawk-moth

Wingspan: 40–50 mm. Small and rather bee-like, with transparent wings, except for a narrow outer brown margin. **HABITAT** Grasslands (often calcareous) and woodland glades where *Ajuga* abounds. This day-flying moth occurs up to 2,000 m. The larvae feed on Devil's-bit Scabious *Succisa pratensis* and Field Scabious *Knautia arvensis*. **SEASON** April to May also August. **SIMILAR SPECIES** ***H. fuciformis* Broad-bordered Bee Hawk-moth** (wingspan: 38–48 mm [not mapped]) has wings with a broad outer brown margin.

*Hemaris tityus*

*Mimas tiliae* *Smerinthus ocellata* *Laothoe populi*

*Agrius convolvuli*

*Acherontia atropos*

*Sphinx ligustri*

*Sphinx maurorum* [KB]

*Hemaris tityus*

*Hemaris fuciformis* (left), (right) [PC]

### *Macroglossum stellatarum* Humming-bird Hawk-moth

Wingspan: 40–45 mm. Bee-like, grey with various darker markings, hindwings orange. **HABITAT** Gardens, parks and others where this day and night-flying species nectars on *Buddleja* and others, hovering about, often at speed. The larvae mainly feed on bedstraws *Galium* and *Rubia*. **SEASON** All year.

*Macroglossum stellatarum*

### *Daphnis nerii* Oleander Hawk-moth

Wingspan: 90–110 mm. Olive-green. **HABITAT** Dry river beds and hillsides with scattered Oleander *Nerium oleander* (the larval foodplant). **SEASON** August to September, but sometimes earlier, for example migrants.

*Daphnis nerii*

### *Prosperinus proserpina* Willowherb Hawk-moth

Wingspan: 36–60 mm. Forewings various shades of green, hindwings mainly yellowish. **HABITAT** Damp woodland clearings and edges and others. The main foodplants are willowherb *Epilobium* and evening-primrose Oenothera. **SEASON** Late May to early June (July in the Pyrenees).

*Prosperinus proserpina*

### *Hyles euphorbiae* Spurge Hawk-moth

Wingspan: 70–85 mm. Broad forewing band reaching tip. **HABITAT** Grassland and woodland edges, even mountains to 1,900 m. The larvae are variable in colour (pictured left) and mainly feed on spurge *Euphorbia*. **SEASON** July to August.

*Hyles euphorbiae*

### *Hyles gallii* Bedstraw Hawk-moth

Wingspan: 65–85 mm. Narrower forewing bands than *H. euphorbiae*. **HABITAT** Grasslands and woodland cleared areas in mountains to 2,000 m. The larvae feed on willowherb *Epilobium* and bedstraw *Galium*. **SEASON** May to June and August to September.

*Hyles gallii*

### *Hyles livornica* Striped Hawk-moth

Wingspan: 60–85 mm. White-striped forewings. **HABITAT** Various open sites, often on migration. The larvae feed on various plants including dock *Rumex*, *Polygonum* and vine *Vitis*. **SEASON** Late February to October, including migrants travelling almost anywhere in Europe to the north of the breeding area shown on Map 6.

*Hyles livornica*

### *Deilephila elpenor* Elephant Hawk-moth

Wingspan: 60–75 mm. Pink and olive-green forewings and body; hindwings pink and black. **HABITAT** Various including floodplains of rivers and streams, damp woodlands, urban areas, even to 1,500 m in mountainous areas. The larvae feed mainly on willowherb *Epilobium* and bedstraw *Galium*. **SEASON** June to September.

*Deilephila elpenor*

### *Deilephila porcellus* Small Elephant Hawk-moth

Wingspan: 40–55 mm. Pink and yellowish-brown. **HABITAT** Grasslands where the larvae feed mainly on bedstraw *Galium*. **SEASON** Late May to August.

*Deilephila porcellus*

### *Hippotion celerio* Silver-striped Hawk-moth

Wingspan: 60–80 mm. Conspicuous, narrow silver forewing stripe. **HABITAT** Various where adults seek suitable flowers and ideally the main larval foodplant vine *Vitis* is present. **SEASON** June to October, including migrants which occasionally arrive earlier.

*Hippotion celerio*

### *Marumba quercus* Oak Hawk-moth

Wingspan: 85–100 mm. Grey or pale to dark brown. **HABITAT** Woodlands, sometimes in hilly areas to 1,500 m. The larvae feed mainly on shrubby oak *Quercus* bushes. **SEASON** May to September.

*Marumba quercus*

*Macroglossum stellatarum*

*Daphnis nerii*

*Prosperinus proserpina*

*Hyles euphorbiae* (left), larva (right) [PC]

*Hyles gallii*

*Hyles livornica*

*Deilephila elpenor* (left), larva (right)

*Deilephila porcellus*

*Hippotion celerio*

*Marumba quercus*

## Family Geometridae – GEOMETRID MOTHS

A large family of varied small to medium-sized moths, broad with triangular forewings and slender bodies. The larvae have only two pairs of prolegs (hindlegs) and often loop as they move.

### *Idaea aureolaria* Golden-yellow Wave

Wingspan: 12–18 mm. Bright yellow with fringes and lines blackish. **HABITAT** Grasslands including mountainous areas. **SEASON** June to early August.

### *Idaea degeneraria* Portland Ribbon Wave

Wingspan: 18–25 mm. Variable dark brown shading. **HABITAT** Open places. **SEASON** March to October.

### *Schistostege decussata* Rayed Sash

Wingspan: 25–33 mm. Whitish with brown lines. **HABITAT** Mountainous areas, often seen by day. The larvae feed on spurge *Euphorbia*. **SEASON** June.

### *Scopula ornata* Lace Border

Wingspan: 18–25 mm. White with delicate grey and brown borders. **HABITAT** Grasslands, including mountainous areas. **SEASON** May to October.

### *Scopula tessellaria* Dusky-brown Wave

Wingspan: 22–28 mm. Whitish and dark brown chequered, including fringes. **HABITAT** Grasslands, including mountainous areas. **SEASON** June to July.

### *Scopula submutata* Mediterranean Lace Border

Wingspan: 20–25 mm. Easy to confuse with *S. decorata*, but markings distinct. **HABITAT** Open areas. **SEASON** April to October.

### *Rhodostrophia calabra* Narrow Rose-banded Wave

Wingspan: 28–33 mm. Yellowish with crimson lines and bands. **HABITAT** Grasslands and scrub, including mountainous areas where it is easily disturbed by day. **SEASON** May to June.

### *Cyclophora puppillaria* Blair's Mocha

Wingspan: 20–26 mm. Speckled, pinkish-brown. **HABITAT** Woodlands on oak *Quercus*. **SEASON** All year.

### *Rhodometra sacraria* Vestal

Wingspan: 20–25 mm. White or yellow with bold pink or brown cross-band. **HABITAT** Grasslands, including urban areas, easily disturbed by day. **SEASON** All year.

### *Scotopteryx peribolata* Spanish Carpet

Wingspan: 28–33 mm. Characteristic markings. **HABITAT** Sites with broom *Cytisus*. **SEASON** August to November.

Moth trapping in **Casares, Andalucia, Spain**. Penny Hale and the author examining a moth trap set up by Penny in her garden. This attracts numerous geometrid and other moths. Most go inside the trap, but some moths settle on the outside of the trap, or on nearby vegetation.

*Idaea aureolaria*

*Idaea degeneraria*

*Schistostege decussata*

*Scopula ornata*

*Scopula tessellaria*

*Scopula submutata*

*Rhodostrophia calabra*

*Cyclophora puppillaria*

*Rhodometra sacraria*

*Scotopteryx peribolata*

*Schistostege decussata* [KB]

*Idaea aureolaria*

*Idaea degeneraria*

*Scopula ornata*

*Scopula tessellaria*

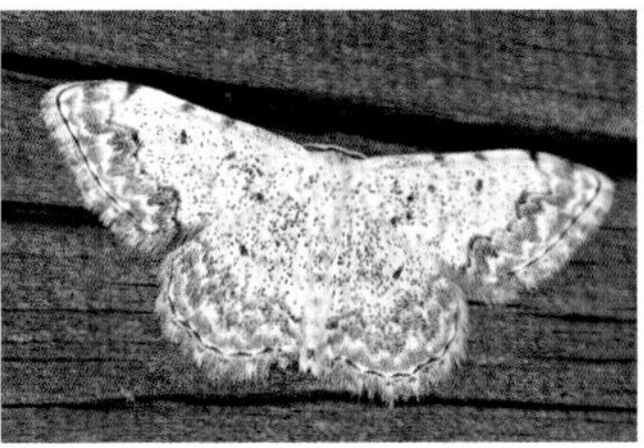

*Scopula submutata*

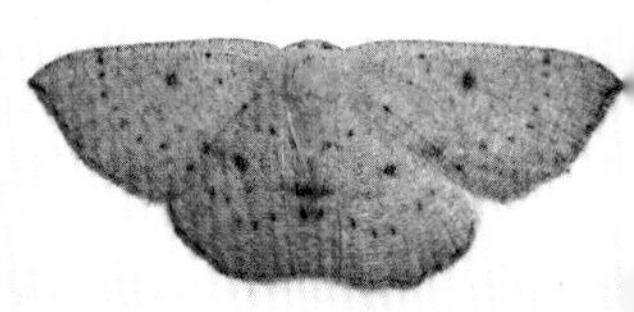

*Cyclophora puppillaria*

*Rhodostrophia calabra*

*Rhodometra sacraria*

*Scotopteryx peribolata* [PH]

### *Lythria cruentaria* Pale-rose Saffron
Wingspan: 18–22 mm. Yellow with pink cross-bands. **HABITAT** Grasslands and woodland edges, easily disturbed by day. **SEASON** April to August.

*Lythria cruentaria*

### *Epirrhoe tristata* Small Argent & Sable
Wingspan: 21–24 mm. Black or brown and white. **HABITAT** Grasslands, often calcareous, where the larvae feed on bedstraw *Galium*. **SEASON** May to August.

*Epirrhoe tristata*

### *Euphyia vallantinaria*
Wingspan: c.28 mm. A well-marked dark carpet moth, which could be confused with other species. **HABITAT** Grasslands, first reported as new to Europe (in Andalucía) in 2011 and since in Malaga area of Spain. This is another example of species expanding their range, in this case from northern Africa. **SEASON** September to October.

*Euphyia vallantinaria*

### *Cosmorhoe ocellata* Purple Bar
Wingspan: 20–24 mm. White with broad central purplish band. **HABITAT** Gardens and woodlands, where the larvae feed on bedstraw *Galium*. **SEASON** May to September.

*Cosmorhoe ocellata*

### *Odezia atrata* Chimney Sweeper
Wingspan: 25–27 mm. Black or dark brown with white forewing tip. **HABITAT** Grasslands and woodland edges. These day-fliers are also found in mountainous areas. **SEASON** June to August.

*Odezia atrata*

### *Eupithecia centaureata* Lime-speck Pug
Wingspan: 15–23 mm. White with darker markings, including large black or bluish blotch. **HABITAT** Open areas including gardens. **SEASON** All year.

*Eupithecia centaureata*

### *Aplocera praeformata* Purple Treble-bar
Wingspan: 34–40 mm. White with orange marks and dark bands distinctively shaped. **HABITAT** Various grasslands including mountainous and woodlands where the larvae feed on St John's-wort *Hypericum*. **SEASON** July to August.

*Aplocera praeformata*

### *Chiasma clathrata* Latticed Heath
Wingspan: 23–30 mm. Rests like a butterfly and sometimes confused for one. **HABITAT** Grasslands, day and night flying. The larvae feed on medick *Medicago* and clover *Trifolium*. **SEASON** April to September.

*Chiasma clathrata*

### *Itame vincularia* Fettered Dyer
Wingspan: 28–32 mm. Greyish with dark brown bands and black mark. Black-dotted. **HABITAT** Woodlands and scrub, where the larvae feed on buckthorn *Rhamnus*. **SEASON** January to October.

*Itame vincularia*

### *Petrophora narbonea* Sienna Silver-line
Wingspan: 20–26 mm. Brownish-grey with two yellow lines. **HABITAT** Scrublands, where the larvae feed on *Teucrium*. **SEASON** March to April, then August to October.

*Petrophora narbonea*

**Sardinia, Italy**: Wooded slope on the central mountains, habitat for various moths, also *Papilio hospiton* (page 264). [WW]

*Lythria cruentaria* [TN]

*Epirrhoe tristata*

*Euphyia vallantinaria*

*Eupithecia centaureata*

*Odezia atrata*

*Cosmorhoe ocellata*

*Aplocera praeformata*

*Itame vincularia*

*Chiasma clathrata* (left), (right) [PC]

*Petrophora narbonea*

### *Plagodis dolabraria* Scorched Wing
Wingspan: 28–33 mm. Wings with a rather scorched appearance. **HABITAT** Woodlands, various foodplants. **SEASON** April to August.

*Plagodis dolabraria*

### *Opisthograptis luteolata* Brimstone Moth
Wingspan: 32–37 mm. Pale yellow wings, with brown markings. **HABITAT** Woodlands and gardens, often in urban areas; various foodplants (larva pictured left). **SEASON** April to October.

*Opisthograptis luteolata*

### *Pseudopanthera macularia* Speckled Yellow
Wingspan: 25–28 mm. Yellow with brown blotches. **HABITAT** Woodland rides and edge. **SEASON** May to July.

*Pseudopanthera macularia*

### *Selenia lunularia* Lunar Thorn
Wingspan: 32–41 mm. Characteristic wing shape and dark areas. **HABITAT** Woodlands and parks. **SEASON** April to August.

*Selenia lunularia*

### *Odontopera bidentata* Scalloped Hazel
Wingspan: 33–45 mm. Scalloped wings. **HABITAT** Woodlands, various foodplants including coniferous trees. **SEASON** May to July.

*Odontopera bidentata*

### *Crocallis auberti* Aubert's Scalloped
Wingspan: 33–40 mm. Forewings brown, cross-lines often pale, in some forms dark. **HABITAT** Slopes, the larvae feeding on *Coronilla valentina*. **SEASON** September to December.

*Crocallis auberti*

### *Crocallis dardoinaria* Dusky Scalloped Oak
Wingspan: 36–43 mm. Straw, central mark on forewings with four small black spots. **HABITAT** Scrublands. **SEASON** June to November.

*Crocallis dardoinaria*

### *Ourapteryx sambucaria* Swallow-tailed Moth
Wingspan: 45–60 mm. Pale lemon wings, short tails. **HABITAT** Woodlands, gardens and others on various plants. **SEASON** June to August.

*Ourapteryx sambucaria*

### *Biston strataria* Oak Beauty
Wingspan: 40–56 mm. Attractive banded wings. **HABITAT** Woodlands, often on oak *Quercus*. **SEASON** February to April.

*Biston strataria*

### *Nychiodes hispanica* Spanish Annulet
Wingspan: 38–48 mm. Dark species with little variation. **HABITAT** Mountainous areas in Spain apparently restricted to Andalucía, including Sierra Nevada 700 to 2,100 m. The larvae feed on *Genista* and gorse *Ulex*. **SEASON** June to September.

*Nychiodes hispanica* ♂

*Nychiodes hispanica*

*Plagodis dolabraria*

*Opisthograptis luteolata*

*Pseudopanthera macularia*

*Selenia lunularia*

*Odontopera bidentata*

*Crocallis auberti* [PH]

*Crocallis dardoinaria*

*Ourapteryx sambucaria*

*Biston strataria*

***Menophra japygiaria* Brassy Waved Umber**
Wingspan: 24–33 mm. Light to dark brown. Distinctive wavy black lines and paler areas. **HABITAT** Various. The larvae feed on *Olea*, *Rhus* and *Zizyphus*. **SEASON** All year.

*Menophra japygiaria*

***Ematurga atomaria* Common Heath**
Wingspan: 25–35 mm. Variable, ♂ yellowish-brown or grey (feathery antennae), ♀ often whitish. **HABITAT** Various grasslands and clearings. **SEASON** April to August.

*Ematurga atomaria*

***Gerinia honoraria* Scalloped Barred**
Wingspan: 39–50 mm. Brown or yellowish with angular, scalloped wings. Outer margin of forewings with brown and white edged lines either side of darker band, but hindwings with only one line. **HABITAT** Woodland edges. **SEASON** Practically all year.

*Gerinia honoraria*

***Hylaea fasciaria* Barred Red**
Wingspan: 23–35 mm. Variable, usually red or green but other colours possible. **HABITAT** Coniferous woodlands. **SEASON** May to September.

*Hylaea fasciaria*

***Charissa mucidaria* Coppery Taupe**
Wingspan: 20–30 mm. Russet-tinged with whitish and grey. Some authors regard the subgenus *Euchrognophos* as a valid genus. **HABITAT** Low and high elevations, where the larvae feed on umbellifers. **SEASON** All year.

*Charissa mucidaria*

***Siona lineata* Black-veined Moth**
Wingspan: 35–45 mm. White, veins darker, black on underside (pictured left [PC]. **HABITAT** Grasslands, day and night fliers. **SEASON** May to July.

*Siona lineata*

***Aplasta ononaria* Rest Harrow**
Wingspan: 21–26 mm. Light brown to greyish with reddish banding; rather speckled. **HABITAT** Grasslands, particularly limestone to 2,200 m. The larvae mainly feed on restharrow *Ononis*. **SEASON** May to August.

*Aplasta ononaria*

***Pseudopterpna coronillaria* Gorse Emerald** [Jersey Emerald]
Wingspan: 26–33 mm. Grey with darker lines and pale outer line. **HABITAT** Grasslands and sparse woodlands to 1,700 m. The larvae feed on broom *Cytisus* and others. **SEASON** March to November.

*Pseudopterpna coronillaria*

***Thetidia smaragdaria* Essex Emerald**
Wingspan: 25–34 mm. Green with white lines and white spots on forewings. **HABITAT** Rocky grassland slopes and river banks to 2,200 m., where the larvae feed on various Asteraceae. **SEASON** Mid May to September.

*Thetidia smaragdaria*

***Phaiogramma etruscaria* Etruscan Viridian**
Wingspan: 20–25 mm. Light green with various markings and mottling. **HABITAT** Scrublands and slopes, with various foodplants used. **SEASON** April to October.

*Phaiogramma etruscaria*

*Menophra japygiaria*

*Ematurga atomaria* ♂ (left) [PC], ♀ (right)

*Gerinia honoraria*

*Hylaea fasciaria*

*Charissa mucidaria*

*Siona lineata*

*Aplasta ononaria*

*Pseudopterpna coronillaria*

*Thetidia smaragdaria*

*Phaiogramma etruscaria* [PH]

## Family Notodontidae – PROMINENTS and ALLIES

Most species in this family have strange, humped larvae, which feed on trees, mainly in woodlands.

**_Thaumetopoea pityocampa_ Pine Processionary**
Wingspan: 29–45 mm. Grey, forewing with crescent mark. **HABITAT** Coniferous woodlands, where this species is a major pest. The tent-like silk nests are often seen high in pine *Pinus* trees and the larvae are well known for their processions, crawling in nose-to-tail columns in about April. As well as having protection of numbers, hairs from the larvae are known to cause allergic reactions in humans and mammals. **SEASON** Mid May to October.

*Thaumetopoea pityocampa*

**_Cerura vinula_ Puss Moth**
Wingspan: 45–80 mm. Whitish with various black spots and grey lines. **HABITAT** Woodlands and others, the spectacular larvae feeding on willow *Salix* and poplar *Populus*. **SEASON** April to August.

*Cerura vinula*

**_Cerura erminea_ Feline**
Wingspan: 45–70 mm. Rather like *C. vinula*, but *C. erminea* is easily recognised by its mostly black abdomen. **HABITAT** Woodlands and others. **SEASON** April to July.

*Cerura erminea*

**_Furcula bifida_ Poplar Kitten**
Wingspan: 44–48 mm. Central forewing band with straighter edge than in closely related species. **HABITAT** Open woodlands, where the larvae feed on poplar *Populus*. **SEASON** May to September.

*Furcula bifida*

**_Harpyia milhauseri_ Tawny Prominent**
Wingspan: 40–52 mm. Grey with black streaks and lines, also brown patches. **HABITAT** Various. The larvae feed on willow *Salix* and poplar *Populus*. **SEASON** March to September.

*Harpyia milhauseri*

**_Stauropus fagi_ Lobster Moth**
Wingspan: 48–70 mm. Yellowish-brown. **HABITAT** Woodlands, where the spectacular larvae (pictured left [PC]), hence the name 'lobster', mainly feed on beech *Fagus*. **SEASON** May to September.

*Stauropus fagi*

**_Peridea anceps_ Great Prominent**
Wingspan: 52–72 mm. Greenish-brown. **HABITAT** Woodlands, the larvae feeding on oak *Quercus*. **SEASON** March to June.

*Peridea anceps*

**_Pheosia tremula_ Swallow Prominent**
Wingspan: 46–64 mm. White wedge in forewing corner long. **HABITAT** Various, on poplar *Populus* and willow *Salix*. **SEASON** April to September.

*Pheosia tremula*

**_Phalera bucephala_ Buff-tip**
Wingspan: 45–70 mm. Twig mimic, with yellow patch at tip of forewings. **HABITAT** Various, the larvae often feeding on a number of trees including willow *Salix*, birch *Betula* and oak *Quercus*. **SEASON** May to September.

*Phalera bucephala*

**_Clostera curtula_ Chocolate-tip**
Wingspan: 36–38 mm. Chocolate-tipped forewings. **HABITAT** Mainly woodlands on poplar *Populus* and willow *Salix*. **SEASON** April to August.

*Clostera curtula*

*Thaumetopoea pityocampa* ♂

*Cerura vinula* (left), larva (right)

*Cerura erminea* ♂

*Furcula bifida* ♂

*Stauropus fagi* ♂

*Harpyia milhauseri*

*Peridea anceps*

*Pheosia tremula*

*Phalera bucephala* (left & right)

*Clostera curtula*

## Family Erebidae – TIGER & TUSSOCK MOTHS, RED UNDERWINGS & ALLIES

This family includes well known, mainly colourful moths formerly in families such as Lymantriidae (tussock moths) and Arctiidae (tigers, ermines & footmen) and others placed in the Noctuidae.

### *Calyptra thalictri* Vampire Moth

Wingspan: 46–60 mm. Brown, distinctive shape, forewings with a strong basal lobe. **HABITAT** Woodlands or sometimes open areas. The larvae feed on meadow-rue *Thalictrum*. The moth is a so-called 'vampire' as ♂s can suck blood from vertebrates (including humans) through skin. However, the proboscis is normally used to pierce fruit. **SEASON** June to August.

*Calyptra thalictri*

### *Lymantria monacha* Black Arches

Wingspan: 44–54 mm. White with several black jagged cross-lines. **HABITAT** Woodlands, where the larvae feed on oak *Quercus*. **SEASON** Late June to August.

*Lymantria monacha*

### *Lymantria dispar* Gypsy Moth

Wingspan: 48–65 mm. Dark brown ♂ and white ♀ with jagged cross-lines. **HABITAT** Woodlands, where the distinctively marked larvae feed on various trees and can be a pest. **SEASON** June to September.

*Lymantria dispar*

### *Euproctis chrysorrhoea* Brown-tail

Wingspan: 36–42 mm. White, ♂ abdomen mainly brown, raised when disturbed. **HABITAT** Open areas with hedges or similar, where larval webs may be plentiful on the likes of *Prunus*, hawthorn *Crataegus*, willow *Salix*, bramble *Rubus* and others. Like some other hairy larvae, these cause allergic skin reactions in some humans. **SEASON** June to August.

*Euproctis chrysorrhoea*

### *Orgyia antiqua* Vapourer

Wingspan: 25–38 mm. ♂ Orangey-brown, with dark lines and large white spots on each forewing, wingless ♀ brown (c.15 mm in body length). **HABITAT** Various including urban areas, associated with a wide range of trees. ♂s are day-fliers, often mistaken for butterflies. **SEASON** June to August.

*Orgyia antiqua*

### *Orgyia trigotephras* Mediterranean Vapourer

Wingspan: 20–25 mm. ♂ Similar to *O. antiqua*, but distinctly marked (♂ pictured left [PH]). **HABITAT** Various including urban areas. **SEASON** May to July.

*Orgyia trigotephras*

### *Ocneria rubea* Gypsy Rose

Wingspan: 30–35 mm. Brown. **HABITAT** Woodlands, where the larvae feed on oak *Quercus* and Strawberry-tree *Arbutus unedo*. **SEASON** May to July, September to October.

*Ocneria rubea*

### *Arctornis l-nigrum* Black V Moth

Wingspan: 52–60 mm. White, with black 'v'-like mark on each forewing. **HABITAT** Woodlands, where the larvae feed on beech *Fagus* and others. **SEASON** Mid June to early October.

*Arctornis l-nigrum*

### *Spilosoma luteum* Buff Ermine

Wingspan: 29–42 mm. White or cream to buff, with a row of black dots. **HABITAT** Various. **SEASON** June to October.

*Spilosoma luteum*

### *Diacrisia sannio* Clouded Buff

Wingspan: 28–50 mm. ♂ with yellow forewings, orange in ♀. **HABITAT** Various, ♂s are day-fliers. **SEASON** May to October.

*Diacrisia sannio*

*Calyptra thalictri* [MS]

*Lymantria monacha*

*Euproctis chrysorrhoea* (left) [RC], larvae (right)

*Lymantria dispar* mating pair [HB]

*Ocneria rubea*

*Spilosoma luteum*

*yia antiqua* mating pair (top), larva (bottom)

*Arctornis l-nigrum*

*Diacrisia sannio*

***Phragmatobia fuliginosa*** **Ruby Tiger**
Wingspan: 26–38 mm. Brown forewings, hindwings bright pink with dark marks. **HABITAT** Open areas by day. **SEASON** April to October.

*Phragmatobia fuliginosa*

***Cymbalophora pudica*** **Discrete Chaperon**
Wingspan: 35–43 mm. Cream with black blotches on forewings, hindwings with few black spots. **HABITAT** Open areas. **SEASON** Late July to November, sometimes in Spain also May to June.

*Cymbalophora pudica*

***Parasemia plantaginis*** **Wood Tiger**
Wingspan: 30–42 mm. Distinctive but variable bold tiger-like markings. **HABITAT** Open areas, ♂s are day-fliers. **SEASON** May to August.

*Parasemia plantaginis*

***Arctia caja*** **Garden Tiger**
Wingspan: 45–78 mm. White forewings with large dark brown blotches. Hindwings red with large bluish spots. **HABITAT** Open areas including gardens. The hairy larvae (pictured left) feed on various plants. **SEASON** June to August.

*Arctia caja*

***Arctia villica*** **Cream-spot Tiger**
Wingspan: 42–66 mm. Black forewings with cream patches. Hindwings yellow with black spots and blotches. **HABITAT** Open areas. **SEASON** February to August.

*Arctia villica*

***Atlantarctia tigrina*** **The Tiger**
Wingspan: 32–50 mm. Similar to *Arctia caja* but distinct pattern on wings. Hindwings orange with back spots and red flushes. **HABITAT** Rocky areas, 600 to 1,600 m. The larvae feed on *Genista*, *Syringa* and others. **SEASON** April to July.

*Atlantarctia tigrina*

***Rhyparia purpurata*** **Purple Tiger**
Wingspan: 35–52 mm. Yellow forewings with brown spots. Hindwings red with black spots. Larva (pictured left). **HABITAT** Open areas. **SEASON** June to September.

*Rhyparia purpurata*

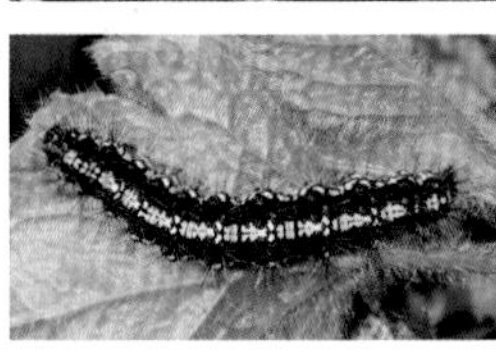

***Callimorpha dominula*** **Scarlet Tiger**
Wingspan: 42–58 mm. Black forewings with white and yellow spots. Hindwings red with black spots and blotches. Larva (pictured left [PC]). **HABITAT** Open areas, including wetlands, where adults are easily disturbed. **SEASON** June to August.

*Callimorpha dominula*

***Euplagia quadripunctaria*** **Jersey Tiger**
Wingspan: 42–58 mm. Black and white striped forewings. Hindwings red, orange or rarely yellowish-white, with black blotches. **HABITAT** Open areas, where adults are active by day. In mountains to 2,000 m. **SEASON** July to mid September.

*Euplagia quadripunctaria*

***Tyria jacobaeae*** **Cinnabar**
Wingspan: 28–45 mm. Black forewings with red markings and spots, hindwings red with black margins. **HABITAT** Grasslands. The conspicuous orange and black banded larvae (pictured left) of these day-fliers feed on Ragwort *Senecio jacobaea* and others. **SEASON** May to July.

*Tyria jacobaeae*

*Phragmatobia fuliginosa* *Cymbalophora pudica* *Parasemia plantaginis* [PC]

*Arctia caja* *Arctia villica*

*Rhyparia purpurata* *Callimorpha dominula*

*Atlantarctia tigrina* [KB] *Euplagia quadripunctaria* *Tyria jacobaeae* [PC]

***Utetheisa pulchella*** **Crimson Speckled**
Wingspan: 27–41 mm. White forewings with pink or red and black spots. **HABITAT** Grasslands, often coastal sites such as dunes from which they periodically migrate north. **SEASON** April to November.

*Utetheisa pulchella*

***Spiris striata*** **Feathered Footman**
Wingspan: 30–35 mm. Yellow forewings. ♂s black-striped, with feathery antennae. **HABITAT** Grasslands including high altitudes, where the larvae feed on grasses. Adults are day-fliers. **SEASON** May to September.

*Spiris striata*

***Miltochrista miniata*** **Rosy Footman**
Wingspan: 25–33 mm. Pink with wavy black-marked forewings. **HABITAT** Wet and dry woodlands to 1,100 m., the larvae feeding on algae, mosses and lichens. **SEASON** Mid May to August.

*Miltochrista miniata*

***Lithosia quadra*** **Four-spotted Footman**
Wingspan: 35–55 mm. ♂ forewings grey with yellow base, as well as yellow head and thorax. Legs and base of thorax bluish. The ♀ yellow with two dark large spots on each forewing. **HABITAT** Woodlands, the larvae feeding on mosses and lichens of branches and trunks, particularly oak *Quercus*. **SEASON** June to early August.

*Lithosia quadra*

***Eilema lurideola*** **Common Footman**
Wingspan: 28–38 mm. Forewings grey with yellow margin; hindwings yellow. **HABITAT** Woodlands. **SEASON** April to October.

*Eilema lurideola*

***Dysauxes ancilla*** **Handmaid**
Wingspan: 22–25 mm. Brown forewings with three large whitish spots. Hindwings brown with yellow band. **HABITAT** Open areas. The larvae feed on ragwort *Senecio* and plantain *Plantago*. **SEASON** June to September.

*Dysauxes ancilla*

***Dysauxes punctata*** **Famulus**
Wingspan: 20–22 mm. Brown forewings with several large whitish spots (mating pair pictured left). **HABITAT** Open areas. **SEASON** Mid May to mid September.

*Dysauxes punctata*

***Amata phegea*** **Nine-spotted**
Wingspan: 28–40 mm. Bluish-black wings with white spots. Abdomen with two yellow bands and antennae white-tipped (various similar species in Europe). **HABITAT** A day-flier in open areas, the larvae feeding on plantain *Plantago*, dock *Rumex* and bedstraw *Galium*. **SEASON** Mid May to July.

*Amata phegea*

***Eublemma cochylioides***
Wingspan: c.20 mm. Forewings yellowish with purple outer half; within latter two whitish spots are distinctive. **HABITAT** Rocky grasslands. **SEASON** July to November.

*Eublemma cochylioides*

***Eublemma ostrina*** **Purple Marbled**
Wingspan: 16–23 mm. Pale brown with darker markings, often with purple in outer half and white markings. **HABITAT** Rocky grasslands. **SEASON** All year.

*Eublemma ostrina*

*Utetheisa pulchella*

*Spiris striata* ♂ (left), ♀ (right)

*Miltochrista miniata*

*Lithosia quadra* ♂ (left), ♀ (right)

*Eilema lurideola*

*Dysauxes punctata* [PC]

*Amata phegea* [MS]

*Dysauxes ancilla*

*Eublemma cochylioides*

*Eublemma ostrina*

### *Catocala elocata* French Red Underwing

Wingspan: 80–86 mm. Grey forewings less distinct than the similar *C. nupta*, red and black hindwings. **HABITAT** Woodlands, where the larvae feed on poplar *Populus* and willow *Salix*. **SEASON** July to October.

*Catocala elocata*

### *Catocala fraxini* Clifden Nonpariel

Wingspan: 84–100 mm. Largest European *Catocala*, hindwings black with central violet-blue band. **HABITAT** Woodlands, where the larvae (pictured left) mainly feed on Aspen *Populus tremula*. **SEASON** July to November.

*Catocala fraxini*

### *Catocala fulminea*

Wingspan: 54–58 mm. Characteristic markings, hindwings yellow with black bands and markings. **HABITAT** Woodlands, where the larvae feed on *Prunus*, hawthorn *Crataegus*, oak *Quercus* and others. **SEASON** Late June to early September.

*Catocala fulminea*

### *Catocala mariana*

Wingspan: 40–44 mm. Similar to *C. fulminea* but smaller, forewings with less zigzag-like lines. **HABITAT** Woodlands, where the larvae feed on oak *Quercus*. **SEASON** May to June.

*Catocala mariana*

### *Catocala nymphaea*

Wingspan: 58–64 mm. Similar to *C. fulminea*, forewings distinctive. **HABITAT** Woodlands, where the larvae feed on oak *Quercus*. **SEASON** June to August.

*Catocala nymphaea*

### *Catocala nymphagoga* Oak Yellow Underwing

Wingspan: 35–43 mm. Distinctive forewings. **HABITAT** Woodlands, where the larvae feed on oak *Quercus*. **SEASON** May to July.

*Catocala nymphagoga*

### *Catocala nupta* Red Underwing

Wingspan: 78–84 mm. Grey forewings, red and black hindwings. **HABITAT** Woodlands, where the larvae feed on poplar *Populus* and willow *Salix*. **SEASON** June to October.

*Catocala nupta*

### *Catocala promissa* Light Crimson Underwing

Wingspan: 50–68 mm. Greyish-brown forewings with various markings, red and black hindwings, the latter central band gently wavy. **HABITAT** Woodlands, where the larvae (pictured left [DG]) feed on oak *Quercus*. **SEASON** July to August.

*Catocala promissa*

### *Catocala sponsa* Dark Crimson Underwing

Wingspan: 58–74 mm. Similar to *C. promissa*, sometimes darker. Hindwings with the black central band 'W' shaped. **HABITAT** Woodlands, where the larvae (pictured left [DG]) feed on oak *Quercus*. **SEASON** July to early September.

*Catocala sponsa*

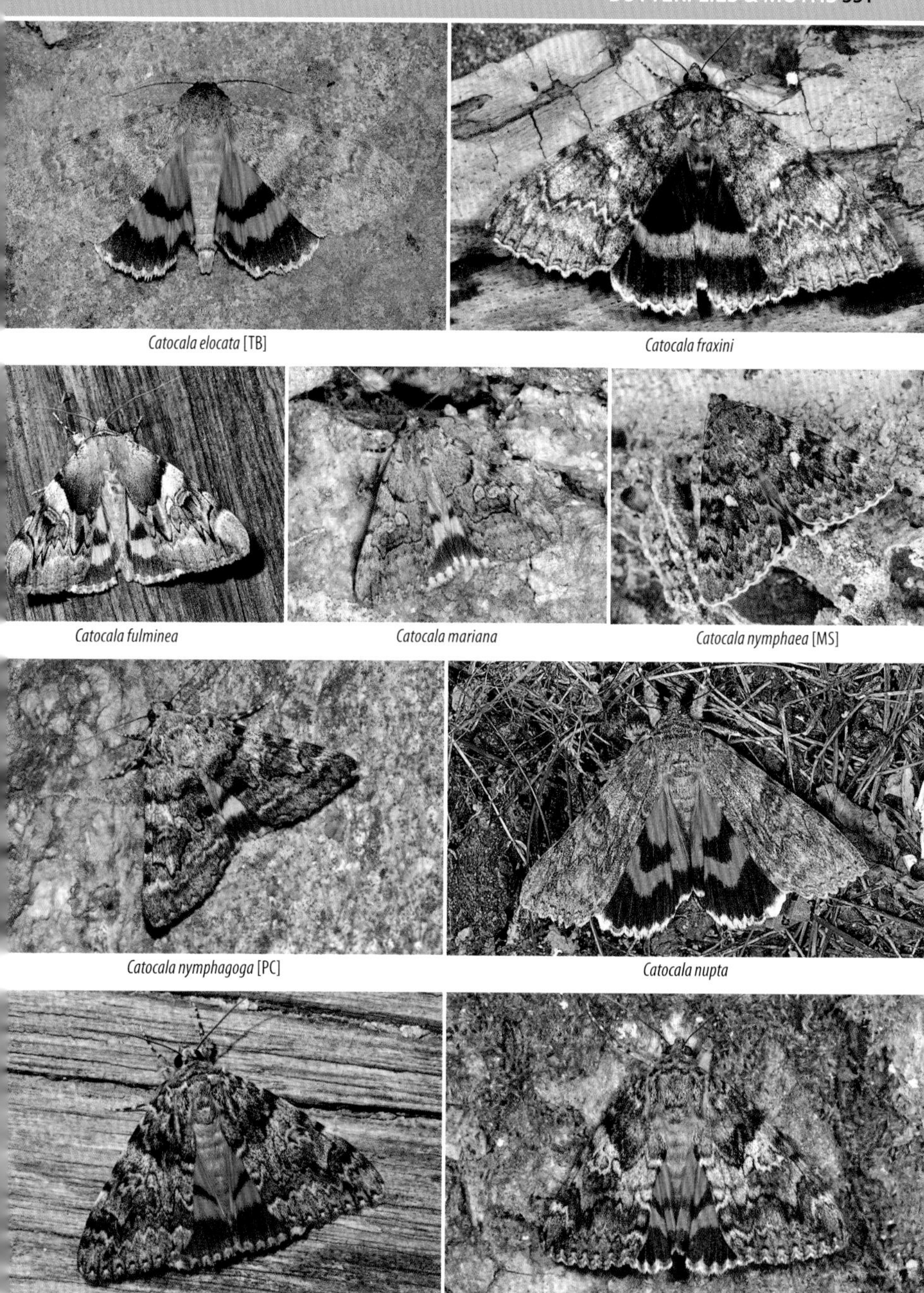

*Catocala elocata* [TB]

*Catocala fraxini*

*Catocala fulminea*

*Catocala mariana*

*Catocala nymphaea* [MS]

*Catocala nymphagoga* [PC]

*Catocala nupta*

*Catocala promissa*

*Catocala sponsa*

**_Euclidia glyphica_ Burnet Companion**
Wingspan: 28–34 mm. Forewings brown-banded; hindwings orange and dark brown. **HABITAT** Day-fliers in grasslands, where the larvae prefer bird's-foot-trefoil *Lotus* and clover *Trifolium*. **SEASON** May to August.

*Euclidia glyphica*

**_Euclidia mi_ Mother Shipton**
Wingspan: 30–34 mm. Forewing pattern said to resemble the profile of Mother Shipton, a 16th-century English witch. **HABITAT** Day-fliers in grasslands, where the larvae feed on leguminous plants and grasses. **SEASON** April to September.

*Euclidia mi*

**_Dysgonia algira_ Passenger**
Wingspan: 38–44 mm. Brown forewings with lighter bands. **HABITAT** Various. The larvae often feed on bramble *Rubus*. **SEASON** May to September.

*Dysgonia algira*

**_Ophiusa tirhaca_ Green Drab**
Wingspan: 60–70 mm. Forewings green with brown border and brown central spot. **HABITAT** Various. The larvae feed on *Pistacia*, *Rhus* and others. **SEASON** February to October.

*Ophiusa tirhaca*

**_Zethes insularis_**
Wingspan: 35–37 mm. Brown with distinctive darker bands. **HABITAT** Various, where the larvae feed on *Pistacia*. **SEASON** March to September.

*Zethes insularis*

## Family Euteliidae – EUTELLIDS
A small family of moths, typically resting with wings folded and abdomen curled upward.

**_Eutelia adulatrix_**
Wingspan: 23–34 mm. Brown with whitish, black and metallic blue markings. **HABITAT** Various, including rocky slopes where the larvae mainly feed on *Pistacia*. **SEASON** March to October.

*Eutelia adulatrix*

## Family Noctuidae – NOCTUIDS
A large family of medium-sized, often brown moths, with forewings often longer than deep, designed for powerful flight.

**_Chrysodeixis chalcites_ Golden Twin-spot**
Wingspan: 32–42 mm. Forewings brownish with metallic gold areas and two central silver spots, sometimes joined. **HABITAT** Various, sometimes regarded as a pest in greenhouses. **SEASON** May to December.

*Chrysodeixis chalcites*

**_Macdunnoughia confusa_ Deswick's Plusia**
Wingspan: 36–42 mm. Forewings brownish with distinctive metallic silver mark. **HABITAT** Open areas, or light woodlands. As with related species, strongly migratory. **SEASON** April to November.

*Macdunnoughia confusa*

**_Autographa gamma_ Silver Y**
Wingspan: 38–46 mm. Grey or brown, forewings with silver 'Y' mark. **HABITAT** Various, including agricultural sites where the larvae are regarded as a pest on field crops. A strongly migratory, day-flying species. **SEASON** All year.

*Autographa gamma*

**_Deltote uncula_ Silver Hook**
Wingspan: 22–25 mm. Olive brown forewings with broad whitish margins and 'hook'. **HABITAT** Wetlands, where the larvae feed on grasses. **SEASON** May to September.

*Deltote uncula*

*Euclidia glyphica*

*Euclidia mi*

*Dysgonia algira*

*Ophiusa tirhaca* [PH]

*Zethes insularis*

*Eutelia adulatrix*

*Chrysodeixis chalcites*

*Macdunnoughia confusa*

*Autographa gamma*

*Deltote uncula* [RC]

***Pseudozarba bipartita***
Wingspan: 16–18 mm. Yellowish-brown forewings with broad central and margins dark brown band, also fringes. **HABITAT** Grasslands. **SEASON** May to November.

*Pseudozarba bipartita*

***Acontia lucida* Pale Shoulder**
Wingspan: 25–30 mm. Forewings blackish with large white blotch; basal area variable from white to grey (pictured below). **HABITAT** Open areas. **SEASON** All year.

*Acontia lucida*

*Acontia lucida*

***Acontia trabealis* Spotted Sulphur**
Wingspan: 19–22 mm. Forewings yellowish with dark brown spots and lines. **HABITAT** Open areas. **SEASON** May to early September.

*Acontia trabealis*

***Tyta luctuosa* Four-spotted**
Wingspan: 22–24 mm. Forewings blackish with large white blotch. **HABITAT** Dry grasslands, a day-flying species. The larvae feed on *Convolvulus*, *Linum* and others. **SEASON** March to October.

*Tyta luctuosa*

***Panemeria tenebrata* Small Yellow Underwing**
Wingspan: 16–19 mm. Dark brown, grey-dusted forewings. Hindwings black with broad yellow band. **HABITAT** Open and lightly wooded areas. **SEASON** Late April to mid June.

*Panemeria tenebrata*

***Synthymia fixa* Goldwing**
Wingspan: 32–40 mm. Brownish and dark green forewings, with black markings; there are usually whitish patches and other markings. **HABITAT** Open areas, where the larvae feed on Pitch Trefoil *Bituminaria bituminosa*. **SEASON** March to July.

*Synthymia fixa*

***Calophasia hamifera***
Wingspan: 27–32 mm. Brownish-white with black markings. **HABITAT** Rocky grasslands. **SEASON** January to July.

*Calophasia hamifera*

***Lophoterges millierei***
Wingspan: 27–33 mm. Brownish with distinctive black lines and white areas. **HABITAT** Open woodlands and bushy grasslands. **SEASON** April to early September.

*Lophoterges millierei*

***Heliothis incarnata***
Wingspan: 28–32 mm. Yellowish with pink markings. **HABITAT** Grasslands, including hilly areas. **SEASON** April to August.

*Heliothis incarnata*

***Heliothis peltigera* Bordered Straw**
Wingspan: 29–40 mm. Pale yellowish or brown with a central blotch on wing edge, sometimes another before tip, alongside darker band. **HABITAT** Various, including cultivated lands. **SEASON** All year.

*Heliothis peltigera*

*Acontia lucida* [PC]

*Acontia trabealis* [PC]

*Tyta luctuosa*

*Panemeria tenebrata*

*Pseudozarba bipartita*

*Synthymia fixa*

*Calophasia hamifera*

*Lophoterges millierei*

*Heliothis incarnata*

*Heliothis peltigera*

***Heliothis viriplaca*** **Marbled Clover**
Wingspan: 25–35 mm. Yellowish-brownish with darker bands. **HABITAT** Various open areas, including mountains to 1700 m. A day and night-flying species. **SEASON** February to September.

*Heliothis viriplaca*

***Spodoptera littoralis*** **Mediterranean Brocade**
Wingspan: 35–40 mm. Forewings light and dark brown, some pale, perhaps whitish veins. Hindwings white. **HABITAT** Various, including agricultural areas where it is regarded as a pest on various vegetables and flowers. **SEASON** April to November.

*Spodoptera littoralis*

***Trachea atriplicis*** **Orache Moth**
Wingspan: 45–50 mm. Forewings greyish-brown with green; pinkish-white central mark. **HABITAT** Woodlands, strongly migratory. **SEASON** Often June to July.

*Trachea atriplicis*

***Actinotia polyodon*** **Purple Cloud**
Wingspan: 31–36 mm. Forewings brown, with pinkish-purple area. **HABITAT** Grasslands. **SEASON** April to August, sometimes later.

*Actinotia polyodon*

***Dryobota labecula*** **Oak Rustic**
Wingspan: 27–31 mm. Forewings dark brown or blackish, with orange or white mark. **HABITAT** Various, on oak *Quercus*. **SEASON** October to December.

*Dryobota labecula*

***Griposia aprilina***
**Merveille du Jour**
Wingspan: 45–52 mm. Forewings lichen green with various black markings. **HABITAT** Woodlands and others, adults often well camouflaged on lichen covered tree trunks. The larvae often feed on oak *Quercus*. **SEASON** August to December.

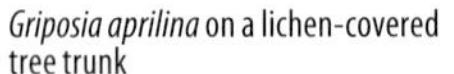
*Griposia aprilina* on a lichen-covered tree trunk

*Griposia aprilina*

***Trigonopora flammea*** **Flame Brocade**
Wingspan: 44–52 mm. Forewings purplish-brown, with bold kidney-shaped pale mark. **HABITAT** Various. **SEASON** October to December.

*Trigonopora flammea*

***Anarta myrtilli*** **Beautiful Yellow Underwing**
Wingspan: 24–28 mm. Forewings reddish-brown or grey, with whitish marbling, hindwings yellow with a broad black border and white fringe. **HABITAT** Various open sites up to 2,000 m, often day-flying. The larvae feed on heathers: *Calluna vulgaris* and *Erica*. **SEASON** May to August.

*Anarta myrtilli*

***Hecatera cappa***
Wingspan: 24–38 mm. Forewings white with some grey and extensive black wavy lines and markings. **HABITAT** Woodlands and scrub. **SEASON** April to September.

*Hecatera cappa*

***Hadena albimacula*** **White Spot**
Wingspan: 28–37 mm. Forewings brown with white spots and markings. **HABITAT** Rocky grasslands, often calcareous. **SEASON** April to July, sometimes also later to September.

*Hadena albimacula*

*Heliothis viriplaca*

*Spodoptera littoralis*

*Trachea atriplicis*

*Actinotia polyodon*

*Dryobota labecula* [PH]

*Trigonopora flammea* [PH]

*Anarta myrtilli*

*Hecatera cappa*

*Hadena albimacula*

**_Mythimna vitellina_ Delicate**
Wingspan: 36–43 mm. Forewings straw with brown central streak and small white central spot. **HABITAT** Grasslands, the larvae feeding on various grasses. **SEASON** March to October.

*Mythimna vitellina*

**_Noctua fimbriata_ Broad-bordered Yellow Underwing**
Wingspan: 45–61 mm. Forewings reddish-brown to greenish. Hindwings yellow with a broad black band. **HABITAT** Open areas and woodlands to 2,000 m. **SEASON** May to September.

*Noctua fimbriata*

## Family Nolidae – BLACK ARCHES & SILVER-LINES

A small family of small, often whitish, grey or sometimes green moths, with rounded forewings; some species could be mistaken for micro-moths.

**_Meganola albula_ Kent Black Arches**
Wingspan: 14–22 mm. White with brown markings. **HABITAT** Woodlands. **SEASON** June to September.

*Meganola albula*

**_Bena bicolorana_ Scarce Silver-lines**
Wingspan: 39–47 mm. Broad, green forewings with two diagonal yellowish-white lines. **HABITAT** Oak *Quercus* woodlands. **SEASON** June to October.

*Bena bicolorana*

**_Pseudoips prasinana_ Green Silver-lines**
Wingspan: 31–40 mm. Green forewings with three diagonal white lines. **HABITAT** Woodlands, on beech *Fagus*, oak *Quercus* or birch *Betula*. **SEASON** June to September.

*Pseudoips prasinana*

**_Earias insulana_ Egyptian Bollworm**
Wingspan: 19–23 mm. Green or brown, sometimes yellowish. Darker lines are sometimes indistinct. **HABITAT** Open areas, a pest of cotton *Gossypium herbaceum* and other crops. **SEASON** April to November.

*Earias insulana*

**MICRO MOTHS** – The so-called micro moths are generally small species, hence are not usually confused with the larger macro moths. Although small, some micro moths have stunning colours and the group is increasing in popularity. A small selection of species from some of the main families is shown.

## Family Adelidae – Longhorns

Wings held roof-like at rest but easily recognised by characteristic long antennae. All are day fliers.

**_Adela reamurella_ Green Longhorn**
Wingspan: 14–18 mm. Metallic dark green. **HABITAT** Woodland edges; day-fliers often swarming around oak *Quercus* and others. **SEASON** April to June.

*Adela reamurella*

## Family Psychidae – Bagworms

Wings held roof-like at rest but easily recognised by characteristic long antennae. A few are ♀s only, reproducing parthenogenetically. Larvae live in silken, moveable cases which include plant fragments.

**_Ptilocephala atrella_**
Wingspan: 15–17 mm. ♂ dark, later almost transparent wings (hindwings elongate compared with related species), feathery antennae and hairy body. **HABITAT** Grasslands, including mountains. **SEASON** June to July.

*Ptilocephala atrella*

## Family Pterophoridae – Plume Moths

Easily recognised as species stand up at rest, with wings extended; in some species hindwings are visible.

**_Pterophorus pentadactyla_ White Plume**
Wingspan: 24–35 mm. White, forewings divided into two plumes, hindwings with three. **HABITAT** Grasslands, where the larvae feed on *Convolvulus*. **SEASON** May to September.

*Pterophorus pentadactyla*

*Mythimna vitellina*

*Earias insulana*

*Noctua fimbriata*

*Meganola albula*

*Bena bicolorana*

*Pseudoips prasinana*

*Adela reamurella*

*Ptilocephala atrella* ♂ (top) [PC], bagworm larva (bottom)

*Pterophorus pentadactyla*

## Family Tortricidae

A large family (most are orange or brown), wlth broad forewings.

**_Tortrix viridana_ Green Oak Tortrix**
Wingspan: 17–24 mm. Pale green. **HABITAT** Woodlands, where the larvae feed in a folded leaf on oak *Quercus* and others. **SEASON** May to July, also a possible later generation about October.

*Tortrix viridana*

## Family Pyralidae

There are many familiar species in this variable family, which have elongate or triangular forewings.

***Stemmatophora brunnealis***
Wingspan: 17–25 mm. Brownish conspicuously marked. **HABITAT** Various open areas. **SEASON** July to September.

*Stemmatophora brunnealis*

***Acrobasis romanella***
Wingspan: 17–20 mm. Brown and grey, with black lines. **HABITAT** Various. **SEASON** April to October.

*Acrobasis romanella*

## Family Crambidae

This large family includes some of the most-colourful micro moths.

***Pyrausta aerealis***
Wingspan: 18–29 mm. Fairly plain brown forewings with a zig-zag yellowish line. **HABITAT** Often heathlands and mountains. **SEASON** June to August.

*Pyrausta aerealis*

**_Pyrausta aurata_ Small Purple and Gold**
Wingspan: 14–18 mm. Dark purple forewings with orange markings. Hindwings with golden band. **HABITAT** Grasslands (often calcareous) and gardens where the larvae feed on Lamiaceae, including *Mentha* and *Origanum*. **SEASON** March to November.

*Pyrausta aurata*

**_Pyrausta cingulata_ Silver-barred Sable**
Wingspan: 12–17 mm. Forewings brownish black, with narrow whitish cross-band. **HABITAT** Often calcareous grasslands to 1,900 m on Lamiaceae. **SEASON** April to September.

*Pyrausta cingulata*

**_Pyrausta despicata_ Straw-barred Pearl**
Wingspan: 14–19 mm. Greyish-brown, with lighter markings. **HABITAT** Grasslands and woodland edges, where the larvae feed on plantain *Plantago*. **SEASON** April to October.

*Pyrausta despicata*

**_Pyrausta nigrata_ Wavy-barred Sable**
Wingspan: 13–17 mm. Forewings black, with wavy whitish cross-band and other markings. **HABITAT** Grasslands to 2,000 m on Lamiaceae, often on bare ground. **SEASON** April to October.

*Pyrausta nigrata*

**_Pyrausta ostrinalis_ Scarce Purple and Gold**
Wingspan: 13–17 mm. Pale yellowish band and spots on dull purple forewings. Further fainter yellowish band towards margin. Hindwings with whitish spots, broad central band and notably a narrower band near margin. **HABITAT** Grasslands (often calcareous) to 2,000 m where the larvae feed on Lamiaceae, including thyme *Thymus*. **SEASON** April to August.

*Pyrausta ostrinalis*

**_Pyrausta purpuralis_ Common Purple and Gold**
Wingspan: 15–22 mm. Forewings bright purple with yellowish markings. Hindwings with pale yellow or whitish spots and band, also a faint line near margin. Notably there is another whitish spot in the basal area, absent in the similar *P. aurata*. **HABITAT** Grasslands (often calcareous) where the larvae feed on Lamiaceae. **SEASON** March to October.

*Pyrausta purpuralis*

*Tortrix viridana*

*Stemmatophora brunnealis*

*Acrobasis romanella*

*Pyrausta aurata*

*Pyrausta aerealis*

*Pyrausta nigrata* [TB]

*Pyrausta purpuralis*

*Pyrausta cingulata*

*Pyrausta despicata*

*Pyrausta ostrinalis*

***Pyrausta sanguinalis* Scarce Crimson and Gold**
Wingspan: 13–18 mm. Forewings yellow with crimson bands and partial margins. **HABITAT** Grasslands (often calcareous) where the larvae feed on thyme *Thymus*. **SEASON** February to October.

***Anania funebris* White-spotted Sable**
Wingspan: 17–23 mm. Each wing black with two large white blotches, possibly another small forewing dot. **HABITAT** Woodland margins and others, where the larvae feed on Goldenrod *Solidago virgaurea*. **SEASON** June to August.

***Ostrinia nubilalis* European Corn-borer**
Wingspan: 24–30 mm. Variable yellowish to brown wings with various dots and lines or bands. **HABITAT** Various, the larvae can be a pest of grain, particularly maize *Zea*. **SEASON** June to October.

***Palpita vitrealis* Olive-tree Pearl**
Wingspan: 22–31 mm. Wings translucent white, upper edge of forewings brown. **HABITAT** Various, a migratory species. **SEASON** All year.

***Nomophila noctuella* Rush Veneer**
Wingspan: 25–34 mm. Forewings brown, elongate and variably marked. **HABITAT** Various, a migratory species. **SEASON** All year.

***Cynaeda dentalis* Starry Pearl**
Wingspan: 24–29 mm. Conspicuous pattern and shape. **HABITAT** Grasslands, where the larvae feed on Viper's Bugloss *Echium vulgare*, *Anchusa* and *Onosma tubiflorum*. **SEASON** May to September.

***Eurrhypis pollinalis* White-spotted Black**
Wingspan: 16–20 mm. Forewings black with brown markings and two large white spots. **HABITAT** Woodland edges, where the larvae feed on broom *Cytisus*, *Genista* and others. **SEASON** Late April to early July.

***Ancylolomia tentaculella***
Wingspan: 30–38 mm. Brown, with whitish streaks. **HABITAT** Grasslands. **SEASON** July to October.

***Chrysocramboides craterella* Dusky Grass-veneer**
Wingspan: 18–24 mm. Yellowish, with brown lines. **HABITAT** Grasslands. **SEASON** May to August.

***Elophila nymphaeata* Brown China Mark**
Wingspan: 25–33 mm. **HABITAT** Wetlands, where the larvae mine leaves of water plants. **SEASON** May to early October.

*Elophila nymphaeata* [PC]

*Pyrausta sanguinalis*

*Anania funebris*

*Ostrinia nubilalis*

*Palpita vitrealis*

*Nomophila noctuella*

*Cynaeda dentalis*

*Eurrhypis pollinalis*

*Ancylolomia tentaculella*

*Chrysocramboides craterella*

*Elophila nymphaeata*

*Pyrausta sanguinalis*

*Anania funebris*

*Ostrinia nubilalis*

*Palpita vitrealis*

*Nomophila noctuella*

*Cynaeda dentalis*

*Eurrhypis pollinalis*

*Ancylolomia tentaculella*

*Chrysocramboides craterella* [PC]

# Order HYMENOPTERA – ANTS, BEES, WASPS & RELATIVES

**Southern Europe & Mediterranean: many of Europe's 16,000 species**

A large order, ranging from tiny parasitic wasps to giant ichneumons. Everyone has heard of bees, wasps and ants (combined, they are known as aculeates) and some are fearful of the reputation they have, in stinging people. However, these are a minority of species. The numbers in this order escalate when one includes 'Parasitica', the poorly known ichneumons and parasitic wasps all belonging to the suborder Apocrita, as do the aculeates. The sawflies belong to a separate suborder the Symphyta. The Hymenoptera typically have two pairs of membranous wings, the forewings larger than the hindwings; they have mouthparts for biting and chewing, feeding on plants, pollen and nectar and wood; some are cleptoparasites (steal food) or parasitoids (parasites that kill their host) of other invertebrates. The life-cycle is one of complete metamorphosis: egg, larva, pupa and adult; larvae are legless except for sawflies which have small fore, mid and hind legs, resembling butterfly and moth caterpillars. A useful species is the Honey Bee *Apis mellifera*, valued for its honey, beeswax and royal jelly. Bees fly to flowers to collect pollen and nectar; wasps feed on nectar but also seek prey in the form of other insects. The fast-flying bees are particularly efficient pollinators of crops and play a significant role in feeding the world's human population, making a huge contribution to the world's economy. The sophisticated behaviour of social insects in a bee-hive or ants nest is remarkable. Then there are some small wasps with a jewel-like beauty. The photographs in this book show a representative selection of species and have often been taken after careful watch of the behaviour of these insects. If watching nests, it is well worth seeing if any parasites enter or investigate, a cautious approach is needed when photographing Hymenoptera, as many species are easily disturbed and quickly fly away. Whilst some of these insects have distinctive features, identification can be a challenge at times and even for specialists voucher specimens are often necessary due to close resemblance to other species.

**HABITAT** Various, but for the most popular group, aculeates (bees, ants and wasps), there is a diverse fauna in sandy sites, particularly coastal areas.

**HOTSPOTS** Sand dune systems along the Mediterranean coast have a wide range of aculeates.

The fixed sand dunes at **Mas Larrieu Reserve Naturelle, Roussillon, France,** are known for the rare reptiles they support but are equally important for the insects, particularly bees and wasps as well as a range of other insects including bee-flies. [PC]

**Tudes, Picos de Europa, Spain** – wildflower meadows here are well known for butterflies, but also attract bees and many other insects.

*Tenthredo scrophulariae* mating pair (Tenthredinidae)

An ichneumon wasp egg-laying (Ichneumonidae)

*Camponotus cruentatus* (Formicidae) behaviour [PC]

*Polistes gallicus,* both ♂s and ♀s at the nest (Vespidae)

*Philanthus triangulum* (Crabronidae) at nest burrow

*Rhodanthidium stricticum* (Apidae) ♂ (left) and ♀ [PC]

## Suborder Symphyta – SAWFLIES & WOODWASPS

Some of the major families are covered. Sawflies are often brightly coloured, weak-flying insects that are mainly active in the day. Some species possess a saw-like ovipositor, but certainly not as long as in *Urocerus gigas*. Adults sometimes nectar on flowers, but often eat other insects. Most larvae are caterpillar-like with fleshy false legs (prolegs) and feed on vegetation; a few induce gall-formation or are leaf miners. Apart from some distinctive species, sawflies are often a challenge to identify to species level.

### Family Cimbicidae – CIMBICID SAWFLIES

Striking large, stout-bodied sawflies, with clubbed antennae. These insects buzz in flight. The cocoon is often attached to the host plant.

**_Abia fulgens_**
Body length: c.11 mm. Green body. Antennae with dark base and tip. **HABITAT** Grasslands, mainly mountainous areas, where the larvae feed on scabious *Knautia maxima*. **SEASON** May to August.

*Abia fulgens*

**_Cimbex femoratus_ Birch Sawfly**
Body length: c.25 mm. Black, yellowish or red spot on abdomen. Yellow antennal tip. **HABITAT** Birch *Betula* woodlands. **SEASON** May to August.

*Cimbex femoratus*

**_Corynis obscura_**
Body length: 7–8 mm. Black body and legs. **HABITAT** Damp grasslands and others, the larvae developing on Marsh Crane's-bill *Geranium palustre*. **SEASON** May to July.

*Corynus obscura*

### Family Tenthredinidae – COMMON SAWFLIES

A varied family, with some colourful distinct sawflies such as ***Tenthredo*** species and including wasp mimics, which have nine segmented antennae. The larvae live on host plants, but some species feed in galls or stems; some are nocturnal. Example species are illustrated.

**_Athalia rosae_ Turnip Sawfly**
Body length: 7–8 mm. Conspicuous shaped species, orange on thorax and abdomen. **HABITAT** Grasslands, often on flowers and sometimes in abundance. The larvae feed on Brassicaceae and are regarded as pests. **SEASON** May to September.

*Athalia rosae*

**_Tenthredo scrophulariae_ Figwort Sawfly**
Body length: 11–15 mm. Black and yellow striped with orange antennae. **HABITAT** Grasslands and others, often on flowers where they hunt for small flies and other prey. The larva (pictured left) feeds on figwort *Scrophularia*. **SEASON** May to August.

*Tenthredo scrophulariae*

### Family Siricidae – WOODWASPS

Large and colourful, stout-bodied, harmless insects with, in the ♀, a very conspicuous ovipositor, used for drilling into conifers to lay a single egg.

**_Urocerus gigas_ Giant Woodwasp**
Body length: 25–40 mm. Colourful, black and yellow (abdomen yellowish with black tip in ♂); rather wasp-like. **HABITAT** Coniferous woodlands, where the ♀ drills into decaying standing pine *Pinus* or fallen trees, the resulting larvae feeding on the dead wood, maturing in two to three years. Adult exit holes are circular. **SEASON** May to October.

*Urocerus gigas*

**_Xeris spectrum_**
Body length: 12–28 mm. Black with whitish lateral stripe on pronotum; legs yellowish-red. **HABITAT** Coniferous woodlands to 2,000 m., either in standing trees or felled trunks. **SEASON** June to August.

*Xeris spectrum*

*Abia fulgens* ♀

*Cimbex femoratus* [PC]

*Corynus obscura* [JE]

*Athalia rosae*

*Tenthredo scrophulariae*

*Urocerus gigas* ♀

*Xeris spectrum* ♀

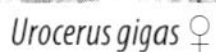

# Suborder Apocrita (Parasitica) – PARASITIC WASPS

The parasitoid Hymenoptera are a rather under-studied group of families, which often tend to be small and difficult to identify (although many ichneumon wasps are large). They nearly always kill the host, which ranges from an aphid, an egg, to butterfly and moth larvae, in fact, a wide range of insect orders. Those living inside the host (either one or up to c.2,000 in the same host) are endoparasitoids, or outside the host ectoparasitoids. Selected families are briefly discussed here, with the Braconidae and Ichneumonidae accounting for much of Europe's Hymenoptera.

## Chalcidoidea (several families) – CHALCID WASPS

Chalcid wasps are often parasitoids on insects of several orders, some are parasitoids on gall-forming wasps.

***Brachymeria tibialis*** [family Chalcididae]
Body length: c.5 mm. Black and yellow; robust with hind femora swollen. **HABITAT** Grasslands, the main parasitoid of burnet moths *Zygaena* species, but also other host moths. **SEASON** June to August.

*Brachymeria tibialis*

***Ormyrus nitidulus*** [family Ormyridae]
Body length: 2–5 mm. Hunched metallic bluish green with red eyes, ♀ with elongate ovipositor, paler knees and tarsi. **HABITAT** Woodlands, a parasitoid of *Andricus* (in oak *Quercus* galls) and others. **SEASON** April to November.

*Ormyrus nitidulus*

***Ormyrus pomaceus*** [family Ormyridae]
Body length: 2–3 mm. Similar in appearance to *O. nitidulus*, antennae dark. ♀s usually smaller, last abdominal segment shorter than in *nitidulus*. **HABITAT** Woodlands, a parasitoid of *Andricus* (in oak *Quercus* galls) and others. **SEASON** June to August or later (c. November).

*Ormyrus pomaceus*

***Torymus flavipes*** [family Torymidae]
Body length: c.2.5 mm. Metallic green. **HABITAT** Woodlands. ♀'s use the long ovipositor to pierce various oak *Quercus* galls. **SEASON** March to October.

*Torymus flavipes*

***Leucospis intermedia*** [family Leucospidae]
Body length: 4–12 mm. Hunched, robust black and yellow species. **HABITAT** Grasslands, a parasitoid of *Osmia* (mason bees). **SEASON** May to September.

*Leucopsis intermedia*

## Family Braconidae – BRACONIDS

Mainly small, drab parasitic wasps with long slender antennae (10 to 50+ segments), black, brown or yellowish. Larvae eat the insides of other larvae.

***Microplitis ocellatae***
Body length: c.2 mm. **HABITAT** Various. The picture opposite shows larvae having emerged from a Poplar Hawk-moth *Laothoe populi* larva and spun cocoons alongside the fresh, dead moth larva. **SEASON** May to September.

*Microplitis ocellatae*

## Family Gasteruptiidae

Remarkably slender parasitic wasps, with a distinctive 'neck'; ♀s of some species have long ovipositors. They are cleptoparasites of stem-nesting aculeates, such as *Hylaeus* species.

***Gasteruption assectator***
Body length: 8–12 mm. Very elongate, but smaller than *G. jaculator*, with shorter ovipositor. **HABITAT** Woodlands, often seen on flowers or investigating dead wood. **SEASON** May to September.

*Gasteruption assectator*

***Gasteruption jaculator***
Body length: 10–18 mm. Very elongate with long ovipositor. **HABITAT** Woodlands, often seen on flowers or investigating dead wood. **SEASON** May to September.

*Gasteruption jaculator*

*Brachymeria tibialis* [SO]

*Ormyrus nitidulus* ♀

*Ormyrus pomaceus* ♂

*Leucopsis intermedia*

*Torymus flavipes* ♀

*Microplitis ocellatae* [ARP]

*Gasteruption assectator* ♀

*Microplitis ocellatae* cocoons by a hawk-moth larva [GE]

*Gasteruption jaculator* ♀

*Rhyssa persuasoria* ♀, is one of the largest species of ichneumon wasp

## Family Ichneumonidae – ICHNEUMON WASPS

Small to large parasitoid wasps, with long antennae (at least 16 segments). Some species are very attractive in colour, others drab. ♀s often have a long ovipositor, such as one of the largest species *Rhyssa persuasoria* (100 mm including the ovipositor [pictured above]), used to lay eggs on or inside larvae of various insects. A selection of other species is shown, some of which exhibit sexual dimorphism i.e. ♂s are different in appearance than ♀s, which adds to confusion in identification, in addition to numerous closely related species. Many are parasitic on Lepidoptera larvae and pupae, living in the host; c.25% of species attack sawflies, with a minority using Coleoptera, Diptera, other orders and spiders.
**HABITAT** Found in many habitats, any flower-rich meadow, garden or woodland is likely to have plenty of ichneumon wasps present on flowers including umbellifers, investigating vegetation or dead wood.

### *Amblyteles armatorius*

Body length 12–16 mm. Black with yellow bands and marks and much of legs. **HABITAT** Various, often grasslands. **SEASON** May to August (♀s hibernate). **HOSTS** Parasitoid of noctuid moth pupae.

*Amblyteles armatorius*

### *Ichneumon sarcitorius*

Body length 10–14 mm. The ♂ is rather wasp-like, yellow or ivory and black, whereas the over-wintering ♀ is red, white and black. **HABITAT** Grasslands, often on umbellifers. **SEASON** May to October (♀s hibernate). **HOSTS** Often noctuid moths.

*Ichneumon sarcitorius*

### *Ichneumon stramentor*

Body length 13–18 mm. Black with conspicuous yellow band on abdomen and markings, including at tip of abdomen. Only ♀s have whitish patch on antennae. **HABITAT** Grasslands and woodland edge. **SEASON** April to July. **HOSTS** Often noctuid moth larvae.

*Ichneumon stramentor*

### *Ophion obscuratus*

Body length 15–22 mm. Usually has abundant creamy markings, unlike most of the other *Ophion* species. **HABITAT** Grasslands. This species is a frequent visitor to moth lights and lighted windows, for example in gardens. **SEASON** August to February. **HOSTS** Noctuid moth larvae.

*Ophion obscuratus*

### *Ephialtes manifestator*

Body length c.20 mm (up to 70 mm including ovipositor). Black with a long ovipositor. Legs orange. **HABITAT** Woodlands. **SEASON** May to September. **HOSTS** A parasitoid of solitary aculeates.

*Ephialtes manifestator*

### *Rhyssa persuasoria* Sabre Wasp

Body length 18–50 mm (♀ 100 mm including the ovipositor). Black with whitish bands and markings. Legs mainly orange. **HABITAT** Coniferous woodlands. Felled logs are a good place to see them investigating and egg-laying by drilling into the wood. **SEASON** May to September. **HOSTS** A parasitoid of *Sirex* (woodwasps).

*Rhyssa persuasoria*

*Ichneumon sarcitorius* ♂ (left), ♀ (right) [PC]

*Ichneumon stramentor* ♀ *Amblyteles armatorius* ♂ *Ophion obscuratus*

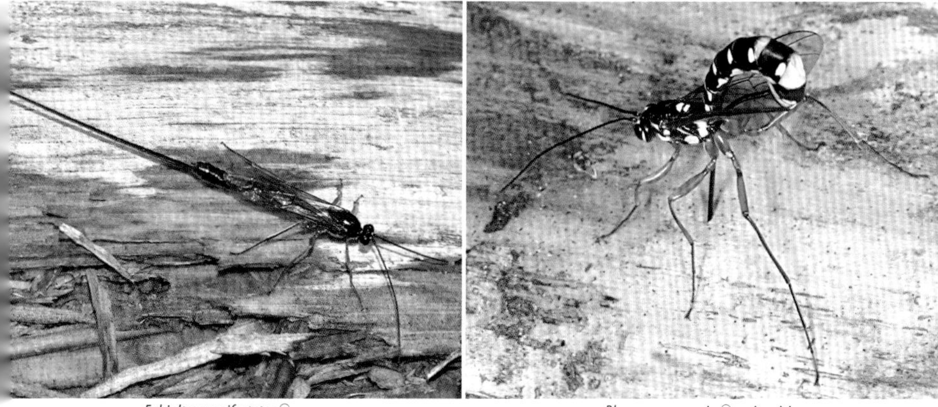

*Ephialtes manifestator* ♀ *Rhyssa persuasoria* ♀, ovipositing

# Suborder Apocrita (Aculeates) – ANTS, BEES & WASPS

## Family Chrysididae – CUCKOO WASPS

Because of their brilliant metallic body colours (blue, green, purple, red), the small and medium-size chrysidids are also known as jewel or ruby-tailed wasps. Adults fly in sunny weather from April to October (depending on species), investigating holes and crevices for nests of other Hymenoptera (other wasps, sawflies and solitary bees). The ♀ enters a host's nest and lays eggs in cells. Resulting cuckoo wasp larvae are parasitoids (causing death of the host) or cleptoparasites (stealing food). Adults feed on nectar and can curl up in defence when threatened by possible predators, or if attacked by a host. A small selection of species is shown.

***Chrysis illigeri***
Body length: 5–8 mm. Head and thorax mostly blue with green; partly red. **HABITAT** Various open areas. **SEASON** May to August. **HOST** *Tachysphex pompiliformis.*

*Chrysis illigeri*

***Chrysura cuprea***
Body length: 8–11 mm. Body mainly red. **HABITAT** Open areas. **SEASON** May to August. **HOST** *Osmia* species.

*Chrysura cuprea*

***Euchroeus purpuratus***
Body length: 8–11 mm. Golden-pink and bluish-violet. 3rd abdominal segment bluish-violet, also 2nd in part. **HABITAT** Open areas, grasslands and sandy sites. **SEASON** June to September. **HOSTS** Probably sphecid wasps.

*Euchroeus purpuratus*

***Hedychrum rutilans***
Body length: 4–10 mm. Abdomen copper or reddish with small green patches. **HABITAT** Open areas. **SEASON** July to August, sometimes earlier. **HOST** *Philanthus triangulum.*

*Hedychrum rutilans*

## Family Tiphiidae – TIPHIID WASPS

Small to medium-sized wasps, ♀s ant-like and wingless [except in *Tiphia*] but ♂s winged; parasites of beetle larvae (scarabaeids and tiger beetles), which they sting and paralyse, before laying eggs.

***Methocha articulata***
Body length: 7–12 mm. Black head and abdomen, otherwise red. **HABITAT** Coastal dunes, inland heathlands on sandy soils. **SEASON** May to September. **HOSTS** Tiger beetles *Cicindela* and *Cylindera* species.

*Methocha articulata*

## Family Mutillidae – VELVET ANTS

Ant-like wasps, ♀s are wingless but ♂s fully winged; abdominal bands with silvery hairs. Velvet ants can sting painfully in defence and if handled, they stridulate. They walk fast and are seldom easy to photograph. They are parasites of certain ground-nesting bees and wasps.

***Mutilla europaea* Large Velvet Ant**
Body length: 9–14 mm. Large, robust black, red and white wasp. **HABITAT** Sandy areas. **SEASON** April to September, ♀s over-winter. **HOSTS** Bumble bees, occasionally Honey Bees.

*Mutilla europaea*

***Nemka viduata***
Body length: up to 13 mm. ♀ with a red thorax (back in ♂), black and white abdomen (red-banded in ♂). **HABITAT** Various, in sandy areas. The mating process lasts c.2 hours. **SEASON** May to August. **HOSTS** *Bembix bidentata* and other wasps.

*Nemka viduata*

***Ronisia barbarula***
Body length: 12–17 mm. Large, triangular mark between eyes. **HABITAT** Open, sandy or stony areas, often waiting around nests of host species. **SEASON** April to September. **HOSTS** Various bees and Sphecidae.

*Ronisia barbarula*

*Chrysis illigeri*

*Chrysura cuprea* [SO]

*Hedychrum rutilans* ♀ [JE]

*Euchroeus purpuratus* [NR]

*Methocha articulata* ♀

*Mutilla europaea* ♀

*Ronisia barbarula*

*Nemka viduata* mating pair [PC]

## Family Scoliidae – MAMMOTH WASPS

Robust black wasps, often marked with yellow; males have much longer antennae. These wasps are parasitoids of scarab beetle larvae.

### *Colpa sexmaculata*

Body length: 18–24 mm. ♀ black with six yellow spots on the abdomen; wings dark bluish brown. The slender ♂ has brown-veined wings and often twice as many, paler spots. **HABITAT** Grasslands. **SEASON** July to September. **HOSTS** Beetle larvae.

*Colpa sexmaculata*

### *Megascolia bidens*

Body length: 22–40 mm. Similar to *M. maculata*, but most of antennae yellow [not black] and ♂ with only one pair of yellow abdominal blotches. **HABITAT** Grasslands. **SEASON** May to September. **HOSTS** *Oryctes nasicornis* and other large beetle larvae.

*Megascolia bidens*

### *Megascolia maculata* Large Yellow-headed Scoliid Wasp

Body length: 22–42 mm. Largest European wasp, a robust black species with yellow head in ♀s only (orange-headed ♀ pictured below [CG]); two pairs of bold yellow abdominal blotches. **HABITAT** Grasslands, often at great speed. ♀s look to trace, paralyse and lay an egg on a European rhinoceros beetle larva. **SEASON** May to October. **HOSTS** *Oryctes nasicornis, Lucanus cervus* and other large beetle larvae.

*Megascolia maculata*

### *Scolia hirta*

Body length: 13–18 mm. Black with two continuous yellow abdominal bands. ♀s with shorter antennae (pictured left [KM]), as with all related species. Wings smoky brown. **HABITAT** Grasslands, often on flowers. **SEASON** May to September **HOSTS** *Cetonia aurata* and other beetle larvae.

*Scolia hirta*

### *Scolia hortorum*

Body length: 11–18 mm. Black with two yellow abdominal bands. ♀s with orange head and two yellow abdominal bands, ♂ s more variable with a pair or more of divided yellow blotches. **HABITAT** Grasslands, often on flowers. **SEASON** May to September. **HOSTS** *Cetonia aurata* and other beetle larvae.

*Scolia hortorum*

### *Scolia sexmaculata*

Body length: 9–15 mm. Smaller species, black with three smaller pairs of yellow spots (sometimes only two pairs). Brownish wings. **HABITAT** Grasslands, often on flowers. **SEASON** May to September. **HOSTS** Beetle larvae.

*Scolia sexmaculata*

*Colpa sexmaculata* ♂ (left), ♀ (right) [both PC]

*Megascolia bidens* ♂

*Megascolia maculata* ♀ [PC]

*Scolia hirta* ♂

*Scolia hortorum* ♂

*Scolia sexmaculata* ♂

## Family Formicidae – ANTS

The remarkable social behaviour of these insects has always fascinated people. The life-cycle often lasts more than one year, with nests in dead wood, soil, under a stone or raised above ground in a mound of earth or plant debris. Whilst some species of ants eat seeds, many feed on the honeydew secreted by aphids, which they then protect. Some species sting or bite in defence. ♂s of most species and queens are winged, workers always wingless. The queens shed their wings after mating. A selection of species is shown.

### *Camponotus cruentatus*

Body length: 6–14 mm. Conspicuously shaped head. Front half of abdomen reddish. **HABITAT** Various, woodland edge, in sunny spots often on slopes in calcareous areas, under stones. This aggressive species is often in mountainous areas up to 1,000 m, where it dominates and displaces some of its main competitors, defending its food sources against other ants. One of these food sources is honeydew secreted by aphids. **SEASON** May to September (active in daylight only in spring and autumn, but all day in summer).

### *Camponotus ligniperdus*

Body length: 6–15 mm. Thorax reddish. **HABITAT** Woodland edge and stony banks, often nesting under stones. **SEASON** May to September.

### *Camponotus pilicornis*

Body length: 7–13 mm. Paler reddish thorax. **HABITAT** Various, including woodland edge. **SEASON** May to September.

### *Camponotus vagus*

Body length: 6–13 mm. Large black ant, with hairy abdomen. **HABITAT** Woodland edge or open areas, where nests are built in dead wood, or sometimes under stones. Larger 'major workers' act as guards. **SEASON** May to September.

*Camponotus vagus*
Queen and workers [RG]

### *Formica rufa* Southern Wood Ant

Body length: 4–10 mm. Black and red. **HABITAT** Deciduous woodland or edges of coniferous trees. The often large nest mounds positioned to take in spring sunshine and provide shade at other times. **SEASON** March to October.

### *Formica rufibarbis* Red-barbed Ant

Body length: 4–12 mm. Black with a light red thorax; pronotum and mesonotum with standing hairs. The queen has a red thorax with dark patches. **HABITAT** Often grasslands up to 2,000 m, often rapidly walking on short pathside vegetation or granite rocks. They often nest under rocks. **SEASON** April to October.

### *Formica sanguinea* Slave-maker Ant

Body length: 6–10 mm. More red than *F. rufa*. Known as 'Slave-maker' because nests can be formed by social parasitism i.e. a mated queen secures acceptance in the nest of another *Formica* species. Workers of various *Formica* species are then expected to perform nest duties. The species can operate without 'slaves', but assuming an army is formed with slaves, they will attack nests of other species of *Formica* ants (including those of existing slaves), kill the queen and return with larvae and pupae to rear or eat. **HABITAT** Open woodland, in dead tree stumps or logs. **SEASON** April to October.

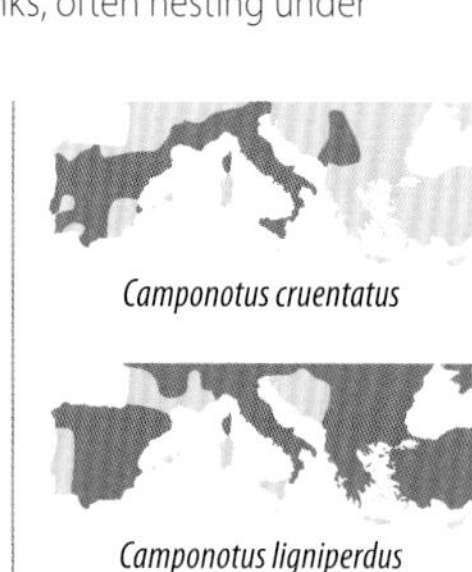

*Camponotus cruentatus*

*Camponotus ligniperdus*

*Camponotus pilicornis*

*Camponotus vagus*

*Formica rufa*

*Formica rufibarbis*

*Formica sanguinea*

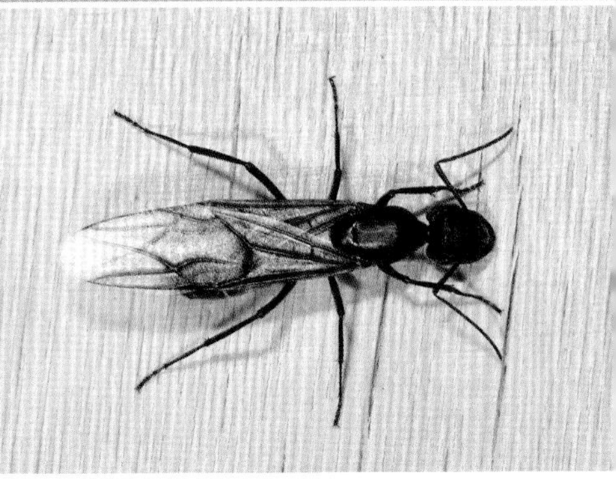

*Camponotus cruentatus* (left), winged ♀ (right)

*Camponotus ligniperdus* (left), queen (right)

*Camponotus pilicornis* major worker

*Camponotus vagus* [PC]

*Formica rufa* queen

*Formica rufibarbis*

*Formica sanguinea*

***Lasius flavus* Yellow Meadow Ant**
Body length: 3–5 mm. Yellow. **HABITAT** Grasslands or open woodland, where nest mounds are easily recognisable. **SEASON** June to August.

***Lasius niger* Small Black Ant**
Body length: 4–5 mm. Black. **HABITAT** Various open areas, frequently gardens and built-up areas; often the familiar 'black ant' entering houses attracted by food, nesting under pavements, stones and similar. **SEASON** April to October.

***Aphaenogaster senilis***
Body length: 4–10 mm. Black, with brownish mandibles and tarsi. **HABITAT** Open sunny areas, including sand dunes. **SEASON** May to October.

*Aphaenogaster senilis* [KBe]

***Crematogaster scutellaris***
Body length: 4–8 mm. Red head, black thorax and abdomen. **HABITAT** Various, the nests usually in dead wood, also stone walls. **SEASON** March to October.

***Messor barbarus***
Body length: 4–12 mm. Black. Conspicuously shaped head, particularly in major workers (head reddish). **HABITAT** Various, including woodland edge, where they collect seeds. Major workers defend the nest. **SEASON** April to September.

***Myrmica scabrinodis***
Body length: 4–5 mm. Reddish brown, similar to other *Myrmica* species which are distinguished from the shape of the base of the antennal scapes. Pair of spines at the back of the thorax. **HABITAT** Various, including gardens. Nests under stones or bare soil and often preys on *Lasius flavus* with whom they sometimes share a mound. **SEASON** April to September.

## Family Pompilidae – SPIDER-HUNTING WASPS

Very active solitary wasps, often seen investigating sandy slopes or taking short flights. Many species have a slender black or black and red abdomen, with long legs. Most spider-hunting wasps nest in the ground and provision each nest cell with one paralysed spider. It is fascinating to observe the spider being dragged at rapid pace and somehow squeezed into the burrow.
A selection of species is shown.
**HABITAT** Sandy soils, including coastal areas and inland, wherever the prey occurs.

***Cryptocheilus discolor***
Body length: c.30 mm. Large orange wasp with black abdomen. Wings orange with black tips, glimmering metallic blue in part. A larger relative ***C. alternatus*** [not pictured] has a yellow abdomen with black stripes. **HABITAT** Sandy areas, often on flowers. **SEASON** June to September.

***Cryptocheilus egregius***
Body length: c.15 mm. Black with red patch on abdomen and various whitish markings. **HABITAT** Sandy areas. **SEASON** May to September.

*Lasius flavus*

*Lasius niger*

*Aphaenogaster senilis*

*Crematogaster scutellaris*

*Messor barbarus*

*Myrmica scabrinodis*

*Cryptocheilus discolor*

*Cryptocheilus alternatus*

*Cryptocheilus egregius*

*Lasius flavus* [PC]

*Lasius niger* queen

*Crematogaster scutellaris* [KBe]

*Aphaenogaster senilis*

*Messor barbarus*

*Myrmica scabrinodis*

*Cryptocheilus discolor*

*Cryptocheilus egregius* ♀ [SO]

## Family Vespidae – SOCIAL, POTTER & MASON WASPS

Social wasps live in large colonies within nests constructed of wood pulp. A single queen is served by several hundred smaller workers who bring in wood pulp and food in the form of caterpillars and other insects. New queens and ♂s are produced from summer onwards. They are well known as certain species regularly live in and around houses. Although the abdomen is often variable in pattern, the various species can often be identified by looking at the head and thoracic colour patterns. Workers and queens can give a nasty sting, but despite their bad reputation, they can be useful by killing pests such as caterpillars, which are fed to the larvae. Queens hibernate over winter in outhouses, log piles and crevices and re-emerge in March. In autumn certain species feed on fallen fruit, including *Vespa crabro*, which is frequently seen flying fast from flower to flower in the hope of preying on other insects, or flying into crevices in rotting wood. Fragments of wood fibres (pulp) are brought back to the nest as building material. Aerial nests are found in hollow trees in mature woodlands and parks, usually from May to October. New queens and ♂s (the latter with longer antennae) emerge from the nest in September to October, mate and disperse. The ♂s and workers die, but the queens hibernate to form a nest in spring. The potter and mason wasps are solitary wasps, until recently regarded as a distinct family. Like social wasps, they are master builders with amazing construction skills and are fascinating to watch, although it is a challenge to find them completing this process. Whatever structure is made it is provisioned with prey, most likely caterpillars of butterflies and moths or beetle larvae. Wasps can be cautious when approached and in extreme cases solitary wasps can abandon a nest, so photographers need to exercise care in obtaining behavioural images.
**HABITAT** Various, including coastal areas, gardens and woodlands wherever suitable prey occurs.

### *Delta unguiculatum* Great Potter Wasp

Body length: 16–26 mm. **HABITAT** Various, where they can obtain mud for nest construction, such as river banks. **SEASON** May to September.

*Delta unguiculatum*

### *Eumenes coarctatus* Heath Potter Wasp

Body length: 9–15 mm. Remarkably narrow 1st abdominal segment. **HABITAT** Sandy sites including heathlands, with sources of water, such as ponds, pools and streams. Nests are clay pots, attached to vegetation. The ♀ collects water, visits an area of dry clay and adds water to form a small ball of clay, held between jaws and forelegs. She flies back to the nest and builds a pot in 2–3 hours assuming conditions are good. The vegetation is searched for moth larvae, which are stung to paralysis and placed in the pot, which is then sealed. A remarkable several pots could be stacked one on top of the other. **SEASON** April to September.

*Eumenes coarctatus*

### *Eumenes subpomiformis*

Body length: 9–15 mm. **HABITAT** Sandy sites including dunes, with sources of water, such as ponds, pools and streams. **SEASON** April to September.

*Eumenes subpomiformis*

### *Cephalochilus labiatus*

Body length: c.18 mm. Black and yellow, including clypeus. Various white markings and abdominal bands. **HABITAT** Usually seen by water, such as edges of pools and streams. Apparently uncommon in southern Iberia and France and first recorded from Turkey in 2000. **SEASON** June to August.

*Cephalochilus labiatus*

### *Rhynchium oculatum*

Body length: up to 30 mm. Reddish brown, abdomen with some black, also a yellow band and broader area at sides. Wings reddish brown with black/blue-tinged tips. **HABITAT** Nests in cut reeds, where mud nests are constructed for the offspring, which feed on moth larvae. **SEASON** June to September.

*Rhynchium oculatum*

### *Pseudepipona herrichii*

Body length: 9–11 mm. Black with cream stripes [also orange in Spain, as in the UK, elsewhere yellowish]. Legs reddish. **HABITAT** Various, including heathland, with a combination of exposed ground for nesting, water sources to wet the soil for nest-building, suitable flowers for nectar and plentiful prey. **SEASON** June to July.

*Pseudepipona herrichii*

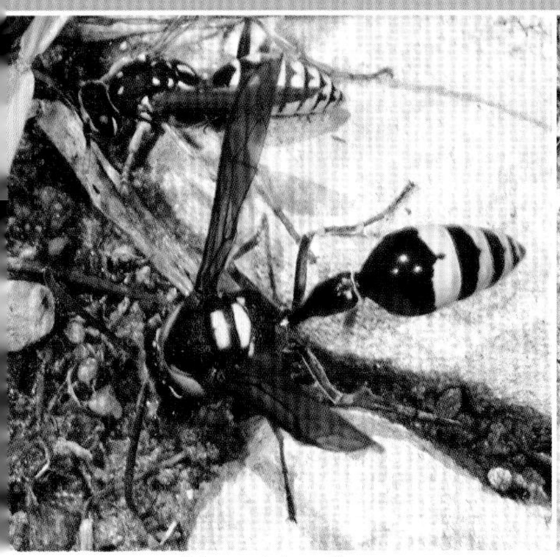

*Delta unguiculatum* ♀

*Eumenes coarctatus* ♀

*Eumenes subpomiformis* ♀

*Cephalochilus labiatus* ♀

*Rhynchium oculatum* ♀ [SR]

*Pseudepipona herrichii* ♀

***Polistes*** are large, black and yellow social wasps, making a single comb nest, suspended from vegetation or a building, provisioning the nests with prey. They often visit flowers to hunt prey, or strip wood for nest-building. Nests are sometimes guarded by several workers.

***Polistes bischoffi***
Body length: 10–15 mm. Black and yellow (upperside of antennae black), with black cheeks; clypeus mainly yellow in ♀s, which are very similar to *P. biglumis*. **HABITAT** Grasslands and woodlands. **SEASON** April to October.

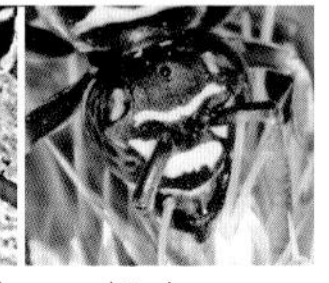

***Polistes dominula* European Paper Wasp**
Body length: 9–13 mm. Yellow and black, with yellow immediately beneath eyes; mandibles black. Underside of final abdominal segment yellow or partly yellow. Similar to some other *Polistes* species but clypeus plain yellow or black spotted in ♀ (inset picture left), transverse black stripe in ***P. nimpha*** ♀ (inset picture right [JE]) and antennae orange beyond 3rd segment, only shared with *P. gallicus*. **HABITAT** Grasslands and woodlands with plentiful flowers at various altitudes. **SEASON** April to October.

***Polistes gallicus***
Body length: 10–16 mm. Yellow and black, with yellow mandibles or at least yellow spot. Black beneath eye. Underside of final abdominal segment black. Similar to other *Polistes* species but clypeus yellow or with black spot in centre in ♀ helps narrow it to species level; often confused with *P. dominula*. **HABITAT** Various mainly open areas, including grasslands and woodlands with plentiful flowers. This is the most widely distributed *Polistes* species in Spain. **SEASON** April to October.

***Dolichovespula*** are large black and yellow striped social wasps with long cheeks. They chew wood and make large paper nests. Adults feed on sap, nectar and honeydew; young are fed on chewed-up invertebrates. Queens over-winter in outbuildings or under bark. Although species are similar in appearance, studying the face pattern helps to confirm identification.

***Dolichovespula media* Median Wasp**
Body length: 15–22 mm. Distinguished by the yellow thoracic markings, like an inverted pair of '7's (face pictured below left). Queens (pictured below centre & right) are sometimes confused with *Vespa crabro* (the *V. crabro* thorax has no yellow markings though). **HABITAT** Various, where they often build large nests in hedges and trees. **SEASON** June to October.

***Dolichovespula saxonica* Saxon Wasp**
Body length: 11–17 mm (face pictured left). **HABITAT** Various, including woodland, where they build large nests in or around buildings and bushes. **SEASON** April to August.

***Dolichovespula sylvestris* Tree Wasp**
Body length: 13–19 mm. A clear yellow face (pictured left) with a single black spot (sometimes absent). **HABITAT** Various, often in gardens, forming small nests above ground in eaves and bird boxes, or in trees and bushes. Also nests in the ground. **SEASON** May to September.

*Polistes bischoffi*

*Polistes dominula*

*Polistes gallicus*

*Polistes nimpha*

*Dolichovespula media*

*Dolichovespula saxonica*

*Dolichovespula sylvestris*

*Polistes bischoffi* ♀ at nest

*Polistes dominula* ♀

*Polistes gallicus* ♀ (left), ♀s at nest (right)

*Dolichovespula media* worker

*Dolichovespula saxonica* queen

*Dolichovespula sylvestris* ♂

***Vespa*** are attractive, very large, black or brown and yellow social wasps. They nests in holes in trees, house roofs and outbuildings, preying on many insects to feed their larvae. Europe's largest social wasps are feared by many people. Nests are often guarded by several workers. All except ♂s can sting.

### *Vespa crabro* Hornet

Body length: 15–28 mm. Brown and brownish yellow, with black markings. As well as other *Vespa* species, it could be confused with queens of *Dolichovespula media* (which has yellow markings on the thorax, unlike *V. crabro*). **HABITAT** Various, but mainly woodlands. Occasionally in gardens. **SEASON** April to October.

### *Vespa orientalis* Oriental Hornet

Body length: 25–35 mm. Reddish brown which thick yellow abdominal bands and a yellow patch between the eyes. **HABITAT** Various, in underground or aerial nests, the latter usually in an enclosed space such as roof spaces or walls. They attack the Honey Bee *Apis mellifera*. **SEASON** April to November.

### *Vespa velutina* Yellow-legged Hornet

Body length: 20–30 mm. Black and yellow (brownish yellow in the slightly larger *V. crabro*). **HABITAT** Various, including woodlands and populated areas. Accidentally introduced to Europe from Asia and first recorded in south-west France in 2004. More aggressive than *V. crabro*, they can be a nuisance around bee hives, attacking *Apis mellifera*. **SEASON** April to October.

***Vespula*** are large black and yellow striped social wasps with short cheeks, otherwise similar in appearance and habits to *Dolichovespula*. Examine the face pattern to confirm identification. The two species shown are most likely to be perceived as pests in the home and garden.

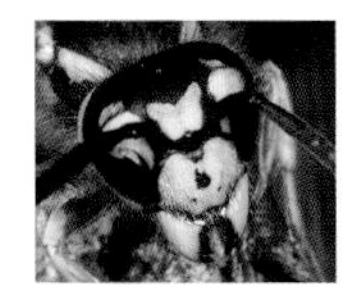

### *Vespula germanica* German Wasp

Body length: 12–20 mm. Three black facial spots between the eyes (pattern varies). Cheeks yellow, lacking a black patch (pictured left). **HABITAT** Various, often seen in gardens and parks. **SEASON** March to November.

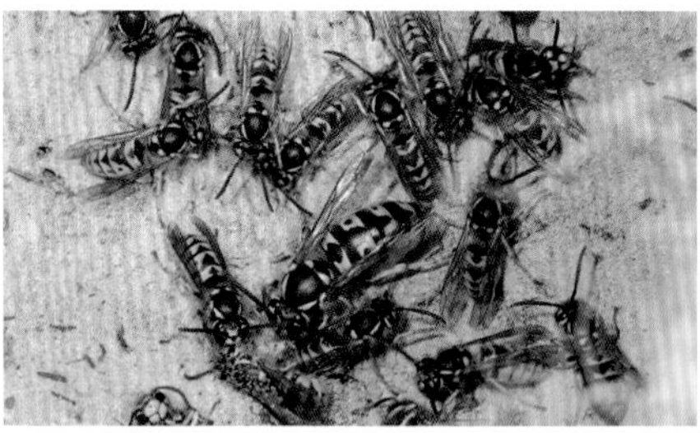

*Vespula germanica* queen (centre) with workers

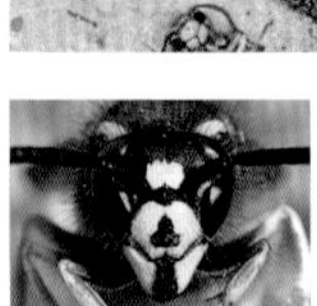

### *Vespula rufa* Red Wasp

Body length: 10–20 mm. Two reddish areas on 2nd abdominal segment (face pictured left). **HABITAT** Various, often in gardens and parks. **SEASON** March to November.

### *Vespula vulgaris* Common Wasp

Body length: 11–19 mm. Conspicuous face, with central black 'anchor' mark towards base. Cheeks yellow with a black patch (pictured left). **HABITAT** Various, often seen in gardens and parks, readily enters houses. Nests in the ground as well as aerial situations (a typical cavity-nester) and can be aggressive. **SEASON** March to November.

*Vespa crabro*

*Vespa orientalis*

*Vespa velutina*

*Vespula germanica*

*Vespula rufa*

*Vespula vulgaris*

*Vespa crabro* worker

*Vespa orientalis* [TB]

*Vespa velutina* worker [PC]

*Vespula germanica* worker

*Vespula rufa* ♂

*Vespula vulgaris* worker

## Family Sphecidae – SAND WASPS

Sphecids are long-legged, elongated hunting solitary wasps of various insects and spiders. These wasps are sometimes seen carrying caterpillars, grasshoppers or spiders, depending on the species of wasp, to be buried in an underground nest. An egg is then laid on the paralysed prey. These active wasps may be seen on the sand, around the nests, hunting or occasionally visiting flowers. Photographers need approach them slowly, as these wasps are wary of quick movement; they are often active but calmly waiting for the spilt second they remain motionless will produce good results.

*Ammophila pubescens*

*Ammophila sabulosa*

*Isodontia mexicana*

*Podalonia affinis*

*Prionyx kirbii*

*Sceliphron spirifex*

### *Ammophila pubescens* Heath Sand Wasp

Body length: 13–19 mm, often slightly smaller than the similar *A. sabulosa* and has slightly different forewing markings. **HABITAT** Heathlands and sandy areas, where they attack moth larvae, rarely sawfly larvae, provisioning the cells progressively i.e. sealed nests are re-opened and extra food added periodically. **SEASON** June to September.

### *Ammophila sabulosa* Red-banded Sand Wasp

Body length: 14–24 mm. Similar to *A. pubescens* and other species in the same genus. In good light has a bluish tinge at the end of the abdomen. **HABITAT** Coastal dunes and cliffs and inland heathlands. Nests are mass-provisioned with moth larvae. **SEASON** June to September.

### *Isodontia mexicana* Grass-carrying Wasp

Body length: 18–20 mm. Black, with a hairy body; wings smoky brown. **HABITAT** Sandy soils where they hunt for bush and tree-crickets to feed their offspring. Nests in cavities are lined with grass. An accidental introduction from the USA, spreading throughout Europe. **SEASON** June to September.

### *Podalonia affinis* Mud Wasp

Body length: 13–20 mm. Much shorter petiole [slender stalk between thorax and abdomen] than *Ammophila* and much hairier. However, there are various European *Podalonia* and *Ammophila* species which may cause confusion. **HABITAT** Mainly sandy soils, particularly coastal areas, where they hunt for moth larvae. **SEASON** May to September.

### *Prionyx kirbii*

Body length: 13–18 mm. Abdomen red and black, white-ringed. **HABITAT** Various. Predates grasshoppers, including species much larger than themselves. **SEASON** May to September.

*Prionyx kirbii* with grasshopper prey *Aiolopus strepens* [NO]

### *Sceliphron spirifex*

Body length: 15–29 mm. Black with a long yellow waist and various yellow markings. Legs yellow, black-banded. **HABITAT** The mud nests are often on structures such as walls. The wasps may be seen on flowers, hunting for suitable spiders to prey on, and by water. **SEASON** May to September.

*Ammophila pubescens* with prey

*Ammophila sabulosa* with prey

*Isodontia mexicana* [PC]

*Podalonia affinis* ♀

*Prionyx kirbii*

*Sceliphron spirifex*

## Family Crabronidae – DIGGER WASPS

Crabronids are solitary wasps at one time regarded as part of the family Sphecidae. These digger wasps visit flowers for nectar and prey on various arthropods, including bees, beetles, bugs and spiders. They nest variously in the ground, dead wood and hollow stems. Many species have attractive yellow and black striped abdomens, including several large, widespread *Cerceris* species. *Philanthus triangulum* occurs in sandy areas; ♀s catch Honey Bees and carry them home upside-down to their underground nests. A selection of species is shown for some genera, including those most likely to be encountered. Photographers need to be cautious, as the wasps are wary of quick movement; they are often so active that it is difficult to even obtain sharp images in nature. Identification to species level can also be a challenge mainly in smaller species and is not really possible without a voucher specimen.

**HABITAT** Various with sandy soils, such as coastal sites.

### *Lestica clypeata*

Body length: 8–12 mm. Black and yellow, ♂s with a distinctive elongated head. **HABITAT** Various at woodland edges, where they nest in dead wood and collect adult Lepidoptera as provision for their larvae. **SEASON** May to September.

### *Bembix oculata*

Body length: 11–18 mm. Black and yellow (often cream or whitish in ♂s), ♀s with pair of black eyespots on 2nd abdominal segment. Abdominal tip black. **HABITAT** Open sandy areas, where they prey on flies. **SEASON** May to September.

### *Bembix rostrata*

Body length: 15–24 mm. Distinctive black and yellow, cream or whitish-banded abdomen (♂ pictured left [JE]); labrum extended and beak-like. **HABITAT** Sandy areas, where they prey on large flies. Adults make a conspicuous buzzing sound in flight **SEASON** June to August.

### *Bembix sinuata*

Body length: 17–23 mm. Black and cream or yellow, ♀s with wavy cream abdominal bands. **HABITAT** Open sandy areas, where they prey on flies. **SEASON** May to September.

### *Gorytes laticinctus*

Body length: 9–13 mm. Recognised by its body shape. Face yellow; yellow band on 2nd abdominal segment occupying at least a third. **HABITAT** Coastal such as dunes, and inland, including gardens, woodland. They nest in the ground in various soil types. Burrows link to several cells provisioned with froghopper nymphs and adults. **SEASON** June to August. **CLEPTOPARASITE** *Nysson trimaculatus.*

### *Astata boops*

Body length: 9–13 mm. Recognised by its shape and large eyes. **HABITAT** Coastal such as dunes, and inland, heathlands where it is often seen on the ground or visiting umbellifers. **SEASON** June to August. **CLEPTOPARASITE** *Hedychridium roseum.*

*Lestica clypeata*

*Bembix oculata*

*Bembix rostrata*

*Bembix sinuata*

*Gorytes laticinctus*

*Astata boops*

*Bembix oculata* ♂ (left) [PC], ♀ (right)

*Bembix rostrata* ♀ with prey [JE]

*Bembix sinuata* ♀ [PC]

*Lestica clypeata* ♂

*Gorytes laticinctus* ♀

*Astata boops* ♀

***Cerceris albofasciata***
Body length: 8–13 mm. Black with whitish-yellow bands and mostly red legs. **HABITAT** Sandy areas. **SEASON** June to August.

*Cerceris albofasciata*

***Cerceris arenaria* Sand Tailed Digger Wasp**
Body length: 8–12 mm. Of various commoner species, the conspicuous yellow banding readily distinguishes it from similar species. **HABITAT** Coastal including dunes, inland various, where they prey on weevils, then carrying them upside-down to the nest. **SEASON** June to August.

*Cerceris arenaria*

***Cerceris flaviventris***
Body length: 12–14 mm. Variable, but extensive orange body and legs (Spain, illustrated). In form *lusitana* (Portugal) black and yellow are dominant colours. **HABITAT** Sandy areas, such as sand dunes; restricted to Iberia. **SEASON** May to August.

*Cerceris flaviventris*

***Cerceris sabulosa***
Body length: 6–11 mm. Whitish or yellow bands, but could be confused with similar species. **HABITAT** Sandy areas and others including gardens, burrowing in flat soil. Part of a group of *Cerceris* species that preys on adult bees; this species is common in the Mediterranean. **SEASON** May to September.

*Cerceris sabulosa*

***Philanthus triangulum* Bee-wolf**
Body length: 8–17 mm. **HABITAT** Often coastal including dunes and lowland heathlands, where they prey on the Honey Bee *Apis mellifera*, paralysing them and then carrying them upside down to the nest. Often seen nectaring on various flowers, or hunting about them. **SEASON** July to September.

*Philanthus triangulum*

***Philanthus venustus***
Body length: 6–11 mm. **HABITAT** Often coastal, including dunes, where they prey on bees. **SEASON** May to September.

*Philanthus venustus*

***Tachysphex panzeri***
Body length: 7–14 mm. Greenish-yellow eyes, base of the abdomen red. ♂ (pictured below [PC]) with golden facial hair. Legs at least partly red. There are numerous species in this genus. **HABITAT** Sandy areas, where they prey on grasshoppers. **SEASON** July to August.

*Tachysphex panzeri*

***Tachytes panzeri***
Body length: 10–15 mm. First two abdominal segments red. Could be confused with some *Tachysphex* species. **HABITAT** Sandy areas, where they prey on grasshoppers. **SEASON** Mid May to mid September.

*Tachytes panzeri*

*Cerceris albofasciata* ♀ [JE]

*Cerceris arenaria* mating pair

*Cerceris flaviventris* ♀

*Cerceris sabulosa* ♀ [JE]

*Philanthus triangulum* ♀s

*Philanthus venustus* ♂

*Tachysphex panzeri* ♀ [JE]

*Tachytes panzeri* ♀ [JE]

## Family Apidae* – BEES *some authors recognise more than one family

A familiar sight visiting flowers, bees are popular with many people, although some are wary of them stinging. However, ♀s only use their stings in defence and, with the exception of the Honey Bee, do not die afterwards. Bees range in size from 4 mm to 25 mm in body length and most European species are solitary i.e. each nest is the work of a single ♀, working alone to excavate and provision her nest burrow. Whilst some bees may be seen nesting in large numbers they are not necessarily exhibiting social behaviour, only the bumble bees, honey bees and some halictine bees are truly social insects. Bees are probably best known for their role in pollinating flowers, their hairy legs and underside of the abdomens of ♀s are adapted to help gather pollen, which is taken back to their nests, in pollen baskets, or specialised clusters of hairs (combs and brushes) on part of the hind tibiae. The larvae feed on the pollen and nectar. The usually much smaller solitary bees are the largest but least well studied of the group. Solitary bees nest in a variety of places above ground, such as in walls, wood and in the ground. The ♀ lays eggs, and some abandon the nest. Solitary bees are considered to be very efficient pollinators. Bumble bees and many solitary bees have some cuckoo bees [cleptoparasites], which benefit from the work of others. Certain bees are also parasitised by various insects, particularly other bees, flies, stylopids and wasps.

*Colletes hederae*

### *Colletes hederae* Ivy Bee

Body length: 10–16 mm. Distinctive sandy yellow abdominal hair bands. Often flies later than relatives. **HABITAT** Open places sometimes gardens or sandy areas, wherever there is a plentiful supply of ivy *Hedera*, on which it prefers to forage; known to be expanding in range. **SEASON** August to November. **CLEPTOPARASITES** Possibly *Epeolus cruciger* and *E. variegatus*. The blister beetle *Stenoria analis* is a known parasite.

*Hylaeus variegatus*

### *Hylaeus variegatus*

Body length: 6–8 mm. ♂ black (whitish face), first two segments of ♀ abdomen is red, otherwise black; abdomen white striped. Face with two yellow triangular markings). **HABITAT** Various, including grasslands and forest edges. **SEASON** June to September.

*Andrena agillissima*

### *Andrena agillissima* Violet-winged Mining Bee

Body length: 11–16 mm. Dark with conspicuous white hairs on head and thorax. Wings dark with a bluish reflection. **HABITAT** Various, nesting in cliffs and walls. **SEASON** May to July. **CLEPTOPARASITES** *Nomada fulvicornis* and *Sphecodes* species.

*Andrena flavipes*

### *Andrena flavipes* Yellow-legged Mining Bee

Body length: 9–13 mm. Pale abdominal hair bands and yellowish pollen hairs on hind tibiae. **HABITAT** Various, including chalk grassland, coastal cliffs, sandpits and woodland. **SEASON** March to August. **CLEPTOPARASITE** *Nomada fucata*.

*Andrena florea*

### *Andrena florea* Bryony Mining Bee

Body length: 10–13 mm. Wide red abdominal band in both sexes. **HABITAT** Commons, gardens, heathlands and woodland where bryony *Bryonia* occurs (its almost exclusive pollen source). **SEASON** May to July.

*Andrena hattorfiana*

### *Andrena hattorfiana* Large Scabious Mining Bee

Body length: 13–17 mm. Robust, black species, often with red bands in both sexes. Wings smoky brown. Golden hairs on thorax in fresh specimens. **HABITAT** Grasslands, including in mountains, calcareous and sandy soils, on scabious *Knautia*. **SEASON** June to August. **CLEPTOPARASITE** *Nomada armata*.

*Halictus maculatus*

### *Halictus maculatus* Box-headed Furrow Bee

Body length: 8–10 mm. Medium-sized *Halictus*, with rather large, almost square head. **HABITAT** Grasslands, including mountainous areas. **SEASON** April to September (males from July). **CLEPTOPARASITES** *Sphecodes* species.

*Halictus scabiosae*

### *Halictus scabiosae* Great-banded Furrow Bee

Body length: 12–15 mm. Black abdomen with yellow transverse hair-bands, much more elongate ♂s. **HABITAT** Light soils, sandy areas particularly coastal. **SEASON** June to September.

*Colletes hederae* ♂ (left), ♀ (right)

*Hylaeus variegatus* ♀ (top & bottom) [both PC]

*Andrena agillissima* ♀

*Andrena flavipes* ♀ [PC]

*Andrena florea* ♂

*Andrena hattorfiana* ♀

*Halictus maculatus* ♀

*Halictus scabiosae* ♀

***Lasioglossum morio*** **Brassy Mining Bee** [Green Furrow Bee]
Body length: 5–7 mm. Metallic brassy sheen, ♂ with long antennae (♀ pictured left [PC]). **HABITAT** Various open areas, often nesting in banks of bare slopes. **SEASON** March to October. **CLEPTOPARASITES** *Sphecodes* and *Nomada* species.

*Lasioglossum morio*

***Lasioglossum xanthopus*** **Orange-footed Furrow Bee**
Body length: 9–12 mm. Orange hind tibiae and tarsi. **HABITAT** Calcareous grasslands and coastal sites, including high altitudes. **SEASON** April to October (males from August). **CLEPTOPARASITE** *Sphecodes spinulosus.*

*Lasioglossum xanthopus*

***Nomioides minutissimus***
Body length: 3–4 mm. Small, metallic green species with yellow markings. **HABITAT** Various well vegetated grasslands and sandy areas, including dunes. **SEASON** June to September. **CLEPTOPARASITE** *Sphecodes* spp.

*Nomioides minutissimus*

***Sphecodes gibbus*** **Humped Sphecodes**
Body length: 7–12 mm. Very similar to many other *Sphecodes*, red abdomen with black tip, but this species is larger than most with less black at the tip. **HABITAT** Open areas. **SEASON** Late April to mid September. **HOST** *Halictus rubicundus.*

*Sphecodes gibbus*

***Dasypoda argentata***
Body length: 13–16 mm. Rather variable, with several features helping to distinguish this species from relatives. An example includes in ♀ fore tibiae with orange hair. **HABITAT** Sandy soil. **SEASON** Late June to mid August.

*Dasypoda argentata*

***Dasypoda hirtipes*** **Hairy-legged Mining Bee**
Body length: 12–15 mm. ♀ with long golden pollen-collecting hairs on the hind tibiae; pollen-laden bees look like they have pantaloons. The ♂ is hairier than the ♀. **HABITAT** Mainly coastal dunes and inland, heathlands with sandy soil. **SEASON** June to August.

*Dasypoda hirtipes*

***Anthidium manicatum*** **Wool Carder Bee**
Body length: 9–17 mm. Black, with a variable number of yellow abdominal spots and bands. **HABITAT** Various, often observed in gardens, seeking flowering labiates and vetches. Nests above ground in existing cavities in dead wood, hollow stems and crevices in mortar. Many ♂s are larger than ♀s and are quite aggressive, chasing off, or even killing, any perceived rivals in their territories. **SEASON** May to September. **CLEPTOPARASITE** *Stelis punctulatissima.*

*Anthidium manicatum*

***Rhodanthidium sticticum***
Body length: up to 15 mm. Black with orange abdominal bands. **HABITAT** Grasslands, including mountainous areas, where they nest in empty shells of snails. **SEASON** May to July.

*Rhodoanthidium sticticum*

***Megachile parietina*** **Black Mud Bee**
Body length: 14–18 mm. Robust-looking black bee (buff-haired on abdominal segments 1–3 in ♂s), with darkened wings. **HABITAT** Grasslands, including mountainous areas in Spain. Builds very hard nests of mud attached to rocks and walls. **SEASON** April to June. **CLEPTOPARASITES** *Stelis nasuta, Dioxys* species.

*Megachile parietina*

*Lasioglossum morio* ♂

*Lasioglossum xanthopus* ♀

*Nomioides minutissimus*

*Sphecodes gibbus* ♀

*Dasypoda argentata* ♀ [JE]

*Dasypoda hirtipes* ♀

*Anthidium manicatum* ♀

*Rhodoanthidium sticticum* ♀

*Megachile parietina* ♀ [TB]

**_Nomada armata_ Armed Nomad Bee**
Body length: 9–14 mm. Attractive black, red and yellow marked. **HABITAT** Grasslands, including calcareous. **SEASON** Mid May to July. **HOST** *Andrena hattorfiana.*

*Nomada armata*

**_Nomada sexfasciata_ Six-banded Nomad Bee**
Body length: 11–15 mm. Black and yellow. When viewed laterally, lower face clearly elevated. **HABITAT** Open areas, including coastal cliffs. **SEASON** Late April to June. **HOSTS** *Eucera* species.

*Nomada sexfasciata*

**_Epeoloides coecutiens_**
Body length: c.9 mm. Green eyes. Abdomen with extensive red areas. **HABITAT** Damp areas where the host flies. **SEASON** July to mid August. **HOST** *Macropis* species.

*Epeoloides coecutiens*

**_Eucera longicornis_ Long-horned Bee**
Body length: 12–16 mm. Large species, with brown thoracic hairs. ♂s have yellow faces and extremely long antennae. Various similar species. **HABITAT** Open areas, including coastal cliffs and dunes, where sites are rich in legumes. **SEASON** May to July. **CLEPTOPARASITE** *Nomada sexfasciata.*

*Eucera longicornis*

**_Amegilla quadrifasciata_ White-banded Digger Bee**
Body length: 9–12 mm. Hairy orange thorax, black and white striped abdomen. **HABITAT** Various, nests excavated in loose soils. **SEASON** March to June, sometimes also later in the season. **CLEPTOPARASITE** *Thyreus histrionicus.*

*Amegilla quadrifasciata*

**_Anthophora plumipes_ Hairy-footed Flower Bee**
Body length: 14–17 mm. Hairy, large mainly black ♀, with orange hairs on hind tibiae; ♂ with brown or greyish hairs and yellow face. **HABITAT** Coastal cliffs, gardens, parks and woodland. Often nests in burrows in mortar of old buildings. **SEASON** March to May, sometimes later. **CLEPTOPARASITE** *Melecta albifrons.*

*Anthophora plumipes*

**_Melecta obscura_**
Body length: 12–17 mm. Black and whitish, markings distinguish it from closely related species. **HABITAT** Various, including grasslands. **SEASON** April to July. **HOSTS** *Habropoda tarsata* and *Anthophora* species.

*Melecta obscura*

**_Thyreus histrionicus_**
Body length: 8–13 mm. Attractive black and white bee, with closely related species. **HABITAT** Various, including grasslands. **SEASON** April to July. **HOSTS** *Amegilla* species.

*Thyreus histrionicus*

**_Xylocopa violacea_ Violet Carpenter Bee**
Body length: 20–28 mm. Black species; dark brown wings with blue and violet reflections. Whilst ♀s, may be difficult to identify to species level from photographs, ♂s of *violacea* have a distinctive reddish area towards the tip of the antennae (pictured left). **HABITAT** Grasslands, gardens and coastal areas. ♀s nest in burrows in wood. **SEASON** April to September.

*Xylocopa violacea*

*Xylocopa violacea* nest entrance in a wooden fence

*Nomada armata* ♂

*Nomada sexfasciata* ♀

*Epeoloides coecutiens* ♀ [JE]

*Eucera longicornis* ♂ (left), ♀ (right)

*Amegilla quadrifasciata* ♀

*Anthophora plumipes* ♂ (left), ♀ (right)

*Melecta obscura* [TB]

*Thyreus histrionicus* [PC]

*Xylocopa violacea* ♀

## SOCIAL BEES: Honey Bees, bumble bees and associated cuckoo bees

***Bombus*** are mainly large hairy bumble bees, c.12–25 mm (queens larger). The queen is the egg-layer, workers (sterile ♀s) care for the larvae, whilst older workers fly to find nectar and pollen. The queen emerges in spring following hibernation and collects pollen from available flowers. The pollen is stored in the nest, which, depending on species, may be underground or above ground. Eggs are laid on the pollen, and a small supply of nectar stored up in the nest for feeding. In late summer or autumn, some of these eggs have developed into queens and ♂s, leaving the old queens, workers and ♂s to die. Only the new queens hibernate, to start the cycle again. Each colony has up to around 200 bees depending on species. Several species are cuckoos in the nests of other bumble bees and are usually less abundant than the host; some of these species have darkened wings, are less hairy and the hind tibiae narrower. Care is needed in identification owing to the similarity of several species and the differences between workers, ♂s and queens. ***Apis*** is the genus which includes the Honey Bee, managed for centuries; often seen collecting pollen in a basket formed by hairs on the hind tibia. Each colony has an amazing working and communication structure. They reproduce by fission (swarming), the old queen and many workers splitting from the existing colony; these swarms may occasionally be found in the wild, but most are from hives. Queens are ♀s resulting from workers feeding them exclusively on royal jelly and once mated, commence egg-laying duties. Drones are the infrequently seen ♂s, easily recognised by their large eyes which meet at the top of their heads. Unlike drones, workers (♀s, but smaller than queens) have a barbed sting and their varied duties include feeding the offspring, guard duty, foraging and receiving pollen. Assuming they resort to stinging in defence of the nest, the bees die, unlike other bees.

*Bombus hypnorum*

### *Bombus hypnorum* Tree Bumble Bee
Very distinctive pattern compared with other species with head black, thorax brown, and abdomen black with white tail. **HABITAT** Gardens, also open areas and woodlands. **SEASON** March to September.

*Bombus incertus*

### *Bombus incertus*
Distinctive black and white, with orange tail. **HABITAT** Restricted to higher ground in Anatolia (where it is common), to Transcaucasia and northern Iran. **SEASON** March to September.

*Bombus mesomelus*

### *Bombus mesomelus*
Greyish white, with black band; abdomen yellowish-orange. **HABITAT** Restricted to mountains of southern Europe. Subspecies *alboluteus* has a wide range, although some populations are fragmented. **SEASON** April to September.

*Bombus niveatus*

### *Bombus niveatus*
Black and white, with orange tail. The whitish areas are replaced by yellow in the subspecies *vorticosus*. **HABITAT** Grasslands and mixed woodland edge, mainly around the Aegean sea, including mountainous terrain. **SEASON** March to September.

*Bombus pascuorum*

### *Bombus pascuorum* Common Carder Bumble Bee
An orange bee. Various subspecies with different colour forms. **HABITAT** Mainly woodlands, irrigated lands and gardens, but avoiding some of the warmer parts, such as much of southern Iberia. **SEASON** March to October.

*Bombus terrestris*

### *Bombus terrestris*
One brownish yellow band on thorax, another at front of abdomen, white tail, closely related to *B. lucorum*. Known as the Buff-tailed Bumble Bee in the UK, mainland European specimens lack the buff tail. **HABITAT** Grasslands, gardens and woodlands. **SEASON** February to November.

*Apis mellifera*

### *Apis mellifera* Honey Bee
Body length: 12–16 mm. Eyes hairy. Variable in colour; abdomen colour largely orange with black bands, to mainly reddish or black. **HABITAT** Found in most habitats. Numbers have been reduced by disease caused by *Varroa* (an external mite). Beekeepers have experienced unusual die-offs of colonies in recent years. *Vespa velutina* is also well known for killing Honey Bee workers. **SEASON** March to November.

*Bombus hypnorum* queen

*Bombus incertus* [PR]

*Bombus niveatus* ♂ [PR]

*Bombus pascuorum*

*Bombus mesomelus* worker [PR]

*Bombus terrestris* [SO]

*Apis mellifera* drone (left), worker (right)

# APPENDIX 1 – References

This selection is of useful, mainly recent field guides and other references, that often provide links to more detailed works, from particular regions or countries. Various species files on-line are useful taxonomic databases, some including numerous photographs of species. Academic works covering small parts of the fauna are therefore not normally listed in this book.


**INSECTS, general guides**

Brock, P.D. (2015) *A comprehensive guide to insects of Britain & Ireland*. Newbury: Pisces Publications [useful illustrations/text on European species also found in Britain. Originally published 2014, reprinted in 2015].

Chinery, M. (1993) *Insects of Britain and Northern Europe*. 3rd Edition. London: HarperCollins Publishers.

Chinery, M. (2012) *Insects of Britain and Western Europe*. 3rd Edition. London: Bloomsbury Publishing.

Gullan, P.J. & Cranston, P.S. (2014) *The insects: an outline of Entomology*. 5th Edition. Chichester: Wiley Blackwell [general introduction to insects].

McGavin, G. (2010) *Pocket Nature. Insects and Spiders*. London: Dorling Kindersley.

Leraut, P. & Blanchot, P. (2002) *Les Guides du Naturaliste -- Le guide entomologique*. Paris: Delachaux & Niestlé [brief coverage of c.5000 species].

Rojas, D. & M.A. (2016) *Invertebrados del Campo de Gibraltar*. Almería: Guante Blanco [useful photographic guide to selected insects and other invertebrates of a popular part of southern Spain and Gibraltar].

Sutton, P. (2015) Recent developments regarding the entomological fauna of Corfu (Kérkira). *Antenna* 39(1): 3-14.

Zúbrik, M., Kunca, A. & Csóka, G. (2013) *Insects and diseases damaging trees and shrubs of Europe*. Verrières le Buisson: NAP [a colour atlas].

Faune de France (www.faunedefrance.org/bibliothequevirtuellenumerique) [pdf's of some titles (in French) on various insect groups downloadable here; check the home page for current titles not yet on pdf, which often cover Europe, not just France].

Fauna Ibérica (www.fauna-iberica.mncn.csic.es) [works on various insect families in Iberia].

Forum Natura Mediterraneo (www.naturamediterraneo.com) [helpful photo galleries on some orders].

The ecology of Commanster (www.commanster.eu/commanster) [good coverage of some insect orders and comprehensive references. Some of these Belgian species are also found in southern Europe and the Mediterranean].

**MEDITERRANEAN AND EUROPE; general guides and nature sites**

Sterry, P. (2000) *Collins Complete Guide to Mediterranean Wildlife*. London: HarperCollins Publishers [basic coverage of insects (less than 50 pages), but a useful general introductory guide to wildlife].

The following include site details:

Gibbons, B. (2009) *Wild France: The Animals, Plants and Landscapes*. London: New Holland.

Farino, T. (2009) *Wild Spain: The Animals, Plants and Landscapes*. London: New Holland.

Crossbill guides (crossbillguides.org) [cover various regions, always including information on the fauna and flora].

Travellers' Nature Guides (Oxford University Press) [useful works, with guides on France, Greece and Spain published in 2003/4].

Butterfly Conservation European Interests Group (www.bc-europe.eu) [information/links on butterfly sites in Europe].

Fauna Europaea (all European animal species online) www.fauna-eu.org [species and maps, with links to illustrations].

**ALIEN INSECTS**

Roques, A. *et al.* (eds) (2010) *Alien terrestrial arthropods of Europe*. Vols 4:1 & 4:2. Sofia: Pensoft.

**EPHEMEROPTERA [Mayflies]**

Bauernfeind, E. & Soldán, T. (2012) *The Mayflies of Europe*. Ollerup: Apollo Books.

**ODONATA [Dragonflies and Damselflies]**

Askew, R.R. (2004) *The Dragonflies of Europe*. 2nd Edition. Netherlands: Brill.

Boudot, J.-P., & Kalkman, V.J. (eds) (2015) *Atlas of the European dragonflies and damselflies*. Zeist: KNNV.

Dijkstra, K.B. & Lewington, R. (2006) *Field Guide to the Dragonflies of Britain and Europe*. Gillingham: British Wildlife Publishing.

Maravalhas, E. & Soares, A. (2013) *As Libélulas de Portugal* (*The Dragonflies of Portugal*). Portugal: Booky Publisher [in Portugese and English].

European Odonata (www.odonata.eu)

Société française Odonatologie [French Odonatology Society] (www.libellules.org)

**PLECOPTERA [Stoneflies]**

Plecoptera Species File (plecoptera.speciesfile.org)

**DERMAPTERA [Earwigs]**

Harz, K. & Kaltenbach, A. (1976) *Die Orthopteren Europas* III (*The Orthoptera of Europe* III). Series Entomologica 12. Hague: Junk [covers Dermaptera and various orders related to Orthoptera].

Dermaptera Species File (dermaptera.speciesfile.org)

**ORTHOPTERA [Bush-crickets, Crickets, Grasshoppers and allies]**

Bellman, H. (1985) *A Field Guide to the Grasshoppers and Crickets of Britain and Northern Europe*. London: Collins.

Bellmann, H. & Luquet, G.C. (2009) *Guide des Sauterelles, Grillons et Criquets d'Europe Occidentale*. Les Guides du Naturaliste. Paris: Delachaux & Niestlé [in French with a CD of songs; covers 164 species].

Fontana, P., Buzzetti, F.M., Cogo, A. & Odé, B. (2002) *Guida al riconoscimento e allo studio di cavalette, grilli, mantidi e insetti affini del Veneto (Blattaria, Mantodea, Isoptera, Orthoptera, Phasmatodea, Dermaptera, Embiidina)*. Guida Natura 1. Vicenza: Museo Naturalistico Archeologico di Vicenza.

Harz, K. (1969) *Die Orthopteren Europas* I (*The Orthoptera of Europe* I). Series Entomologica 5. Hague: Junk.

Harz, K. (1975) *Die Orthopteren Europas* II (*The Orthoptera of Europe* II). Series Entomologica 11. Hague: Junk.

Heller. K.-G., Korsunovskaya, O., Ragge. D.R., Vedenina, V., Willemse, F., Zhantiev, R.D. & Frantsevich, L. (1998) *Check-list of European Orthoptera*. Articulata, Beiheft 7: 1-61.

Ragge. D.R. & Reynolds, W.J. (1998) *The songs of the grasshoppers and crickets of western Europe*. Colchester: Harley Books.

Grasshoppers of Europe (www.grasshoppersofeurope.com) [includes links to many other books].

Orthoptera Species File (orthoptera.speciesfile.org)

**EMBIOPTERA [Webspinners]**

Embioptera Species File (embioptera.speciesfile.org)

**PHASMIDA [Stick insects]**

Brock, P.D. (1991) *Stick-Insects of Britain & the Mediterranean*. London: Fitzgerald Publishing.

Brock, P.D. (in preparation) *Stick and leaf insects of the world*. Verrières le Buisson: NAP.

Phasmida Species File (phasmida.speciesfile.org)

**MANTODEA [Praying Mantids]**

Battiston, R., Picciau, L., Fontana, P. & Marshall, J. (2010) *Mantids of the Euro-Mediterranean*. Verona: WBA Handbooks 2. [a book covering 127 species from North Africa, the Middle East and Europe].

Mantodea Species File (mantodea.speciesfile.org)

**BLATTODEA [Cockroaches]**

Harz, K. & Kaltenbach, A. (1976) *Die Orthopteren Europas* III (*The Orthoptera of Europe* III). Series Entomologica 12. Hague: Junk [covers Blattodea and various orders related to Orthoptera].

Blattodea Species File (blattodea.speciesfile.org)

**PSOCODEA [Lice and Booklice]**

Psocodea Species File (psocodea.speciesfile.org)

**THYSANOPTERA [Thrips]**

Fauna Europaea (www.fauna-eu.org) [key Thysanoptera to search for list of European species].

Orden Thysanoptera (sea-entomologia.org/IDE@/revista_52.pdf) [of Iberia].

**HEMIPTERA [Bugs]**

Lupoli, R. & Dusoulier, F. (2015) *Les Punaises Pentatomoidea de France*. Fontenay-sous-Bois: Éditions Ancyrosoma. [well illustrated guide to French shieldbugs, including many species found in the Mediterranean area]

Faune de France: this series includes books [in French] on shieldbugs and others of the Euro-Mediterranean i.e. vols 90 (2005), 93 (2010) & 96 (2013) cover shieldbugs.

Aphid Species File (aphid.speciesfile.org)

British Bugs (www.britishbugs.org.uk) [useful for European species also found in Britain].

Central European Bugs (www.koleopterologie.de/heteroptera) [includes many species also found further south].

Coreoidea Species file (coreoidea.speciesfile.org)

**NEUROPTERA [Lacewings, Owlflies and Antlions], MEGALOPTERA [Alderflies],RAPHIDIOPTERA [Snakeflies]**

Aspöck, H., Aspöck, U. & Hölzel, H. (1980) *Die Neuropteren Europas* (vols 1 & 2). Krefeld: Goecke & Evers.

Wachmann, E. & Saure, C. (1997) *Netzflügler, Schlamm- und Kamelhalsfliegen*. Augsburg: Naturbach Verlag.

Orden Neuroptera (sea-entomologia.org/IDE@/revista_58.pdf) [of Iberia].

Letardi, A. (2016) Atlante fotografico dei Neuropterida della fauna italiana (versione online 1.1) (www.researchgate.net/publication/311256998) [photographic atlas of Italian Neuropterida, with keys; regular updates projected].

**COLEOPTERA [Beetles]**

Bense, U. (1995) *Longhorn beetles: illustrated key to the Cerambycidae and Vesperidae of Europe*. Weikersheim: Josef Margraf.

Chatanet, G. du (2000-2017) Series of European beetle books in French or English. NAP [four volumes published so far].

Gerstmeier, R. (1998) *Checkered beetles: illustrated key to the Cleridae of the Western Palaearctic*. Weikersheim: Josef Margraf.

Harde, K.W. & Severa, F. (1998) *A field guide in colour to Beetles*. Leicester: Blitz Editions (Bookmart).

Nieto, A. & Alexander, K.N.A. (2010) *European Red List of Saproxylic Beetles*. Luxembourg: IUCN. (www.iucn.org/about/union/secretariat/offices/europe/resources/publications/?5372/European-Red-List-of-Saproxylic-Beetles)

Trautner, I. & L. Geigenmüller (1987) *Tiger beetles, Ground beetles: illustrated key to the Cicindelidae and Carabidae of the Western Palaearctic*. Aichtal: Josef Margraf.

Wagner, T. [ed] (series in preparation) *Coleoptera of Europe*. Brill.

Warchalowski, A. (2003) *Chrysomelidae: the leaf-beetles of Europe and the Mediterranean area*. Warsaw: Natura Optima Dux Foundation [illustrated keys].

Coleoptera websites (www.kerbtier.de, www.koleopterologie.de) [two of various European sites which include many photos of European species].

Cerambycidae: longhorn beetles of the Western Palaearctic Region (www.cerambyx.uochb.cz)

**STREPSIPTERA [Twisted-wing parasites]**

Order Strepsiptera (sea-entomologia.org/IDE@/revista_62B.pdf) [of Iberia].

**DIPTERA [Flies]**

Oosterbroeck, P. (2006) *The European families of the Diptera: identification, diagnosis, biology*. KNNV, Uitgeverij.

Dipterists Forum. The Society for the study of flies (Diptera). (www.dipteristsforum.org.uk) [although based in Britain, Forum is widely used in Europe].

**MECOPTERA [Scorpionflies]**

Mécoptères de France et du Paléarctique occidental. Mecoptera from France & western-Palaearctic. (mecoptera.free.fr/accueil.html)

**SIPHONAPTERA [Fleas]**

Fauna Europaea (www.fauna-eu.org) [key Siphonaptera to search for list of European species].

**TRICHOPTERA [Caddisflies]**

Barnard, P. & Ross, E. (2012) *The adult Trichoptera (caddisflies) of Britain and Ireland*. Handbooks for the identification of British insects, Part 1, vol. 17. St. Albans: Royal Entomological Society [useful coverage of species also found in Europe].

Malicky, H. (2004) *Atlas of European Trichoptera*. 2nd Edition. Dordrecht: Springer.

**LEPIDOPTERA [Butterflies and Moths]**

Haahtela, T., Saarinen, K., Ojalainen, P. & Aarnio, H. (2011) *Butterflies of Britain and Europe. A photographic guide*. London: A & C Black.

Leraut, P. (2006-2014) *Moths of Europe*. Verrières le Buisson: NAP. [four volumes available so far, the fifth due for publication soon. Also available in French].

Leraut, P. (2016) *Butterflies of Europe and neighbouring regions*. Verrières le Buisson: NAP.

Pittaway, A.R. (1993) *The Hawkmoths of the Western Palaearctic*. Brill.

Tolman, T. (2001) *Photographic Guide to the butterflies of Britain & Europe*. Oxford: Oxford University Press.

Tolman, T. & Lewington, R. (2008) *Collins Butterfly Guide*. London: HarperCollins Publishers. 3rd Edition [covers Europe].

Tshikolovets, V.V. (2011) *Butterflies of Europe & the Mediterranean area*. Pardubice: Tshikolovets Publications.

Other popular moth series for specialists include the Noctuidae Europaeae series of 13 volumes, some now out of print, Geometrid Moths of Europe and Microlepidoptera of Europe.

Butterflies of France (www.butterfliesoffrance.com)

Butterflies in Italy (www.butterfliesinitaly.com)

EuroButterflies (www.eurobutterflies.com)

European Butterflies and Moths (www.lepidoptera.eu)

European Lepidoptera and their ecology (www.pyrgus.de)

Guy Padfield's European Butterflies Page (www.guypadfield.com)

Moths and Butterflies of Europe and North Africa (www.leps.it)

Saturniidae of the Western Palaearctic (tpittaway.tripod.com/silk)

Sphingidae of the Western Palaearctic (tpittaway.tripod.com/sphinx)

**HYMENOPTERA [Bees, Wasps, Ants and related insects]**

Michez, D., Rasmont, P., Terzo, M. & Vereecken, N.J. (in preparation) *Hyménopteras of Europe*, Volume 1, Apoidae. NAP.

Zahradník, J. & Severa, F. (2000) *A field guide in colour to Bees and Wasps*. Leicester: Blitz Editions (Bookmart).

Atlas Hymenoptera (www.atlashymenoptera.net/)

Checkist of the Western Palaearctic bees (Hymenoptera: Apoidea: Anthophila) (http://westpalbees.myspecies.info/)

Hormigas.org (www.hormigas.org/) [ants of Iberia].

Sphecidae of Europe (sphecidae.hymis.net).

**FLORA**

Thorogood, C. (2016) *Field Guide to the Wild Flowers of the Western Mediterranean*. Kew: Royal Botanic Gardens [includes habitat information].

# APPENDIX 2 – Red List species

IUCN Red list conservation assessments are periodically made and updated, although work is needed on some orders. For example, Phasmida, Neuroptera, Hemiptera, many Coleoptera, Diptera, some Lepidoptera and many Hymenoptera are not yet assessed. It is probable some of the species included in this book would be assessed as Red List. No 'Extinct' species are covered in this work, but Critically Endangered [CR] (extremely high risk of extinction), Endangered [EN] (very high risk of extinction) and Vulnerable [VU] (high risk of extinction) are quantitative criteria designed to reflect varying threats of extinction; all these rare species are regarded as 'threatened'. Species assessed as Near Threatened [NT] may still be rare and close to qualifying as Vulnerable. Not enough is known about Data Deficient [DD] species, but those assessed as being of Least Concern [LC] are not listed below, as they include widespread and common species.

**REFERENCES**

IUCN 2016. The IUCN Red List of Threatened Species. Version 2016-3. <http://www.iucnredlist.org>. Downloaded March 2017.
European Red List (www.iucnredlist.org/initiatives/europe) [latest publications may be downloaded].
Mediterranean Red List (www.iucnredlist.org/initiatives/mediterranean) [information on the conservation status of species in the Mediterranean area].

The following lists only refer to species featured in this book:

**ODONATA [Dragonflies and Damselflies]**
Red List Europe assessments 2010, with note of differences vs Mediterranean Red List, where applicable
*Lestes macrostigma* VU [Mediterranean – NT]
*Calopteryx splendens* [Mediterranean only – VU]
*Epallage fatime* NT [Mediterranean – LC]
*Coenagrion caerulescens* NT [Mediterranean – LC]
*Coenagrion merculiale* NT
*Coenagrion pulchellum* [Mediterranean only – NT]
*Erythromma najas* [Mediterranean only – NT]
*Brachytron pratense* [Mediterranean only – NT]
*Gomphus graslinii* NT [Mediterranean – EN]
*Lindenia tetraphylla* VU [Mediterranean – NT]
*Oxygastra curtisii* NT [Mediterranean – LC]
*Macromia splendens* VU [Mediterranean – LC]
*Cordulia aenea* [Mediterranean only – NT]
*Somatochlora metallica* [Mediterranean – NT]
*Leucorrhinia dubia* [Mediterranean only – NT]
*Orthetrum nitidinerve* VU [Mediterranean – LC]
*Zygonyx torridus* VU [Mediterranean – NT]

**ORTHOPTERA [Bush-crickets, Crickets, Grasshoppers and allies]**
Red List Europe assessments 2016
*Amphiestris baetica* EN
*Baetica ustulata* EN
*Paracalopptenus caloptenoides* NT
*Omocestus bolivari* VU
*Cophopodisma pyrenaea* NT
*Acinipe hesperica* EN
*Asiotmethis limbatus* VU
*Eumigus monticolus* NT
*Eumigus rubioi* NT
*Paranocaracris bulgaricus* EN

**COLEOPTERA [Beetles]**
Red List Europe assessments: Saproxylic Beetles 2010 [based on a selection of 436 species]
*Carabus intricatus* NT
*Typhaeus momus* EN
*Lucanus cervus* NT
*Ateuchetus cicatricosus* NT
*Gnorimus variabilis* NT
*Protaetia affinis* DD
*Osmoderma barnabita* NT
*Propomacrus bimucronatus* NT
*Buprestis splendens* EN
*Ampedus elongantulus* NT
*Cerambyx welensii* NT
*Purpuricenus dalmatinus* DD
*Purpuricenus desfontainii* DD

**LEPIDOPTERA [Butterflies and Moths]**
Red List Europe assessments: Butterflies 2010
*Zerynthia cerisy* NT
*Parnassius apollo* NT
*Driopa mnemosyne* NT
*Parnassius corybas* NT
*Carcharodus flocciferus* NT
*Carcharodus lavatherae* NT
*Pyrgus cirsii* VU
*Thymelicus acteon* NT
*Colias phicomone* NT
*Lopinga achine* VU
*Coenonympha oedippus* EN
*Coenonympha orientalis* VU
*Chazara briseis* NT
*Hipparchia fagi* NT
*Hipparchia statilinus* NT
*Pseudochazara cingowskii* CR
*Cupido decoloratus* NT
*Pseudophilotes panoptes* NT
*Pseudophilotes vicrama* NT
*Glaucopsyche iolas* NT
*Phengaris arion* EN
*Phengaris nausithous* NT
*Polyommatus eros* NT
*Polyommatus golgus* VU
*Turanana taygetica* EN
*Graellsia isabellae* DD

**HYMENOPTERA [Bees, Wasps, Ants and related insects]**
Red List Europe assessments: Bees 2014
*Andrena agillissima* DD
*Andrena florea* DD
*Andrena hattorfiana* NT
*Lasioglossum xanthopus* NT
*Rhodanthidium sticticum* DD
*Nomada armata* NT
*Melecta obscura* DD

# INDEX OF ENGLISH AND SCIENTIFIC NAMES

# GLOSSARY

**ABDOMEN** the third, rear part of an insect (see STRUCTURE OF AN INSECT)
**ABDOMINAL SEGMENTS** subdivisions of the insect abdomen
**ADULT** the final (mature) stage of an insect, during which reproduction occurs
**ANTENNA (plural ANTENNAE)** the paired sensory appendages of the head, also known as 'feelers' (see STRUCTURE)
**BODY LENGTH** length from top of head to end of abdomen, excluding cerci and female ovipositor (when present)
**CERCUS (plural CERCI)** the paired, segmented appendages at the end of the abdomen (see STRUCTURE)
**CLAVUS** in Hemiptera, part of the forewings that lies next to the scutellum (when wings are folded)
**CLEPTOPARASITE** a ♀ seeking prey or stored food from another ♀, usually belonging to a different species i.e. benefiting from the work of others (mainly some Hymenoptera)
**CLYPEUS** plate on lower part of face, to which the labrum is attached
**COCOON** a silk case made by some pupating larvae
**COMPLETE METAMORPHOSIS** egg, larva, pupa, adult e.g. Coleoptera, Hymenoptera, Lepidoptera
**CORIUM** flexible membrane between body or appendage segments (used in Hemiptera)
**DORSAL** upper surface
**EGG** first stage of an insect (hatches into a larva [or caterpillar] in Lepidoptera, a nymph in Hemiptera)
**ELYTRA** see forewings; often used for rigid wing covers of many beetles, which are not used in flight
**ENTOMOLOGY** the branch of zoology concerned with the study of insects [insects are studied by entomologists]
**EXUVIA** larval skin shed during moulting, often used to describe the larval case of Odonata
**EYE** a large eye (compound eye) made up of many separate units (see STRUCTURE)
**FAMILY** in zoological classification, a rank below the Order and above the Genus, ending in '–idae'
**FEMALE** (= ♀) the sex in which eggs are developed
**FEMUR (plural FEMORA)** the third segment and longest part of the insect leg attached to the base of the body by the trochanter and coxa (see STRUCTURE)
**FOREWINGS** paired outgrowths of the second thoracic segment, also known as elytra and tegmina (see STRUCTURE)
**GALL** abnormal plant growth caused by bacterium, virus, fungus, mite or insect
**GENUS** an assemblage of species agreeing in one or more character(s) (the first scientific name of two for each species, e.g. *Aglais* in *Aglais io*)
**HEAD** first division of the insect body, bearing the mouth and antennae (see STRUCTURE)
**HINDWINGS** paired outgrowths of the third thoracic segment, also known as alae
**IMMIGRANT** considered to have reached Europe by natural flight
**INCOMPLETE METAMORPHOSIS** egg, nymph, adult e.g. Hemiptera, Odonata, Orthoptera
**KEEL** ridge, for example of the pronotum in grasshoppers
**KEY** a tabulation of characters of species, genera etc., serving to identify them
**LARVA (plural LARVAE)** immature stage of insects with complete metamorphosis, i.e. hatching from egg, examples being Lepidoptera (also known as caterpillar(s))
**LATERAL** at or from the side
**LENGTH** see body length
**LIFE CYCLE** time between fertilisation of egg and death of adult; successive stages of reproduction, growth and development
**MALE** (= ♂)
**METAMORPHOSIS** includes change during successive stages of development
**MESOTHORAX** the second thoracic segment
**METATHORAX** the third thoracic segment
**MOULT** to shed or cast the skin or outer covering of the body (ecdysis)
**NOCTURNAL** active at night
**NYMPH** the immature stage of insects with incomplete metamorphosis, i.e. between egg and adult, such as in Hemiptera
**ORDER** major groups based on structural differences in classification of insects
**OOTHECA** egg pod, in cockroaches and mantids
**OVUM (plural OVA)** egg
**OVIPOSITOR** the egg-laying apparatus of a female